Gift from Charles Wilson, former zoo director, 8-05

Charles G. Wilson

MAN AND ANIMAL IN THE ZOO:
ZOO BIOLOGY

Man and Animal in the Zoo

ZOO BIOLOGY

HEINI HEDIGER

Translated by Gwynne Vevers and Winwood Reade

With three line drawings in the text and 188 photographs

A SEYMOUR LAWRENCE BOOK

DELACORTE PRESS · NEW YORK

Published in the United States of America, 1969
by Seymour Lawrence/Delacorte Press, New York

Translated from "Mensch und Tier im Zoo"
Albert Muller Verlag, Zurich, 1963
© *Albert Muller Verlag, AG, Ruschlinkon-Zurich, 1965*
Translation © *Routledge & Kegan Paul Ltd., 1969*
Library of Congress Catalogue Card Number : 70-85758

Printed in Great Britain

Contents

Contents

Foreword

My book *Wild Animals in Captivity*, which was published in 1942, soon
went out of print; sub-titled *An outline of the biology of zoological
gardens* it was a first attempt at dealing with the basic principles of
this subject. It was not intended to be a collection of formulae on
how to keep individual species of wild animal in captivity.

There are many problems involved in zoo biology and at that time
I divided these up under the general headings of living space, diet
and the animal-human relationship; today, after more than twenty
years, I believe that these are still the three key factors in the management of wild animals in zoos. The standard by which a zoo animal is
judged should be according to the life it leads in the wild, under the
so-called free conditions of nature. This subject has received a
welcome stimulus as the result of work done in the new branch of
biology concerned with territory in animals.

This book is not intended as a re-statement of the previous material
but should be regarded as supplementary to the original volume. It
provides additional material obtained as a result of undertaking
various research studies, primarily as Director of Basel Zoo from
1944 to 1953 and of Zurich Zoo since 1954, but also as a result of a
number of visits to European and other zoos during which I have
been called upon to act in an advisory capacity. My earlier book, of
which the English and French editions are also out of print, was
written when I was on the staff of Bern Zoo (1938–1944). (Dover
Publications of New York have recently brought out a reprint of the
original English edition.)

During the course of my work I have assembled a considerable
amount of material based on observations and I have gained a great
deal of experience; as a result I have come to the conclusion that
mistakes are repeatedly made in many zoos, both large and small,

I

and that these are attributable to the techniques adopted by those responsible for the management of the animals. The same errors are committed quite needlessly and the same losses are suffered, mostly at the expense of the animals.

Spectacular advances in modern technology, in its widest sense, often lead to a failure to evaluate correctly the significance of the animal in its natural and artificial environments. A considerable part of my new book refers to the dangers which arise from this.

The sub-title emphasizes that a zoo is by no means merely a business concerned with zoology as is still so often assumed; it is concerned far more with human problems.

Man is the only animal that keeps other animals in captivity and that is capable of domesticating wild animals. Without domestic animals the humans concentrated in large cities could not in fact exist, because these animals form the basis of their diet; today the zoological gardens, as will be explained in greater detail, also form a necessary part of the big-city habitat of man.

Apart from man there are very few living organisms which keep other species in a state of dependence. Although not directly comparable but familiar in this respect are those ants which keep members of other ant species as slaves or aphids as "ant-cows". A cage-like siliceous sponge, the Venus' Flower Basket (*Euplectella*) often encloses crustaceans (*Aega spongiphila* and others), which reach the lumen of the mesh-like cylinder of sponge, then grow up and can no longer get out. In this example the mesh acts not only in a negative way by restricting free movement, but also in a positive way: the mesh of the sponge provides protection to the small crustaceans against enemies—in much the same way as the iron bars or other fencing in a zoo provide security for the captive animals.

I

The Seven Aspects of
a Zoological Garden

As already emphasized in the Foreword a zoo is not merely a business organization concerned with animals; it has a great deal more to offer than this and has many different aspects which often have only a tenuous connexion, if any, with animals. There was a time when the director of a zoo, with the aid of a handful of devoted keepers, was available to do everything in the zoo including looking after people, caring for both healthy and sick animals, organizing supplies, taking cash and doing the book-keeping; he even acted as gatekeeper with a big bunch of keys, rather in the manner of a patriarch. This state of affairs, however, largely came to an end with the last century.

Nowadays the running of a zoo, to reduce it to a simple formula, can be considered under the following seven headings, each of which will be described briefly: humans, finance, technique, organization, animals, research.

One: The Humans

Man, in the guise of the visiting public, is still the essential element on which every zoo—without exception—depends for its existence today. There is still no such thing as a purely academic zoo, an autonomous body independent of the public; there are only a few small private establishments or research institutes (e.g. primate centres) which can afford to do without visitors. The public are therefore of supreme importance; together with the animals they are of primary consideration. It can therefore be said that there would be no point in having a zoo, with the exception of an establishment for pure research, which

3

failed to take the public into account. Equally a zoo without animals would be completely senseless (unless it were a zoo museum which we still lack). Here we are not playing idly with ideas or words but we are trying to show that the public and the animals represent the two focal points which have to be balanced one against the other. The central problem in zoo biology is the reconciliation of the demands of the public and the requirements of the animals. For example: in some cases the animal wants cover whereas the public wishes to see it in the open; when the animal is ready for a period of rest the public wants to see it being active. In these circumstances a solution is arrived at by a prolonged and often extremely difficult search for a compromise in the fields of biology, management and organization.

Bearing in mind the confrontation between the interests of the public and the animals, it should be emphasized that the animal houses are not just homes for the animals but are also buildings which must serve the interests of the humans as well. Where there is a considerable difference between the climatic (macro- and micro-climate) requirements of the animals and humans, the provision of conditions suitable for the humans plays the larger part and greater cost is involved. For instance, in a city with cold winters an anthropoid ape house must devote a corresponding part of its area, together with heating or temperature control, to the human visitors; this would either be unnecessary, or of less importance in a tropical or sub-tropical climate. Paths, escalators, notices, labels, lavatories, resting places, kiosks, first aid posts, restaurants and so on, are built exclusively for the use of the public and are often incorrectly allowed for in the planning of new zoos. A zoo cannot be made with installations for the animals alone.

Comprehensive analyses of the public who visit zoos—such as a study of motivation, a breakdown of occupational classes etc., are still things of the future, even though they could be made use of today. So far it is only the entrance gates which have occasionally been investigated, chiefly with reference to the placing of advertisements. In many zoos it is possible to ascertain age groups by means of different types of entrance ticket. Public relations officers were first introduced into zoos in the United States and in the long run the larger zoos of Europe cannot afford to do without them.

4

It is clear that there are many people who visit zoos out of a genuine need for recreation and a healthy interest in the animals; these people represent the positive elements in the public. There is also a minority of negative elements, which includes, for example, all sorts of psychopaths, perverts, criminals and so on. Every zoo suffers from these groups of people and this problem will be referred to in a later chapter.

In the meantime the all-important public does not represent the one and only category of human beings that is significant; people who are on the staff, particularly the keepers are at least of equivalent importance. If one can draw a broad comparison with the world of the motor-car—the paying public can be likened to the petrol, and the staff of keepers to the oil without which the vehicle cannot be kept running. Experience has already been gained of the temporary absence of both these categories of humans: the public, on the one hand, stay away voluntarily during exceptionally bad weather conditions and they are excluded on account of an infectious disease (foot and mouth disease) or because of the escape of a dangerous animal (leopard, cobra); on the other hand, the keepers may go on strike.

A strike of keepers is based primarily on a fallacy. A strike can only be an issue between human beings, usually between a group of employers and employees. It is therefore illogical for non-participants, such as animals, to be drawn into such issues and for social progress to be gained at their expense. Other ways must therefore be found that are more rational and fair, bearing in mind the obvious innocence of the animals.

Even as late as the second half of the last century the keepers in some European zoos had to work from dawn to dusk, and in the summer this meant a sixteen hour day. Sunday brought only a modest reduction in hours and leave was scarcely mentioned. Living conditions for keepers were simple and when anything out of the ordinary took place it made no difference to them when they had to spend the night beside their charges in the animal houses, as for example when an animal was sick or due to give birth. Nowadays this is only done in exceptional cases.

The trade unions, with their rigid and detailed regulations regarding hours of work and related conditions have often interfered not only with the working atmosphere of the keeper staff, but also with the living conditions of the animals in the zoo to a much greater extent than they realize. There is a danger that the qualifications of the keeper will be judged more from the point of view of the trade union than from that of animal husbandry.

This is certainly not said here in any spirit of reactionary criticism, but solely from the viewpoint of zoo biology. From what we know about zoo biology, wild animals are notoriously conservative by nature, every change upsets them, particularly any change in their keepers as they become attached to them to a marked degree. With the short working hours of its keeper and correspondingly quick changes, the animal in the zoo now has to accept long periods of being left on its own. These conditions, which did not exist formerly, present a new challenge involving adaption, and a new selective factor comes into operation. This accounts for certain successes in the husbandry of animals, which were achieved formerly but which either do not now take place at all or are unusual, as for example the breeding of the European otter in London (1846), of the European hare in Paris (1858), of the giant ant-eater in Stuttgart (*c.* 1890), of the echidna in Berlin (1895) and so on. Naturally other factors also came into play.

Strangely enough in the recruitment of keeper personnel one does not always obtain the best results with so-called animal-lovers who have kept and bred animals for years, such as various kinds of fish, reptiles and mammals. This is because amateurs have their own theories and fixed ways of doing things which do not take into consideration the public and conditions in a zoo. Such people are often unable to adapt themselves adequately to the requirements of the new situation. Many of them are firmly attached to their private, amateurish recipes, methods and theories, and already "know the lot".

By contrast new recruits to the staff of keepers who come from quite different walks of life are often more receptive and less prejudiced; they are therefore easier to teach. Naturally there are exceptions. There is still no examination for the job of zoo animal keeper; but there are people who are naturally gifted, often astonishingly so, and also those who come to the job rather late in life. In the Zurich Zoo we prefer young men who have finished some kind of occupational training, varying from gardeners to waiters, metal-workers to

6

carpenters, or sanitary inspectors to bakers. The prerequisite is a natural feeling for animals and nature, which cannot be learnt from books.

A person who is at odds with his fellow humans and who has turned to animals for this reason does not usually make promising material because even an animal keeper has to work with human beings, to a greater extent than one might think at first sight; he has to come into contact with his workmates, his superiors and with the visiting public who are often very critical and hostile.

For those with a vocation the job of animal keeper is doubtless an ideal one. Here vocation and inclination often go hand in hand. Dealing with animals in the fresh air not infrequently provides a healthy outdoor life, so much so that some doctors believe that casualties from other occupations, such as industry, can be sent to the zoo to regain their health.

In many cases this is an over-idealized point of view which arises from the false assumption that a keeper in the zoo only has to deal with animals, whereas as has already been mentioned, he has to get on well with his colleagues, the visitors and his bosses. These requirements must not be overlooked; a love of animals and an enjoyment of nature are not enough in themselves.

Among the human beings connected with the zoo are the directors or *the* Director. Experience has shown that those zoological gardens thrive best and function with the least friction where the direction is in the hands of one man. Innumerable examples could be cited of difficulties that have arisen because too many people have been involved in the direction of a zoo. The danger of this arising stems primarily from the governing body; this problem will be discussed later.

First however a word about the directors. It might be assumed perhaps that a zoo should naturally and logically be directed by a zoologist. This however is not always the case. Here it is of significance to point out that many zoological gardens, strictly speaking all of them, still have one foot or at least a toe, if not in the Middle Ages then in any case in the last century. This is a historically determined situation and it should not be glossed over. Many, if not all zoos still cling to something of the old-fashioned exhibitions of freaks or curiosities, to the days of the old-time menageries, when living treasures

7

were placed on show for hard cash. This mentality has persisted in many places up to the present time. It follows from this that a zoo is a business and the animals therefore are the equivalent of merchandise. In accordance with this concept it is necessary to have a business manager who is to some extent knowledgeable about the appropriate category of goods, that is, the living wild animal. This is merely an objective statement of fact. Today, however, it is just as clearly established that any undertaking which makes use of the designation zoo, ought basically no longer to be a "business", because the wild animal is no longer regarded simply as an item of merchandise.

Today the wild animal is considered to have cultural value; it is regarded as part of our heritage, to which the whole of mankind and particularly future generations, has a legitimate claim. Zoological gardens, to which these living items of culture are entrusted, therefore represent cultural institutions. As such they are required to serve as recreation for human beings, particularly those in large cities, by preserving and stimulating their creative faculties; they are also institutions for popular education and scientific research. The duty to protect these unique cultural items within zoos and outside their confines is inseparably bound up with this concept. The credit for having clearly formulated this characterization of zoos and for having put it into practice goes to the New York Zoological Society: every letter sent out by this large zoological organization bears the progressive heading with the words *Education, Research, Conservation*. It is obvious that a zoo has to serve the needs of the great mass of the public for recreation and relaxation. But it is by no means generally recognized that a great deal remains to be done to put this into effect. A zoological garden which contributes nothing to the promotion of the important subjects of education, research and conservation is just not a zoo in the modern sense, but only a garden with animals—and that is something completely different.

Today there is an unmistakable tendency to put the direction of zoos in the hands of zoologists or veterinary surgeons. But this has not always been so. The International Union of Zoo Directors, which is still influential today, was founded in Rotterdam in 1946. At that time zoo directors of the most varied professional origins belonged to it. Only a few examples need be cited: in addition to zoologists and

8

veterinary surgeons there were also men who had formerly been farmers, musicians, journalists, architects, merchants, accountants, industrialists, administrators, agronomists and so on. There were men with and without academic training, and in this connection it should be emphasized that the professional origin of the directorate was not a yardstick by which the quality of the zoo could be judged as regards organization and animal husbandry. There were excellent zoos which enjoyed a high reputation both in Europe and in America, whose management and presentation were under non-academic direction.

This is doubtless connected with the fact that at that time zoo management was primarily based on practical experience. Thus, the world-renowned Hagenbeck dynasty, for example, was able to promote the image of an international zoo at a time when none of its members held any academic qualification. There are also instances which illustrate the point that successful direction of zoos cannot be achieved on the basis of academic qualifications alone. Young zoologists and veterinary surgeons are helpless to begin with in a zoo and for this reason people who have had experience in the profession but are without academic training have occasionally misused these circumstances in order to establish their own superiority. Graduates or "academic types" could thus be brought into disrepute. In the face of their lack of experience in zoo management this was sometimes an easy game.

In the meantime zoological gardens have not stood still in their development but have changed themselves from undertakings of pure show business into cultural institutions. The question of simply putting on a display for the public is only one of many aspects of the modern zoo. For example, side by side with considerations of display there is the scientific aspect and this must have its place if a zoo is to be a proper zoo in the meaning accepted today. It is therefore essential now that a zoo should have a scientific directorate or a directorate with an associated scientific department or better still with its own administrative and technical departments.

As regards this scientific direction there are today basically two professional groups in the running: zoologists and veterinary surgeons. Representatives of both these professions sometimes make loud claims to priority. What are the facts of the matter?

First of all one should mention with complete impartiality that for hundreds of years we have talked of zoological gardens and not of hospitals for sick animals. If the sick animals in a zoo outnumbered the healthy the matter would then be in doubt. The veterinary surgeons naturally take exception to this and argue that their task is not only to cure sick animals but also to protect them from disease.

It should also be remembered in this connection that directors of zoos have a long history of cooperation with each other: the International Union of Directors of Zoological Gardens, founded in 1946, had a forerunner in 1935, which arose out of the Conference of Directors of German Zoos formed in 1887. On the other hand the zoo veterinary surgeons met together for the first time in 1959 at an international symposium organized by Johannes Dobberstein and Rudolf Ippen (Institute for Comparative Pathology, German Academy of Sciences, Berlin).

Naturally no priority can be derived either for zoologists or veterinary surgeons from this chronological sequence; nevertheless the chronology is not without interest. It shows how long the veterinary surgeons in zoos worked in isolation without fruitful exchange of experience with their own colleagues.

On the problem of whether zoologists or veterinary surgeons should be zoo directors we may finally cite the following. The essence of a zoological garden is emphasized in the term zoo biology, it is essentially biological. The study and the curriculum of the veterinary surgeon, however, generally passes over zoology and zoologically orientated biology, because the veterinary surgeon is usually concerned with a few types of domestic animal and their diseases and not with wild animals. But it is wild animals that form 90 per cent or more of the animal stock in zoological gardens. Taking all domestic animals together they do not represent even a thousandth part of the total number of species in the animal world. Thus the veterinary surgeon does not usually obtain a general view of the animal kingdom. There is no university yet which trains veterinary surgeons for zoo animals. A zoo veterinary surgeon must therefore of necessity apply his experience gained on domestic animals to the wild animal—in so far as this is feasible, after taking into account the characteristics of the animals where these apply. Naturally he can make himself acquainted with the zoology, particularly the basic zoological factors which are relevant for the animals of a given zoo or of zoo animals in general. But much more is required of a veterinary surgeon who is also a zoo director; he must have a comprehensive knowledge of zoology or zoo biology, which includes a certain amount of ecology, ethology and animal psychology.

As a zoologist I could give a long list of amusing experiences which show the gaps in zoological knowledge of the average veterinary surgeon. To illustrate this point I will cite only a few examples which come from my personal experience of working with inexperienced veterinary surgeons in various zoos.

When passing the baboons one day with one of the vets he advised me to get rid of every animal with the "extreme prolapse"; he was referring in fact to a completely normal phase in the sexual cycle in female baboons, which to the uninitiated can of course give the impression of being pathological. Other vets want to know whether elks were ruminants or whether otters hibernated. (The elk is in fact a ruminant like all deer; the otter is a mustelid and like other members of this family it does not hibernate.) If the advice of a veterinary surgeon had been followed a sick capybara (*Hydrochoerus capybara*)—known in German as a "water-pig"—would have been kept cool corresponding with the treatment for domestic pigs. The capybara, however, is a tropical rodent, for which the recommended cool conditions would have meant certain death. (The German name "water-pig" for the largest of all rodents is of course very unfortunate and in the circumstances misleading.) On one occasion I was told by a veterinarian that the hibernation of marmots is caused by a parasitic worm, which of course is certainly not the case. Also veterinary pathologists miss the point when, for example, they diagnose a purely physiological fat store as fatty degeneration.

An interesting book by J. Y. Henderson (1951) tells of the initial helplessness of a veterinary surgeon when faced with wild animals that were completely strange to him in the menagerie of a big circus.

On the other hand, trained zoo veterinarians can certainly produce many instances where zoologists have made absurd diagnoses. Not every zoologist would automatically make a zoo director; he must make himself familiar with the special problems which arise in connection with keeping the wild animal in captivity (zoo biology).

Practical experience in a zoo is just as essential for zoologists as it is for veterinarians. Zoo biology is a special field of work and as such is initially unfamiliar to the members of both professions.

One circumstance ought perhaps to receive special mention: whereas the zoologist is usually aware of the boundaries of his discipline and behaves accordingly, there are occasionally veterinarians who fail to recognize the range and depth of zoological knowledge; they believe that they can assimilate it all in a surprisingly short time, including the results of research on animal behaviour. There are, however, subjects which are true borderline cases as, for example, the field of nutrition in wild animals (*see* Chapter 7), where there is to some extent common ground for the zoologist and the veterinarian.

The question of whether a zoo director should be a veterinary surgeon or a zoologist is rather futile. A director with zoological training must certainly make use of the services of a veterinary surgeon for the care of sick animals, and conversely a director with veterinary training cannot get along without the advice of zoologists. Either of them working on their own will be skating on thin ice and they should work together in fruitful cooperation. This also applies to the subject of the buildings in a zoo. Today zoos are essentially the work of a team. The zoologist is neither a veterinarian nor an architect; the architect working on his own without the advice of zoologists will be faced with insoluble problems, just as the zoologist cannot do without the veterinarian and vice versa.

In addition every zoo director, whether zoologists or veterinarian, is becoming increasingly tied to his desk and in danger of becoming divorced from the animals; administration and organization swamp his original functions and often confuse the issues.

Mention must now be made of yet another category of humans in the zoo: the governing body. According to the organization of the zoo concerned this may be a municipal council, an administrative board, a commission, a group of patrons or others. I will only mention here a few of the main difficulties which can arise—but which need not necessarily do so. The personalities involved are crucial, and the optimum should be sought in good personal relations rather than in the type of organization.

A fundamental difficulty often arises when members of the governing body consider themselves experts in matters in which only the director—because of his training and practical experience—can be expert; the governing body then think that they can interfere with the director and his staff. The results are often much the same as would take place if an administrative member of the board of a railway company stopped a train on an open stretch of the track and instructed the engine-driver to switch the points and drive the train on a non-scheduled route. Or it is as if a member of a hospital management committee were to give the surgeon instructions on how he should carry out a particular operation. These two examples are by no means exaggerated. They demonstrate, amongst other things, that the duties of the governing body are completely different from those of the director and how disastrous, indeed absolutely impossible, interference from above can be.

In several zoos many unnecessary clashes have developed from this state of affairs. One could cite a great number of instances (including some from my own experience). However we are not concerned here with individual cases, but exclusively with basic principles, which must be dealt with briefly because they affect one area, even if a small one, of zoo biology.

I know of one case, in which the director was severely censured by a member of his governing body, because he had acquired an "obviously sick" female chimpanzee as companion for a solitary male chimpanzee. In actual fact the animal concerned was a completely healthy female chimp with the sexual swelling which is a well known and completely normal phase in the oestrous cycle. In another case the director of a zoo in central Europe was told to stock the empty otter pool with crocodiles; this pool was supplied with cold water which would naturally have caused the death of these warmth-loving reptiles. Compliments from the governing body may also be made on a totally erroneous basis; in one case a zoo director was congratulated during the war because, in spite of an extremely difficult position regarding supplies, he had always managed to obtain sufficient meat to feed the elephants! (Elephants are pure vegetarians.)

Cases of this kind still occur from time to time and indeed in some places they are an everyday occurrence, and it is for this reason that the subject must be discussed and analysed. It is naturally true that there are also governing bodies who wisely avoid meddling in professional details, and guide their zoos at a higher level with discretion and breadth of vision. A case described by H. M. Wegeforth (1953, p. 39) from his own experience is of interest in this context.

As President of the San Diego Zoological Society Dr Harry M. Wegeforth rendered great service to the zoo in this city. The zoo is one of the most beautiful in the world and the terrain with its mesas and canyons presents exceptional problems from the point of view of landscape architecture. In the year 1924 Wegeforth had to place before his governing body, in this case a city council, a plan prepared by an expert landscape architect for approval. It so happened that there was no one on this particular governing body who had even the remotest idea about landscape architecture. Wegeforth declined to lay these plans in front of this body and was able to get agreement that the zoo should be allowed to proceed independently in the future.

The majority of conflicts of this nature take place at the level of the governing body and the director; the state of affairs, as described above, is fairly typical. How does it come about that members of bodies governing zoos regard themselves as expert in zoo matters, when in fact they often have no idea of what zoo biology is about?

Many fundamental misunderstandings usually stem from the fact that zoos are regarded as a collection of individual cages or enclosures (although in fact a zoo is something completely different). Some members of governing bodies feel that the fact that they have a couple of aquarium tanks or aviaries at home, or because they have had experience of hunting trips and a few tropical expeditions, gives them the status of experts who have the right to criticize the management of a zoo. Indeed there is no other field in which misguided interference can have such disastrous results as in a zoo.

Seen from the outside the running of a zoo appears to be very simple: it is certainly a simple matter to cut up meat correctly and give it to a lion, an operation which is something that every dog-owner actually performs in feeding his pet—the only difference being that the lion is a little larger. The dog-owner only becomes involved in the problem of nutrition when, in addition to the dog, he keeps a few other animals, perhaps a cat, a budgerigar, an aquarium tank and so on. My advice on a certain type of flooring for the anthropoid ape cages was once referred back to me on the grounds that one of the gentlemen concerned objected to it on account of his experience when keeping rabbits in his youth.

Hunters, particularly big game hunters, often regard themselves as considerable experts on zoos. Many private owners also have a natural interest in the zoo as a result of their experience in keeping pets; they like to be elected to the governing body, they may even have played a part in the establishing of the zoo and therefore regard themselves as "professionals". Due to the fact that a big game hunter has already killed elephants and rhinos, for example, he will regard himself as an expert on all matters concerning large animals and also colleagues on the governing body often think that he must be an expert on these matters. How can a poor little zoo director, who has not shot a single elephant in his whole life be expected to stand up against men who have laid low so and so many animals with their own hands? What right, for instance, has he to discuss the treatment required by the skin of a zoo elephant or the security of the animal? The man who speaks from "great personal experience" must know all about it.

The question of feeding the lions, mentioned earlier, is not as simple as it sounds; in the first place it is not just a question of feeding one lion but several lions as well as many other predatory animals. Therefore very large amounts of meat are involved; these cannot be collected from the nearest butcher in a shopping basket but quantities on this scale have to be organized in advance. Supplies are not always readily available. In some countries, such as Switzerland, there are few horses and cheap cattle meat is not easily procurable. In Zurich, in view of the increasing difficulties, preliminary experiments have already been made with imported whale-meat, which is used almost exclusively for feeding the beasts of prey in Japanese zoos.

The purchase of large quantities of beef and horse-meat involves all kinds of organizational problems: supplies have to be located, arrangements made for inspection of carcasses, transport and storage. In addition there are the problems of suitable transport containers, cold storage, preparation rooms, weighing scales, thawing out facilities, and so on which all have to be considered. Finally the feeding must be carried out not only to suit the animals but also for the convenience of the public, that is, the public must be able to watch it and scheduled times have to be arranged. The traditional weekly fast day must be fixed and adhered to. Times of feeding and fast days are made known to the public through the zoo's publications, in the official guides, brochures and so on.

Thus in the zoo even such an extremely simple process as the dispensing of a piece of meat to a lion is in fact a small cog in a system of wheels and but a fraction of a process with which the amateur pet-keeper is unfamiliar. A zoo is much more than the sum of its individual cages and it is much more than a series of individual operations of the type undertaken by amateurs who keep animals. This additional element is subject to certain rules and regulations of a technical and biological nature. To ascertain, to formulate and apply these correctly is one of the many tasks of zoo biology. In order not to bore the reader only a part of the whole story of feeding the lions has been described here, as an illustration of some of the problems involved in what appears to be a simple matter. One should also mention the labelling of the animals which can be particularly important when predatory animals have to be kept mostly in individual enclosures so that they can consume their ration in peace. Woe betide the zoo if one of the "professional" visitors discovers a lion at feeding time housed in a cage labelled for tiger or puma. He immediately seeks out the nearest keeper, in order to point out the error.

The technical aspects, which are linked with the food, the type of feeding hatches, and the safety precautions together with many others are not dealt with here as one example must suffice to show the differences in keeping animals in zoos and as an amateur. These differences are one of the potential grounds for the attitude of the expert towards the non-expert. There are, however, many other causes.

Quite frequently, for example, pseudo-experts boast that they have looked at a large number of zoos in many countries. From this they believe that they derive special professional expertise. It is certainly interesting and instructional for zoo enthusiasts to get to know other zoos, the more the better. But there is a distinct difference between looking at and really knowing about what goes on. The public sees only one side of a zoo; the angle seen by the staff may be completely different. The underlying organization, its use for scientific purposes and so on are things which cannot be assessed after a quick tour—one might as well try to judge a hospital from its façade or a bank from the public side of the counter.

The governing body should see its real function and its most important task—apart from supervising the commercial aspect of the establishment—as the promotion of its zoo along broad lines; it should seek to consolidate and obtain support for it through business and trade connections with the big organizations of commerce, industry, finance, publicity, etc., so that the zoo can move on from the problems of mere existence to those of a higher order, namely to work of a scientific nature.

Two: Finance

Zoological gardens by their very character are costly in relation to buildings and management. The more they are removed from the concept of a menagerie, the costlier they become; the expenditure of money is necessary if the requirements of the animals—according to the state of our knowledge on life in the wild—are to be taken into account. The growing demands of the public must also be considered and this too costs money.

Here and there the idea still persists that a zoo, providing it is properly run, can be a profitable and money-making concern. Nevertheless this is quite out of the question today and wrong in principle. Not every park with animals, which can be visited on payment of an entrance fee, is a zoo in the modern sense. These commercial concerns are much more like the old-fashioned places where animals are put on show, virtually as wares to be displayed, in which practically nothing is done about education, research and conservation.

From the biological angle, trading in animals is a necessary evil, which should only be accepted in so far as it serves to establish, maintain and balance the stocks in proper zoos. Quite a number of so-called zoological gardens are mixed up in animal dealing. The commercial conception of animals as items of merchandise is sometimes partially concealed by a cloak of culture. In any case nowadays the quality of a zoo cannot be judged by the revenue which arises from dealing in animals, gate receipts or from the turnover on beer, coca-cola, sandwiches and souvenirs.

Naturally, large zoos must offer their visitors facilities for obtaining refreshments but there are limits to the trading which can be carried out in a zoo. Nowadays the animal should no longer be misused as a source of income. It is worth repeating that in the modern sense a zoo must be a cultural institution and serve primarily for recreation, education, research and nature conservation. All commercial aspects are admissible only in so far as they are subordinate to and serve these aims. Every kind of surplus should be devoted to this higher purpose.

In contrast to the majority of botanic gardens which are closely associated with university departments and have come to be supported by them, zoos as a rule are not connected with universities. This arises from their historical origin and is why they are still associated with something of the attitude of a primitive show-booth, the annual fair or the menagerie, and with the making of money.

Today most zoos find themselves in a transitional stage; they are throwing off the last trappings of the menagerie and commercialism and—in accordance with the responsibilities of our times—are developing into cultural institutions, which like libraries and museums serve popular education and science. There is however no financial profit to be gained from these activities. Not all the competent circles (governing bodies, city councils and so on) are yet aware of this state of affairs; thus nowadays most zoos (and by no means only the worst ones) are suffering from financial difficulties.

After an exhaustive investigation Sir Solly Zuckerman, Secretary of the Zoological Society of London, confirmed in 1959 that almost every major zoo in the world is dependent upon funds from official sources. For a cultural institution this is obviously acceptable in principle; the difficulty lies in the fact that all zoos are not yet recognized as cultural institutions.

As is well known there are national zoos, as, for example, in Washington, D.C., and the one in Paris (Vincennes) which comes under the Department of Education. Others are municipal (e.g. Frankfurt, Bern) or private as Basel (joint stock company), Zurich (cooperative society), and Berlin (limited liability company), or they belong to scientific societies as in London (The Zoological Society of London) and the Bronx Zoo in New York (New York Zoological Society).

There are as many different legal forms of zoos, as the variety in the extent and type of their financial resources. In some cities there is a special zoo tax, that is a tax for the benefit of the zoo, as in St Louis (Missouri); a similar arrangement exists in San Diego

(California). Other cities and states distribute subsidies at regular or irregular intervals of time. Some zoos charge no entrance money or only a token payment, often only on certain days. The Bronx Zoo in New York receives money from the city for the whole of the upkeep, for all the food and the basic wages of the staff. The New York Zoological Society covers the cost of the scientific staff, the purchase of animals and contributes significantly towards improvements. In Zurich there exists the anomaly, that the zoo has to hand over ten per cent of the entrance monies to the city and canton in the form of a ticket tax, but opportunities exist to compensate for this financial levy by corresponding subsidies.

It is remarkable that although there are financial misers in almost all zoos, the number of zoos continues to increase throughout the world. Where none yet exists, a new one will be built and where one is already in existence it will be enlarged. This is true from Japan to central America and from southern Africa to Canada.

This apparently paradoxical situation is attributable to the fact that zoos are no longer regarded as luxury phenomena, which one or another city can afford; they are now regarded more as an essential constituent of the human big-city habitat. Zoos have carried out changes to meet this climate of opinion or are at least proceeding to develop along these lines. Originating from the menagerie they have become cultural institutions and, at the same time, necessary constituents of every large city in the service of its social and mental hygiene. This aspect will be referred to again in a later chapter.

It comes as a shock to some people, particularly to those members of zoo governing bodies who are in the world of business, that all hope of making a profit must be abandoned but although they find it difficult, they have to accept the facts. At one time, in the period of the menageries, amusement parks and so on, it was possible to show zoological curiosities at a profit, but this is no longer possible today; the animal has now lost its role as an article of commerce and has taken on the image of a valuable gift on loan from our vanishing fauna, thus it has virtually acquired a complete change of status.

The significance of exhibiting groups of native human beings, like rare animals, is worth referring to in this context. Up to the Second World War some zoos were able to make ends meet by the temporary exhibition of groups of exotic natives (Sudanese, Red Indians, Lapps

19

and so on). The representatives of strange races of man (for reasons which will not be analysed here) acted as a magnet in city zoos and were often a major attraction. But can anyone imagine nowadays putting the representatives of overseas ethnic groups on show, like strange animals, for the payment of an entrance fee?

Three: Space

In this section I do not intend to go into the spatial requirements of animals in the wild and in the zoo as this will be dealt with in detail in the chapter on "Building for animals". Only the following basic statement need be repeated here: the ideal solution for a zoo is not to provide an exact imitation of the natural habitat, but rather to transpose the natural conditions in the wild, bearing in mind biological principles, into the artificial ones of the zoo.

Here we shall be touching on the question of space in a much wider sense. At one time when the building of new animal houses or whole zoos was under consideration, it was the practice for a group of the people concerned—who were not always professionals—to visit the relevant installations in other zoos; as a result, whatever they saw was imitated, often an exact copy was made, or in some cases the buildings were larger or smaller, with or without trifling differences. The result was that in many cases the planning and building of zoos was devoid of new ideas and merely went round in a circle, at least for several decades, if not for a hundred years. Today, however, things are different.

The ease and speed of modern travel enables the interested parties to visit several different countries, involving more than one nationality, and to inspect buildings in widely differing climates. This has doubtless contributed to the breaking down of well-established patterns and to the appreciation of new ideas; a creative approach has been stimulated and has even resulted in some bold innovations. In spite of this zoo architecture still follows lines that in many cases are much too conservative.

How difficult it is, for example, to get architects to come to the point where they will accept the challenge of getting away from the cube, a suggestion I made years ago in *Break away from the cube* (*Los vom Kubus*, 1956). Fascinated by the cubic form of human dwellings—

a shape that is completely alien to nature—architects have confined all animal life, from fish to giraffe, from snake to gorilla, in this particular spatial form. In zoo architecture it is not the simplest and the cheapest type of building which should be given primary consideration but the type of building which comes nearest to meeting the biological requirements. The cube, indeed a straight line of any kind, is unbiological.

The African House in Zurich Zoo which accommodates rhinoceroses, hippopotamuses, shoebills and cattle egrets was opened in 1964 and it is an example of how it is possible to build animal houses without using cubical forms; it also shows that there is no need for the flooring of an animal enclosure to be as horizontal and smooth as that of a human sitting-room. Something of the "wildness" of the natural landscape should be introduced, appropriately adapted, into the living areas destined for wild animals.

Richard Neutra (1962), the well-known American architect (whose family incidentally came from Zurich) was one of the first to abandon the cube and the smooth vertical wall surfaces for human dwellings, in favour of a form which was closer to nature. The demand for this is even more urgent and obvious when it comes to accommodating animals. It involves breaking with a rigid principle in more ways than one. This demand has occasionally been misinterpreted, particularly in the effort to avoid cubical shapes, and has resulted in an animal house with cubical areas that have only been slightly displaced, in that they have been given a rhomboid form.

In his article on *Proxemics*, the study of man's spatial relations, E. T. Hall (1963, a and b), inspired by biology, shows the intimate relationship between the subject—whether man or animal—and the surrounding space; this may help towards satisfying the needs of identification and may also contribute decisively towards good health or, on the other hand, it may lead directly to ill-health.

Animals which have been domesticated over a period of thousands of years have diverged from their natural forms, through the influences of breeding imposed by man, and have become largely emancipated from their spatial relationships. Because of the successes gained in this field, it is often erroneously thought that this can also be applied to wild animals and that the same effect can be achieved by dividing up a cube into large or small areas. The amount of space available is still held to be significant, whereas in fact the quality of the space, its form and the nature of the surfaces exposed to the animals are generally speaking of greater importance.

Four: Technique

Keeping wild animals in captivity usually entails a certain amount of apparatus and machinery which takes up space; this makes the artificially constructed home of the animal diverge from its natural habitat. Zoological gardens which are situated in cold climates or those with hard winters must keep their tropical animals in specially conditioned accommodation; anyone who lives inland and wishes to keep delicate marine animals, such as fish, must provide aeration, filtration and heating equipment. Where large quantities of water are in circulation suitable pumps, filter beds and so on must be available. Pumps had to be installed at Zurich Zoo right from the start, simply to get rid of the waste effluent.

Complicated machinery often proves to be necessary also in places where one would not expect it, for example the filter beds in oceanaria lying close to the sea, in which small toothed whales and large fishes are kept. The use of water in open circulation nearly always has to be abandoned in favour of total or partial filtration. In this connection the opening of the Seven Seas Panorama in 1961 in Brookfield Zoo, Chicago, provided a special landmark as dolphins were kept in captivity inland, fully emancipated from the sea, for the very first time; the accommodation for the dolphins is heated and under cover, and artificial salt water was used, first at a concentration of 2 per cent salt and since 1964 at 1 per cent. The water is passed through the filters at the rate of about 170 gallons per minute.

Many different kinds of machine have to be installed in a zoo, not only to provide suitable living conditions but also in connection with the preparation, cleaning and transport of the food. The larger the size of the establishment the greater the amount of machinery which is necessary. Rationalization and mechanization techniques are also being applied in zoos but not to the same extent as in the modern rearing of domestic animals, where, for example, the dispensing of food and the removal of dung are carried out by conveyor belts controlled from a switchboard. Machines that are designed for

22

a few types of domestic animals fortunately cannot be put to such extreme use in zoos on account of the wide variety of wild animals involved.

When installing machines in the zoo there are two basic principles which should not be overlooked: wild animals and machines are at completely opposite ends of the pole; every machine is an exquisitely unbiological piece of equipment. For this reason it is essential that machinery is installed as discreetly as possible. This means that all noise and vibration from the machines must be kept from the animals as far as possible.

The second basic principle which must be applied to zoos in this connection is that—by contrast with establishments for rearing domesticated animals—the maximum effort must be made to counteract all domestication effects. Wild animals in a zoo must be looked after in such a way that they retain all their typical characteristics, with the sole exception of the urge to escape which in the wild also disappears in the absence of enemies (for example on islands).

In endeavouring to avoid all the effects of domestication, the machines for preparing food should be looked at critically. This problem will be discussed in greater detail in a later chapter. In nature, for the majority of wild animals there is no uniform food mixture of the type that is put in front of our cattle and poultry; on the contrary there is a great variety of food, both qualitatively and quantitatively, and conditions also vary as to the possibility of acquiring it. Therefore in the zoo one must beware of the standardization of food machines.

Some of the machinery in the zoo is required more for the welfare of the visitors than that of the animals; this applies particularly to ventilation equipment. In the first half of the 20th century, even if there was any system of ventilation at all it was usually extremely primitive, and ventilation by mechanical means did not exist. Even today in some places people believe that they can get by without mechanical ventilation and that the public should be expected to put up with stale or foul air. The animal houses that are the worst in this respect are those of the big cats, apes and monkeys, and the small mammals; these require particularly careful treatment. With the big cats it is primarily a question of dealing with the fumes of ammonia; these are difficult to combine chemically and often very penetrating,

23

and it is absolutely essential that these are kept away from the visitors. These fumes also attack plants. Thus, for example, in the big cat house in Zurich Zoo it is still not possible today (1964) to keep plants alive indoors; when the house was constructed (1933) the ventilation equipment—a primitive blower—was installed the wrong way round, since when it has not been possible to put it into operation. An improvement is planned.

The smell in the ape and monkey houses is caused by the active metabolism of the animals, similar to that in man, by which odours are released that are widely diffused and active over long periods of time. In the anthropoid ape house of Zurich Zoo which was opened in 1959, separate air-conditioning was installed in the enclosures of individual species or groups; it was found that it was possible to establish that the smells of the excrement, urine and sweat, were specific to the individual groups of ape.

Among the small mammals which nearly always possess a variety of skin glands (for marking, etc.), their secretions often produce unpleasant smells. All termite eaters have a specific smell. Ungulates, both the artiodactyls and the perissodactyls, fill their houses with scent, which is less offensive to the human nose; on the other hand, most pigs produce unpleasant smells.

In principle, all animal houses should be ventilated or air-conditioned; this should also be done on grounds of hygiene. The sight of visitors holding handkerchiefs to their noses, at one time typical of all animal houses, should be a thing of the past; in the zoo, animals and men should be in separately ventilated areas.

The division of the zoo's technical equipment, particularly the machinery, into one group which serves the animals and another which serves the humans is an obvious one; there is a third group however which serves both.

The convenience of visitors, for example, is served by a specially designed escalator which was first used in a zoo at San Diego in 1962; at that time it was the longest in the world (over 100 yards).

Automatic feeding machines, delivering a certain quantity of food to the interior of the cage or enclosure, on the insertion of a coin outside the cage, probably gives more pleasure to the humans than to the animals which in any case have been given the necessary food supplies. Such automatic feeders should be used to a greater extent in the future; hitherto only expensive prototypes have been installed in a few zoos, as for example the one in Zurich Zoo which was installed in 1959 in front of one of the air-conditioned anthropoid ape cages. After the insertion of a coin the chimpanzee receives a handful of popcorn, hazelnuts or small biscuits. The apes soon follow the preparatory movements of the visitor with interest and the highest ranking ape takes up a position, ready for the arrival of the food from the automatic vendor. This gives man and animal the chance to establish some kind of enjoyable contact in spite of the airtight barrier of glass. It brings in money, gives the animals welcome activity and the automatic feeder can be controlled precisely with regard to quality and quantity. The automatic machine in Zurich Zoo can be temporarily put out of action at any time and a notice to this effect displayed.

An automatic fish-feeding machine would doubtless be an important attraction at a sea-lion pool. Similar apparatus could also be used successfully for elephants, bears, many ungulates and so on, after the animals have been trained to perform simple tasks.

The difficulty is that different animal groups require different types of food (e.g. fish, pellets, groundnuts); machines have to be adapted for each type and prototypes can be very expensive. An enterprising manufacturing firm which was willing to undertake the mass production of suitable automatic machines would undoubtedly find a considerable market among the zoos all over the world.

In 1957 visitors in the Exotarium at the Frankfurt Zoo were issued with ultra-short wave receivers; by using these listening devices they were able to hear a running commentary on the animals as they were walking round. This was the first time that this kind of equipment was put into operation in a European zoo, although similar machines had already been in use for some time in American museums. It was in 1962 in the National Zoo in Washington that I first saw a short-wave radio in use; this gave radio communication between the director walking round the zoo and his office. J. A. Davies of the Bronx Zoo in New York described in 1963 (*Animal Kingdom*, No. 5) the use of a walkie-talkie radio for intercommunication between keepers during the introduction to each other of two adult gorillas. There is no doubt that similar equipment from the radio industry will soon find general application in zoos.

I would recommend to all zoos which keep sea-lions, other seals and fish-eating whales, the use of a "fish-hook detector". This has not yet been made but its production by some enterprising firm would be worthwhile because although fish caught in the sea (herring, whiting, etc.) are normally netted, on occasions they contain fish-hooks. In some zoos and particularly in circuses, which have a considerable amount of capital invested in their performing groups, conscientious keepers spend hours daily in checking each fish by hand before it is fed to the animals. Nevertheless, in spite of a most careful check a hook deeply embedded in the flesh may escape detection. My invention would ensure that all fish to be used as food would move along a conveyor belt past a sensitive detector, which would give a signal at the presence of a metal object, stopping the conveyor belt. By this means many valuable fish-eating exhibits would be protected from injuries by lethal foreign bodies, particularly from perforations of the stomach and intestine.

Five: Organization

Nowadays many zoos are large concerns employing hundreds of staff, looking after thousands of animals, thereby making it impossible for the director to continue to supervise details. Thus something important has been lost. Up to the Second World War, one of the elementary duties generally performed by the director of zoos in Europe was known as "the inspection". This is still carried out today in small zoos but it is no longer possible in large concerns.

The word "inspection" comes from the Latin verb *inspicere*, meaning to look into. The morning inspection of the director—referred to almost everywhere as a thing of the past—consists of a looking-into and an active examination of all cages, dens and enclosures; it includes the inspection of all spaces and corners of the establishment. This daily check which is in fact both energetic and tiring is usually referred to by naïve visitors to the zoo as the director's "morning walk".

Anyone who did not feel tired after doing an inspection lasting two or three hours would not have carried it out properly. This elementary function of a zoo director in the classical tradition has died

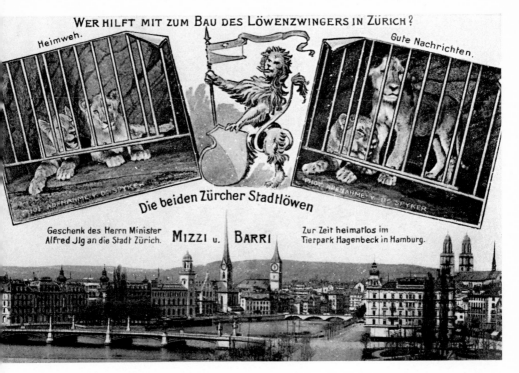

Fig. 1   Dated about 1900, a sentimental and anthropomorphic appeal for funds to provide quarters for two lions presented to the city of Zurich. An example of animals being accepted before suitable accommodation is available.

Fig. 2   The Tuatara (*Sphenodon punctatus*) from New Zealand prefers living at a lower temperature than any other reptile, namely at 12°C (54°F); unlike other reptiles, it requires a cool cage, without heating.

Fig. 3   The first escalator to be installed in a zoo was at San Diego in 1962; at that time it was the longest in the world.

Fig. 4   In London Zoo the African Oxpecker (*Buphagus*) is supplied with a model, made out of sacking, to act as a substitute for the bodies of large ungulates.

out or has already become a matter of history. It is worth attempting to describe it here because, in general, many younger members of the zoo profession do not know anything about it; also I would like it to be retained wherever possible and rather than let it die out I would like to promote it, in so far as this is feasible under the present conditions in large zoos.

Two main points of the classical inspection make it difficult to retain in large zoos, namely the supervision of the entire stock of animals and the overall competence of the person undertaking the inspection. Although present-day rationalization scarcely permits anything else the inspection is not achieved by subdividing a large zoo into several broad categories of inspection, involving more than one inspector and with authority divided among several officials. In a zoo, however, priority should be given in principle not to rationalization, but to considerations of biology (Biologisierung)—and the two are often diametrically opposed. Here also the whole is more than the sum of its parts, although nowadays this fact often has to be neglected.

The ideal form of inspection consists of the critical checking of every detail by one individual—moreover always by the same person —and the issuing of instructions for carrying out immediate improvements concerning matters which have been open to criticism. The paramount objective of the zoo inspection is to examine the results of the unique confrontation between man and animal, as presented by conditions in a zoo.

In former times the small zoos, which were, so to speak, run on patriarchal lines, were stamped with an individual character, through the personality of the director who was responsible for every detail. With the growth of zoological gardens this ideal form of inspection soon became impossible; administration, the keeping of appointments and so on, pressed more and more into the foreground, so that at first the inspection had to be curtailed periodically from the point of view of its extent and thoroughness. It is significant that an overseer is frequently interposed between the director and the keeper; this is done for example in Germany and applies generally in Europe. In America, where the majority of zoos did not pass through this phase, another system was prevalent: there the division was made primarily on a functional basis, according to animal groups; individual curators were given responsibility, for example, for mammals, birds, reptiles, aquarium and so on. Under this system it was often possible for the curators to undertake an inspection in the old style in their own sections; sometimes however there was no tradition on which to work and the overall competence, as mentioned previously, was lacking. Thus, for example, maintenance work is often entrusted to a special service or works department, which is not always available for every section and it often works along general lines instead of meeting individual specifications.

In the old-style inspection it was necessary to extend one's powers of observation, using all one's senses and not only one's eyes. Sight for example was useful for checking the condition of the buildings and particularly the state of cleanliness of the paths; plants had to be included as well as the external appearance of the animal enclosures (cages, paddocks, dens), particular attention being paid to labels, wire-netting and locks. Labels might be missing altogether, put in the wrong place or be out of date. Wire-netting—if it is not of top quality—has a tendency to rust, to split and then to give rise to dangerous foreign bodies in the cage or even to get into the insides of the animals and thus cause injuries. Where necessary, orders must be issued for repairs and maintenance work and this also applies, of course, to all the following matters of a technical nature.

Fastenings of animal enclosures have a fatal tendency, to put it politely, to be left undone or not properly locked and secured. Since 1954 in Zurich Zoo, therefore, there are twelve rules for keepers, the first of which is well known and it reads: "In the zoo, all doors (also windows, sliding bars, hatches) must not just be shut but fastened and checked." In spite of this clear instruction, various animals have since found their way out, including gibbon, wolf, axis deer and Chapman's zebra.

In November 1963 a group of zebras was able to get out of its paddock owing to the fact that the mesh of the paddock fencing had contracted in the cold weather, causing the bolt to withdraw from its slot. The animals were quite quiet and it was possible to drive them straight back into their paddock. This could not be done with a black panther and an ordinary leopard which broke out earlier and both these animals had to be shot. At that time (1933) the black panther had been living in the woods in the vicinity for about two months and had caused serious alarm amongst the local people (Hediger 1950, p. 66).

In a zoo, however, locks not only have to be checked in order to prevent animals escaping but also as a means of preventing the unauthorized entry of humans. On one occasion in Zurich Zoo a boy suffering from a mental disorder had momentarily eluded his escort and after going through two open doors and a third which he opened himself, he got into the cage occupied by adult chimpanzees. Fortunately it was possible to keep the chimps away from the boy by the immediate use of fire-hoses and he was removed unhurt. In the year 1944 a woman got into the elephant stall in Zurich Zoo through an unfastened window and was killed by the bull; this tragic incident will be referred to again later.

Basically the principle of double security is to be recommended and applied strictly: that is, care should be taken in every place to see that if an animal escapes from its own enclosure for any reason, it finds itself still within a confined space from which it can be driven back without further risk. Conversely, visitors who have got into a staff room, although forbidden to do so, should still be excluded from the actual animal enclosures by a further barrier. For example the anthropoid ape house in Zurich Zoo, opened in 1959, is arranged in such a way that people who have gone ahead without authorization into antechambers cannot get out again without using a special key in the event of the door shutting behind them. It is as well to remember that double security does not ensure absolute security, but at least one has done one's best.

Having dealt with some of the most important external features which arise during the inspection the internal features of the animal enclosures which require inspection can now be described. For example, the cleanliness, the food and drinking water including their containers, the temperature, the ventilation and the lighting, all require attention. Here checking on the dung is particularly important. Food and water containers have a tendency to accumulate dirt in the form of encrustations or even layers of spoiled remnants of food, fungi, algae, etc. Some animals—from reptiles up to primates—are inclined to foul the containers with their excrement, particularly if these are not properly fixed thus encouraging infection and re-infection with parasites. In order to avoid the possibility of animals

29

fighting over the food, it should be decentralized according to the particular circumstances: that is, there should be more than one feeding station so that animals that are social rivals or socially inferior, can have sufficient space and time in which to feed.

The old-fashioned view that containers for food and water must always be fixed to a wall or to the front wire is still widespread, although it has been shown that wild animals restricted for space in small enclosures will regularly walk up and down close to the walls or wire; under these conditions the containers are in their way. This is particularly important when animals are liable to get excited as they tend to stumble or bump into the containers, injuring themselves and upsetting the containers or fouling their contents. Therefore it is important for these dishes to be placed towards the centre of the cage so that the animals are able to run freely in between the receptacles and the walls. As regards height the containers should be fixed in such a way that the animal is not able to stand in them, but at the same time does not have to put its head in an unnatural position when using them. It is wrong from the biological point of view to fix hay-racks at a great height above the ground (for perissodactyls, such as horses, or for many antelopes, etc.). Ungulates with large antlers or horns are often unable to get the food out of containers that are mounted close to the wall, without straining their necks and risking dislocation.

When zoos are situated in areas of heavy rainfall, one must take take care to prevent puddles and water-holes accumulating in the paddocks outside, because such residual waters usually form danger-ous focal points for parasites, and also hold urine and dung, which may lead amongst other things to glanders. Many animals are partial to this kind of soiled water.

It is particularly important to pay attention to dung during the inspection. Its condition may betray the presence of parasites, intes-tinal disturbances, dietary deficiencies or it may indicate over-excitability; lack of dung is a pointer towards constipation and so on.

On one occasion in Zurich Zoo clots of blood suddenly appeared in the excrement of anteaters and echidnas. According to instructions both species should have been given a few drops of fifteen per cent formic acid in their food every day. However the keeper had failed to order a supply in the normal way, that is on an order form attached to each day's report sheet and instead he had obtained a bottle of "formic acid" from a commercial source. The latter contained an 80 per cent solution, such as is used for industrial purposes, like the defurring of electric kettles. The keeper however used the formic acid as though it were a 15 per cent solution.

Finally we come to considerations concerning the animal itself, beginning with the position it takes up in its enclosure, that is its dispersal in the cage or paddock. As we already know this is not determined by mere chance, for the position adopted by an animal follows a definite pattern, the place that it occupies and the position which it adopts are as expressive of the state of play as the pieces on a chess-board. An animal that is normally active during the inspection which is unexpectedly found lying apathetically in a corner, indicates a change in its relationship with its environment. This change is a pointer that something is amiss and it may even acquire the significance of a symptom. Changes in social relationships may be just as informative. An animal occupying an unusual position in the enclosure may point to an unevenness in the distribution of warmth (a defect in the heating system, a broken window, etc.). It has been my experience that keepers assume that the supply of heat is automatically satisfactory once they have turned on the switch but in fact faults can develop. Not infrequently the behaviour of the animals— whether they be fish or apes—is a more reliable indication regarding the working of the heating system than the mechanical instruments. The position of the animal's body, the rate of respiration, the movement of the tail and so on, may also be important indicators.

The condition of an animal's skin is a marvellous barometer of health, which should not be overlooked during the inspection. The skin is an important intermediary between what goes on inside and outside the animal; it is never just a passive covering into which the animal is packed. It is in fact much more than a mere buffer between two worlds; it is, according to its structure, colour, temperature and so on, an efficient organ of unprecedented versatility and efficiency— even in tortoises. For example, giant tortoises have a carapace which reacts to extremely delicate mechanical and thermal stimuli in the most surprising way. A spiny skinned animal, such as the prehensile-tailed porcupine (*Coendou prehensilis*), will respond to a man stroking it with his hand, according to its mood and degree of tameness.

31

Even the skin of a fish is much more than a scaly or slimy covering and it is not only in chameleons that the skin is expressive of mood. The condition of the plumage in a bird virtually speaks volumes, and a great deal can be learnt about the condition of a mammal from the sheen on its coat and the extent to which the fur stands up. (cf. W. Fiedler, 1964.) Much the same could be said of the nose, eyes and ears; however, it is not possible to go into these characteristics in greater detail here.

So far we have only considered some of the many features which become visibly apparent during an inspection. As already mentioned, however, the inspector must not only use his eyes but also his senses of hearing and smell—in fact all his senses need to be utilized. In so far as his nose is efficient it allows all kinds of checks to be made when he enters an animal house, on matters which relate not only to the ventilation equipment, but for example to disturbances in metabolism, the quality of food and straw, the use of disinfectants, insecticides and rodenticides, and the presence of live or dead mice and so on.

During the inspection ears can be used for checking on mechanical noises, sounds of water, whether they are in the right place or not; the creeking of door hinges, for example, indicates the need for a few drops of oil. Above all it is essential to observe the sounds made by the many animals themselves and equally, to take note of the absence of any normal sounds. It is necessary to be aware not only of vocal sounds but also of other noises made by the animals as they move, their breathing and of course any coughing. Undue noise with the food containers, for instance, or banging on the barriers of the enclosure, may indicate a state of over-excitement.

It would be utterly impossible to give a formula which included everything that should be covered by the inspection; the examples mentioned above should be regarded more as an indication of all the many aspects which require attention. In practice there is a great deal more which should be looked into and even the most zealous observer will not cover everything that should be checked. There are a hundred and one details which need attention in a zoo, far more than in other establishments because there are so many animals which are themselves always changing or bringing about alterations in their surroundings.

Faults and failings which are revealed during the course of the inspection should be dealt with immediately; the logical follow-up is to check that the orders relating to improvements have been carried out. How often in a zoo one hears the stereotyped comment: "I have already told him." The issue of an order is only half the battle; the other half consists in checking whether the order has been properly and sensibly carried out.

This has nothing to do with a neurotic obsession for perfectionism but is the outcome of having accepted the responsibility of removing wild animals from their natural habitat and of keeping them under artificial conditions for the convenience of man. This responsibility ought never to be undertaken lightly because it involves a maximum sense of duty.

Owing to various outside factors there are limits to what can be achieved by this high sense of purpose, nevertheless it should be kept permanently in view as an ideal. By attending to a mass of detail, the expert gains an overall impression of a zoo and, with experience, he learns to assess the effect of outside factors and of any *force majeure*. To the initiated it is possible to distinguish properly between inefficiency, negligence and failures due to external factors.

The overall image presented by a zoo is the sum total of many details. The best run zoo is one in which the detailed action to be taken, as a result of the inspection, is subsequently carried out by a number of assistants who accompany the inspector on his rounds. The assistants see that any instructions regarding diet, maintenance work on enclosures, changes of accommodation, etc., are subsequently executed. In principle this process is comparable to the action which follows the visit of a consulting surgeon to a hospital, in which the assistant medical staff ensure that the treatment prescribed is actually carried out.

Even in a small zoo an astonishing number of details requiring action can accumulate during the course of an inspection and there are only a few people who have such good memories that they can afford to do without notes. In large zoos it is conceivable that each head of department or curator can carry out an inspection of his own section; however, with the best will in the world he cannot always get his wishes carried out as he may need to call on the services of technicians who come under a special department which has its own

33

programme of work. Thus it sometimes happens that items such as rusty wire-netting and defective labels remain in an unsatisfactory state.

It may appear that the amount of space which I have devoted here to the inspection is excessive, particularly as there is hardly anywhere now that it is carried out in the "classical" form as described. Lack of time and working under pressure are the chief enemies of carrying out inspections satisfactorily and often they are even undertaken from a motor-car—a pseudo form of inspection. Nevertheless, if at all possible it is recommended that the old inspection methods should be resumed at least occasionally or area by area.

Let me give just one example to show how important inspection can be in relation to the coordination of animal care and maintenance work. It can be argued that efficient animal keepers are capable of making the necessary observations and taking care of anything that needs doing, thus obviating the necessity for an inspection by one expert. Although this seems to be self-evident, in practice it does not work out. Even good keepers are very conservative at heart and keep clear of innovations and additional work—often consciously, often unconsciously (and this applies not only to keepers!) There is often a marked tendency towards the development of blind spots, through over-familiarity with the job and this increases the more the individual is confined to his own working area. The majority of keepers— at any rate in my experience—have a tendency to remain in one section which is especially congenial to them, even to the extent of shutting themselves off from all other sections.

As the inspection proceeds from one section to another everything is seen with a fresh eye and by comparing the different sections one notices what each one has to offer that is stimulating and exciting or that could be described as of lesser interest. This does not mean that the inspection cannot also have a deadening effect; the person who carries it out can also go stale. But the changes of scene, in looking at completely different sections, certainly lessens the risk of occupational blindness by comparison with people who spend years working in the same sphere of activity.

Let us now see what effect occupational blindness may have on the example I have chosen, namely on maintenance work. The keeper in charge of a section is fully familiar with his animals under the

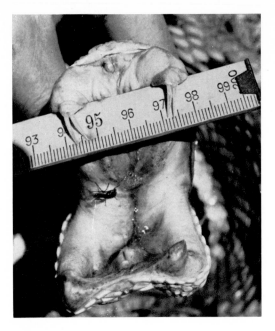
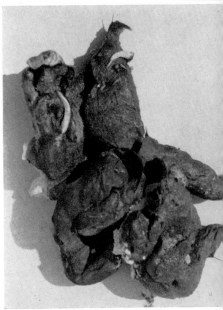

Fig. 5 The open mouth of a rattlesnake (*Crotalus*). Each half of the upper jaw shows a venom fang with an equally large reserve fang. The worn-out fangs are shed and swallowed at intervals of a few weeks.

Fig. 6 Faeces of a rattlesnake (*Crotalus*) containing two of the fangs which have been shed and swallowed.

Fig. 7 Some rattlesnake fangs which were passed out in the faeces. The split-shaped opening for the expulsion of the venom is on the outer curve of the fang near the tip.

Fig. 8 Every couple of weeks venomous snakes of the viper and rattlesnake type excrete the used fangs in the faeces. Rattlesnakes also lose parts of their rattles at infrequent intervals.

Fig. 9 The construction of this type of zoo label, which has more than one section, has proved efficient. Changes can easily be made to any of the four sections.

Fig. 10 The use of a zoo label for this purpose, however, was not foreseen.

Fig. 11   It is important to label exhibits correctly and conveniently for visitors. In Zurich Zoo the names of the animals are given in four languages; in addition there is a picture, a description and a distribution map.

Fig. 12 Machine for feeding hens in the Jardin d'Acclimatation in Paris, after
P. A. Pichot 1873. Biologists made the mistake of attempting to look after
animals by automation even so long as a hundred years ago.

conditions of the daily routine. He does not know the effect created in other sections by the setting-up of scaffolding, by letting noisy machines run, by allowing paint-pots, nails, pieces of metal, splinters of glass, etc., to lie around; the inspector, on the other hand, sees the effect of all this every day in other sections. For this reason the keeper is unable to foresee or to assess sufficiently the possible effects of disturbance created by having workmen in his own section.

As a result of this lack of foresight, large numbers of wild animals have died unnecessarily. The really bad cases of death in the zoo are those that are avoidable; we should therefore devote particular attention to them. It is possible to avoid many of the calamities by giving appropriate instructions at the time of the inspection; workmen have no idea of what may constitute a danger to animals, in so far as they have had no special training or experience of working in a zoo. At all events, the following casualty list shows that all animals— from fish to anthropoid apes—may be injured or killed through the unfortunate way in which workmen carry out their duties.

In 1954 a nine-year-old gorilla became seriously ill with lead poisoning, which it contracted by licking red lead from newly painted iron bars (L. E. Fisher, 1954).

In the London Zoo, R. E. Rewell (1950, p. 493) had to perform a post-mortem on an agouti (*Dasyprocta aguti*). Its death was caused by red lead, which had been left behind in the cage by plumbers mending pipes. Chemical investigation showed clearly the presence of lead in the gut.

Some workmen do not know how dangerous discarded cigarette ends can be—and many aquarium keepers do not wish to know anything about it. When tobacco smoke comes into contact with the surface of the water in aquaria poisoning may take place. Nicotine poisoning may occur even more readily in aquaria when the water is aerated from a smoky atmosphere. In a suitably arranged experiment, fish showed a reaction after only three to five minutes. "After swimming about restlessly for a few minutes the breast fins become rigid, balance is disturbed and paralysis and sinking follow" (W. Schäperclaus, 1954, p. 586). Smoking in the vicinity of the fresh air intake nozzle may be disastrous; the same applies to the gases produced during the mixing and use of certain paints, varnishes and mastics.

People in the zoo who watch giraffes or antelopes standing peace-
fully alongside cranes or noisy machines during building operations
do not usually realize that although these animals have now become
completely indifferent to the disturbance, it was a very different
matter when the building work started; when the first worker arrived
with a surveyor's pole or when the first building lorry drove up, they
may well have taken serious fright and reacted alarmingly; it is only
subsequently that they become accustomed, to an astonishing degree,
to these optical and acoustic nightmares. Above all, craftsmen and
building workers cannot foresee the effects which their everyday
activities may have in the zoo. Many disasters can be avoided by
careful preparation and supervision, particularly at the start of
building operations.

In his report for the year 1954 Dr W. C. Osman Hill, the primatologist who was for many years Prosector of the London Zoo, describes
the case of a Delamere's bushbuck (*Tragelaphus scriptus delamerei*)
which was scared by craftsmen working nearby. As it took flight in
alarm it broke the right tibia in such a way that this bone was
splintered into more than a hundred fragments; there was no chance
of the animal recovering and it had to be put down.

It is clear that under the heading of organization and the theme
of inspection only a few examples can be cited here. There is a wealth
of examples which could be cited if space permitted but one point
must be made here which concerns the basic organization, particularly security measures. So far only the principle of double security
has been mentioned.

In the zoo, overall security must above all be dealt with from
three aspects in the following order of priority: the security of the
visitors, of the staff and of the animals.

Human life must be given preference! The visitor in the zoo has
priority in just the same way for instance that passengers in a ship
must be saved first. The staff in a zoo is in less danger than the
visitors owing to their familiarity with the job, in much the same way
that the ship's crew is more at home on the sea than the passengers.

At this point the statement which seems a truism to all zoo people
should be repeated in parenthesis: it is very much easier to protect
the humans from the animals than vice versa. This will be referred to
again in a later chapter. Brief mention should be made here, however,

of the precautions taken to protect the keeper staff from a risk that is peculiar to zoos, namely from the bites of venomous snakes; this is particularly important because random checks have shown that protective measures are not always properly organized.

I have met more than one zoo director, who has taken me up to a small box in the service room of his reptile house and remarked with pride that everything was available in the box for the immediate treatment of a venomous snake bite. Often in such cases there would be a few phials of anti-venine serum in stock, but not a single sterile hypodermic syringe! The sera were frequently several years old, out of date or completely dried up in crushed ampoules! And often the supplies of the necessary sera were lacking having regard to the particular venomous snakes present in the collection.

On a Brazilian farm, an African cotton plantation or an Indian tea plantation the matter is relatively simple, because in these places it is only necessary to keep a stock of the sera for the treatment of the local venomous snakes. In a large zoo in which the reptile house accommodates venomous snakes from all over the world, it is a much more complicated business and the responsibility is much greater.

Anti-venine sera for practically all venomous snakes from every country must be kept ready for use and this means keeping them in the required state of freshness. To fulfil this task requires continuous organization and financial expenditure which is beyond the capacity of many zoos. In this respect the Zurich Zoo finds itself in a particularly favourable position which might perhaps be emulated elsewhere. The zoo is barely five minutes by car from the Zurich Canton Hospital, and by the generosity of the hospital authorities a stock of all the sera concerned is kept in the hospital dispensary. Should anyone receive a dangerous bite in the Zurich Zoo, the patient is driven as fast as possible in the nearest available car to the casualty department of the Canton Hospital; a report is telephoned to the hospital where the correct serum from the stock held by the dispensary is already waiting.

So far there has only been one occasion on which the services of this organization have been called upon and, as it turned out, this was a false alarm. While the Director was away in Africa a young reptile keeper was cleaning out a small pond in the gaboon viper cage with a sponge. On squeezing out the wet sponge the keeper suddenly

37

felt a sharp prick in the finger; a gaboon viper fang which had got into the sponge had penetrated his skin and become lodged in the musculature of his finger.

The injured keeper and the deputy to the Director who was called in to deal with the situation got into a panic and the patient was rushed to the hospital and given an injection of *Bitis* anti-venine. It was certainly quite right to go through the whole emergency procedure without delay; in fact the precautions were unnecessary but at that time the people concerned did not know that the venom fangs in solenoglyph snakes are periodically shed and usually swallowed. The fangs are then passed right through the stomach and intestines; during the digestive process every kind of venom undergoes complete destruction. After this the fangs are passed out in the faeces. Thus anyone who regularly examines the faeces of captive or wild venomous snakes can establish a considerable collection of fangs in a short time (Hediger, 1958, p. 186).

The list of all the sera available on the market, produced by the American Association of Zoological Parks and Aquariums (T. H. Reed, 1963) is extremely valuable when establishing a stock of the appropriate, fresh sera for use in real emergencies.

These few examples taken from the field of zoo organization must suffice. When one takes into consideration the scale and variety of operations in a large zoo, it is obvious that there are often serious organizational problems which call for analysis by scientific business methods. A large zoo, for example, is responsible for considerable stocks of animals and large staffs, vast numbers of visitors, complicated building and technical installations, problems of supplies and sales including victualling, not to mention training and research departments, etc. One of the most interesting and most fundamental investigations of a zoo involving business methods was undertaken by Alex L. Srbich of the Bureau of Business and Economic Research (San Diego State College) in 1963. Using San Diego Zoo as an example he showed how it was possible to apply modern management techniques to the zoos of large cities.

After making a theoretical analysis of the existing establishments and having established a target for the lowering of costs, for improving the health and longevity of the animal population, the process of putting it all into practice is of course a long and complicated business. However there is no doubt that zoos can also gain many valuable ideas from the experience of modern business management.

In this context the following standard practice which has been put into operation in the Zurich Zoo may be mentioned: every keeper and craftsman has to produce a daily report on a printed form at the end of the working day, the lower portion of which consists of a section headed "orders". The report forms are issued with pages numbered up to fifty. The keeper retains the book with the carbon copies and only hands in the detachable top copy.

Thus every keeper can refer back at any time to his own notes and observations. Young keepers write out the food formulae and other information on every species of animal with which they have to work; they can therefore refer to their own records.

The sections for indenting are torn off and handled by the supplies officer or his assistants. The main part of the report sheet is read by the director or his deputy; this forms the basis for the monthly and annual reports, for entries in the animal stock register and reports to the zoo veterinarian or to the works department.

The book containing the duplicated report sheets has hard covers and on the inside cover the following text is printed as a guide and aide-memoire:

The keeper's report should contain:

1. All changes in animal stock (additions, departures, births, deaths); egg-laying, dates of births and hatchings.
2. All transfers of animals.
3. Signs of illness such as loss of appetite, abnormal faeces, injuries, etc.
4. Drugs, vitamins, food additives dispensed.
5. Signs of oestrus, observation of mating.
6. Special observations, such as moulting of skin and hair, rubbing, antler shedding, etc.
7. Capture or killing of mice, rats, sparrows, etc.
8. Work by gardening and works maintenance department; orders and completion.
9. Special observations made during the inspection, urgent repairs, etc.

10. Booking of days-off to be notified well in advance. Orders should be written on the detachable counterfoil.

The written report does not dispense with the need for verbal reports during the morning inspection, but it standardizes procedure and acts as confirmation. When filling in the report one should *never* think: "the other fellow will write that down", when two or more keepers are engaged on the same job.

In addition to their contract newly arrived keepers in the Zurich Zoo receive a copy of *Working instructions for keepers and other manual workers*. Certain items from this manual may be of interest, e.g.

Paragraph 1. Keepers and men working in the Zoo differ from others in that amongst other things they have to deal not with inanimate material but with sensitive living creatures, for whose care and well-being they are responsible. In Zurich Zoo the animals must be treated in accordance with the principles of animal conservation and of the latest findings of zoo science, extracts of which appear in *Rules for animal keepers* issued as an appendix at the end of the working instructions.

Paragraph 4. The feeding of the animals must follow the precise instructions laid down by the Director, care being taken to avoid all waste of food. The rations are calculated in such a way as to maintain the animals in the best possible health. All animals, including those which are used as food for other animals, must be looked after conscientiously every day. The daily duties of a good keeper include keeping feeding and drinking dishes scrupulously clean.

Paragraph 8. Every keeper is provided with a pass, which he must carry whenever he is in the gardens in civilian clothes and this must be shown to visitors when necessary. While in the gardens every keeper is expected to take part in seeing that the rules are kept. Particular attention must be paid to the following rules which forbid:

the entrance of dogs;
any disturbance of the animals, particularly teasing and feeding them;
climbing over barriers and fences;

40

picking flowers and plants;

committing any nuisance or doing damage of any kind;

playing with balls and hoops, using roller-skates, scooters;

carrying balloons and flags, which may frighten the animals.

Failure to observe the rules should be dealt with courteously but firmly, cases of difficulty should be referred to the director or the police. *Supervision does not consist of passively standing around*, but in actively observing the animals and the visitors. It should be remembered that in principle every visitor is capable of behaving in a stupid way.

On their side the keepers are expected to contribute to keeping the gardens clean and to pick up any litter they see when they are walking around.

Paragraph 11. In the interests of the animals the war against dangerous foreign bodies, such as nails, staples, pieces of wire and so on must be pursued vigorously. It is also the duty of every keeper to combat mice and rats in his section with traps (or by any other method approved by the director). The use of staples, steel-wool and glass-wool is forbidden. Screws should be used instead of nails whenever possible.

It is recommended that the following *Rules for animal keepers*, mentioned in Paragraph 1, should be constantly borne in mind:

1. In the zoo, doors (also windows, slides, bolts, etc.) must not be merely closed, but fastened *and checked*.
2. In the handling of wild animals, *excitement* is *anathema*; every form of excitement is therefore to be avoided wherever possible.
3. Cages, paddocks and transport boxes must be cleaned and disinfected as soon as they are vacated—not just before they are reoccupied.
4. Building or technical work in a cage, paddock or transport box is *not finished until* a careful check has been made to see that no dangerous nails, screws, pieces of wire, splinters and similar objects are either projecting or left lying around.
5. On every occasion before cages and transport boxes are due to be occupied by new animals they should be thoroughly checked to make sure that they are safe; this includes looking for any uneven surfaces, projecting nails, wire and other hazards.

6. The transfer of strong animals, from the size of a fox upwards, either into a transport box or out of it, is only to be done after the box has been properly secured with ropes, supports, etc.

7. The "principle of double security" must be applied at all times in the zoo but especially during the transfer of an animal from one place to another; in the event of it escaping, it should still find itself in an enclosed space. Thus, before any transfer operations are started all doors, windows, ventilation shafts, outlet drains and so on of the enclosure or house in which the transfer is to take place, should be shut and fastened.

8. The care of an animal does not stop after it has been carefully fed and watered; meticulous checking and removal of the dung are also an essential part of animal husbandry—together with a few friendly words.

9. In the artificial rearing of young animals on a bottle, no amount of care will bring results if the baby lacks the necessary bodily warmth; it is also essential, at least after every feed, to see that the gut and bladder are evacuated by gentle stimulation with a damp sponge, swab or something similar.

10. So-called animal-lovers often make clicking and hissing sounds at animals but most animals find these sounds unpleasant; deeper and quieter calls such as "hoo" are certainly more likely to be acceptable to animals which have been caught in the wild.

11. All materials must be used with the greatest economy, with the sole exception of disinfectant. Economy with disinfectants in the zoo is forbidden (this applies also to tincture of iodine or a corresponding substance, which must be applied even after the slightest injury).

12. In the same way that the animals need food and water, doors of cages and paddocks, etc., also require a little *lubrication* from time to time.

Six: The animal

Enough has been said so far to show that a zoo is far from being only a zoological concern. It is no accident that the animal should come sixth in the list of headings; moreover this fits in with the logical and chronological order followed in the establishment of a zoo. It is not

Fig. 13 The habitat of the big-city dweller. Concentration in completely artificial surroundings with nature totally excluded. View of a part of New York (Photographer unknown).

Fig. 14 (*extreme left*) Millions of humans live virtually shut off from nature; they do not see a single green leaf or even a living animal.

Fig. 15 (*left*) In Le Corbusier's 'Cite radieuse' a whole neighbourhood is packed into a habitation unit—it includes streets which look like illuminated tunnels and which enable the inhabitants to dispense entirely with the need to go out into the open.

Fig. 16 (*centre left*) The same sort of picture can be seen all over the world: skyscrapers shoot up out of the original vegetation and drive out the animals from their traditional habitats.

Fig. 17 (*bottom left*) Central Park in New York resembles a green island surrounded by skyscrapers. In addition to this zoo, New York and the surrounding area have four others, the most important of which is the Bronx Zoo.

Fig. 18 (*below*) Where the tropical rain-forest is destroyed it can never grow up again in its original form. With every tree that dies something irretrievable is lost.

Fig. 19 (*bottom*) One area after another of primary forest is uprooted. Wildlife is driven from its original home and is increasingly absorbed into the surrounding areas.

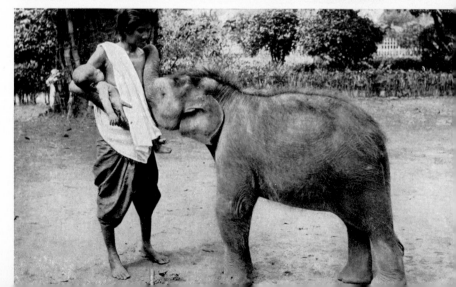

Fig. 20 (*top left*) These Kookaburras (*Dacelo gigas*) regard the outstretched arm of their keeper as an inanimate bit of the surroundings, that is, as a branch to be used as a comfortable perch.

Fig. 21 (*Centre left*) This Canadian Lynx regards its human keeper as a member of its own species and greets him with the head rubbing ceremony which is typical of its species (Photo Three Lions).

Fig. 22 (*bottom left*) For this young Indian Elephant the Siamese woman signifies as a member of its own species, in this case as its mother (Photographer unknown).

Fig. 23 (*above*) A lonely adult male tortoise (*Testudo hermanni*) regards the boot of its keeper as a member of its own species and attempts to mate with it (Photo Rene Honegger).

Fig. 24 (*below*) During the inoculation of an Alpine Ibex (*Capra ibex*) against foot-and-mouth disease a young buck Ibex becomes troublesome by trying to mate with one of the assistants.

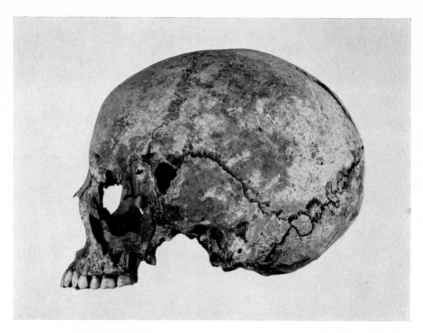

Fig. 25 A Vedda skull with typical injuries caused by a Sloth Bear. In India and Ceylon the Sloth Bear (*Melursus ursinus*) causes many serious accidents and even fatalities among the natives. This is because if it is accidently surprised by them when asleep, it jumps up in alarm and feels it must defend itself. The reaction becomes critical, the human taking on the significance of an enemy. In this situation the bear does not behave, at any rate in the first place, as a man-eater. (Collection of Dr Fritz Sarasin).

Fig. 26 Side-view of the skull of a Sloth Bear (*Melursus ursinus*), showing the powerful canine teeth. As a rule the bear uses another weapon before it bites, namely the claws on its fore-paws. When the bear is standing erect a man is usually struck in the face. (Collection of Natural History Museum, Basel).

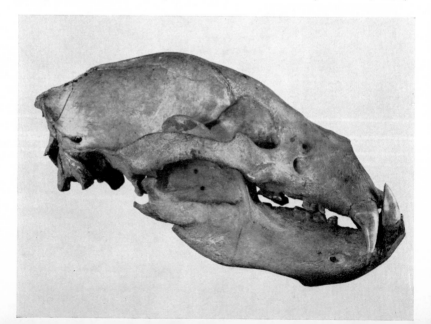

until man himself has found a suitable site, raised the necessary money, laid out the appropriate accommodation and built up the organization, that the animal can finally be introduced.

In practice the sequence of events does not always follow such a tidy pattern. It often happens that some animal or other arrives before there is any suitable accommodation for it or money available. Figure 1 provides a delightful illustration of this situation, for which I am indebted to Herr Hans Haudenschild; it evidently dates from the turn of the century. At that time Alfred Ilg, the Swiss Minister at the Court of the Emperor Menalik of Abyssinia, presented to the City of Zurich—whose coat-of-arms bears two lions—a couple of young lions named Mizzi and Barri; this placed the city in an embarrassing situation, because they were not in a position to look after the animals properly. There was no alternative but to put the two lions in the care of Hagenbeck's world-renowned zoological park at Stellingen near Hamburg. The people in Zurich then set about raising the money for building a cage for the lions. The card reproduced in Fig. 1 appealed for generous donations in the sentimental and anthropomorphic style typical of the time.

Evidently sufficient money did not materialize, because on 17 June 1903 the two Zurich City lions were moved from Hamburg to the Zoological Gardens in Basel (founded in 1874), whose council made an agreement with the City Council of Zurich that the lions should remain the property of the City of Zurich, but should be looked after free in Basel. It was also laid down that any offspring should be divided among the parties to the contract; nevertheless this did not happen. The Zoo in Zurich was not opened until 1929.

This venture in local patriotism illustrates a state of affairs which takes place now and again in the establishment of small zoos. Thus, for example, the first animals for the Animal Park in Goldau, Switzerland, arrived a year before the place was opened. Even today there are still zoo directors who procure or accept presentations before they can look after them properly. Once the animals are in the zoo provisional arrangements have to be made and the demand for a suitable building then becomes pressing. The animal is therefore used as a way of bringing pressure to bear to get the building put up.

From the standpoint of zoo biology this procedure is naturally to be condemned. In spite of the occasional success keeping animals in a makeshift manner on purely tactical grounds for ulterior motives is nevertheless inadmissible. The animals ought to find proper accommodation available for them on their arrival. The planning of accommodation must be coordinated with plans regarding the animal stock.

The concept of planning as applied to an animal collection, however, is so to speak foreign to many zoo men. Collections arise in a much more haphazard way: one takes what comes, even single individuals, perhaps as a chance gift for advertising purposes, an animal that is surplus from a circus passing through, or a surprise presentation from a returning overseas traveller. It should really be quite obvious that any zoo aiming at being worthy of the designation should have animals in its collection which confirm to a certain pattern. It is one of the special responsibilities of the zoos in question to select animals for the collection with due care.

As well as the ordinary zoo there is the thematic zoo, which specializes from the start on a particular group of animals, such as on the endemic fauna perhaps, on domesticated animals as was done by the Halle Zoo or on the animals mentioned in the Bible (Jerusalem Zoo).

Disappointments of several kinds were experienced by many of the zoological parks which either from choice or compulsion restricted themselves to the endemic fauna and to introduced species which had become established (e.g. Basel 1874, Bern 1937). First, the representatives of the endemic animal world proved to be of too little attraction to the public; compared with exotic animals their exhibition value was far too low. This subject will be dealt with in greater detail later on. Secondly, anyone who thought that endemic animals were "easier" to keep soon found out, for example, that many of the popular wild species of Europe—such as roe deer, hare, capercaillie and black grouse, woodcock or snipe, etc.,—are far more difficult to keep than some antelopes, monkeys, parrots, etc. It is therefore understandable that such zoological gardens, in spite of their original statutes and aims, were soon forced to take on exotic animals. Even Jerusalem cannot confine itself to showing only biblical animals; in the Bern Zoo in Dahlhölzli, monkeys, pelicans, giant snakes and marine fish nowadays make popular attractions, and in Basel nothing

44

of the original restrictions envisaged at the time of its foundation are to be seen.

It is possible however to keep certain specialities alongside a quasi-obligatory basic stock of popular exotic large animals. Thus, for example, the monkeys in San Diego and the antelopes in Rome, are unparalleled amongst the rich variety of the rest of the animals on display. A zoo without elephants, lions, tigers, bears, zebras, camels, monkeys, etc., would not be regarded as a zoo by the public; giraffes sea-lions, hippopotamus and ostrich also belong to the basic stock of large animals which are familiar to every child from its picturebooks, and which it therefore expects to see and to meet.

Today we know of about one million different animal species, of which thousands are suitable for keeping in zoos; this means that there are almost endless opportunities for specialization to take place side by side with the basic stock of animals which must also be kept. The larger the number of zoological gardens there are in existence and the more important they become, the more pressing is the need for specialization. Monotony of all kinds should be avoided. The aim should be to achieve the greatest possible variety, so that the visitor to the zoo can see something different and special in every city, both as regards the animal collection and also its presentation. A closer reciprocal division of the animal population between zoos of neighbouring cities would be desirable, but this sometimes fails through the ambition of each zoo to possess the most "complete collection" possible.

Apart from the fact that the attempt to establish a complete collection has proved to be basically an illusion even for small systematic groups, on account of the wealth of species, the desire to do so is a relic of the museum approach which formerly existed. The term "collection" now belongs to the realm of the museum. Striving to fill in gaps in individual collections in order to provide the whole picture is, therefore a legitimate aim of a museum and one that it is capable of carrying out. On the other hand the emphasis in the zoo today is less on collections than on exhibiting a selection of animal species, based on typical family or social groups, under the most natural possible conditions—that is, in breeding groups.

A significant tendency is beginning to emerge: in the future, it will not only be *what* one shows in the zoo, but *how* one shows it. The quantity of species shown must be reduced in favour of the quality of the way in which they are kept and exhibited.

People are only human and naturally the ambition to show the rarest and the most expensive animals will not disappear entirely. The okapi, for instance, was at one time regarded as one of the prestige animals. Originally it was a very expensive animal but the more frequently it is bred in zoos, the cheaper it becomes, thereby lessening its scarcity value and thus reducing the demand for it. In a certain sense the planning of the animal stock is inevitably influenced by such fashions. It is not difficult to predict that in this respect the bongo will be the successor to the okapi and that in Europe the keeping of dolphins will soon become a matter of prestige.

Often arguments based on finance rather than on zoo biology are the decisive factors in planning the stock of animals; money and chance determine what is in a particular zoo rather than geographical location, climate, vegetation, water supplies, access to supplies of food, historical considerations, etc. Run-of-the-mill zoos determined by chance are out of place nowadays; instead, each zoo should have a special character and style of its own. It is obvious that a zoo, say in Athens, must differ in every aspect—particularly architecturally and from the point of view of the animals kept—from a zoo in Switzerland or in Holland.

Some zoos have the ambition (and the concomitant money) to show the maximum number of first importations, a policy which is often advantageous from the publicity and advertising point of view. Sometimes however true scientific interest lies behind this because new knowledge can be gained from such opportunities. This does not apply so much to single specimens, although the relevant museum authorities are often scarcely able to hide their impatience for the specimen to die. From the scientific point of view breeding groups are more important because observations can be made for the first time on their reproductive behaviour and development, and there is the chance that the resulting progeny may be offered to other zoos.

The guide to the Bronx Zoo in New York (R. L. Ditmars and L. S. Crandall, 1945, p. ix), the "leading zoo of the United States" proudly records some unusual and rare animals which it has imported into the United States for the first time: quetzal, umbrella-bird, cock-of-the-rock, musk-ox, platypus, Przewalski's horse, koala, gorilla, bongo, okapi, pygmy hippopotamus, birds of paradise, vampire bat, Komodo dragon, etc.

According to Chalmers Mitchell (1929, p. 7) the oldest document relating to the Zoological Society of London, dated 1 February 1825, proposes the introduction of new quadrupeds, birds or fishes, etc., with a view to their possible use for domestication. Since then the importance attached to the first importation has largely disappeared; considerations of usefulness have largely retreated in the face of considerations of science and prestige.

Seven: Research

However galling it may be for a zoologist it has to be admitted that scientific research is usually placed last in zoological gardens, if indeed it has any place at all. The only exceptions to this rule are the few zoos—like the Bronx Zoo in New York and the London Zoo —which were established by scientific societies. Science only plays a subsidiary role in pretty well all the others. Some zoos believe that they have done enough for science when, instead of burying dead animals, as was generally done formerly, they hand the carcasses over to a museum or for pathological examination. Even today a zoo director with scientific interests is not infrequently regarded with suspicion by his governing body, and it is pointed out to him that a zoo director belongs in the zoo, his duties are confined to looking after the animals inside the zoo and do not include any wider interests or outside activities. Such a simple outlook is both naïve and out of date.

Anyone who finds the above statement somewhat questionable or even malicious, can refer to the annual accounts for zoos, for example those of European zoos, and see for himself whether money is allocated to scientific purposes or not, and if so, the sums that are involved.

We are not concerned here with cases which express dissatisfaction with conditions that are purely local but with the sad state of affairs which exists all over the world and which should be made known in the interests of progress. The attention of the governing bodies should be drawn to the fact that conditions for which they are responsible are reminiscent of the Middle Ages and totally unworthy of the age of space travel. There are serious defects which should be pointed out to the governing bodies; having had their attention explicitly drawn to them, they will find it difficult to answer for their neglect to future generations. The idea that a zoo can still be regarded merely as a business must be finally completely discarded. Nowadays a zoo must be run as a cultural institution and it should no longer be dependent upon the ignorance of people or authorities with old-fashioned ideas.

Even in zoos that are regarded as representatives of well-known institutions the facilities for research are sometimes unbelievably modest. For instance, on 9 September 1961 a gorilla was born in the United States National Zoo in Washington, D.C. This was a most unusual event, namely the fourth gorilla to be born in the history of zoological gardens, the second in the New World.

It was reported in detail by the Director of the National Zoological Park in Washington, Dr Theodore H. Reed, and his colleague B. F. Gallagher in the international journal *Der zoologische Garten* (1963). In view of the fact that insufficient data are available on the onset of sexual maturity and the development of the gorilla, exact weight measurements on the growth of the parents of the Washington youngster would have been of exceptional interest, particularly as when the young pair arrived in Washington they weighed about 20 and 17 pounds respectively.

Detailed weight measurements could not be given in the paper mentioned, because the National Zoo in Washington unfortunately possessed no suitable weighing machine. One finds a corresponding state of affairs in many other zoos; there is often a lack of the most modest research facilities, of laboratories, instruments, equipment and of money for payment to scientific colleagues. The most important exceptions today are the zoos run by the Zoological Societies of London, New York and San Diego, and the zoos in Amsterdam and Berlin-Friedrichsfelde; these zoos have been engaged in large scale activities in the scientific field for years. There must be many more opportunities that are missed which may never recur merely on account of lack of interest and the necessary finance.

In Amsterdam the Zoological Institute of the University is situated in the centre of the zoo, and thus it has quite unique opportunities for making use of live material for demonstration purposes. The zoo is owned by The Royal Zoological Society "Natura artis magistra" which celebrated its centenary in 1938. In 1928 the zoo, known popularly in Amsterdam as Artis, laid out a laboratory for research on animal behaviour in the centre of its ground. It was the first of its kind and for many years it was under the direction of J. A. Bierens de Haan. In 1939 the latter published a review of the very varied investigations which had taken place there. The report finishes with the sentence: "It is to the credit of the Royal Zoological Society that they have placed their animal material and their buildings and equipment at the disposal of these scientific investigations; they can rest assured of the gratitude of the investigators." There are many other zoos which could have followed this example, instead of allowing their animal stock to remain unproductive.

The Zoo at Berlin-Friedrichsfelde, already mentioned as a progressive organization, has extensive and modern research equipment which is closely tied to the German Academy of Sciences. Another zoo in Europe which is prominent in the scientific field is the London Zoo, and its Annual Report for 1963 infers that the research opportunities have been significantly increased by the building of the Nuffield Institute for Comparative Medicine and the Wellcome Institute for Comparative Physiology. Here scientific problems are investigated, which are related not only to the animal, but—thanks to the comparative approach—may also be of decisive importance to man.

Compared with these institutions other zoos are indeed wretchedly equipped. Zurich Zoo, among others, still does not possess a single laboratory. In some places a profitable restaurant is regarded as the most important building in the zoo. A zoo director should no longer keep his mouth shut about this kind of thing, his duty nowadays is to draw attention to it. There is only one planet Earth and only one fauna on the Earth, and already many of its members have been irretrievably lost, before even minor investigations into them have been made.

Biological research today is based mainly on work done on a small number of species kept in laboratories; the wild animals kept in zoos form an important and necessary supplement to this. The laboratory work is done on a narrow basis as many of these laboratory animals are simplified models of their wild ancestors, abstract animal forms or man-made creatures, which, because they have been selected under the artificial conditions of a minimal laboratory existence, tend to develop into extreme forms which do not occur in the wild. There are hidden dangers in the exclusive study of such caricatures of living creatures; these can only be countered by making supplementary observations, for the purpose of comparison, on wild animals, particularly when behavioural problems are involved, in addition to ordinary observations.

For example, in the majority of laboratory animals a quick succession of the generations is required, therefore the animals must have a rapid and uncomplicated method of reproduction. This goal has been achieved so successfully that, e.g. in rats, guinea-pigs, rabbits and others, on bringing together two sexually mature partners one can assume that mating will take place immediately, followed by fertilization. The formula is quite simple: 1 male + 1 female = breeding + young.

Such cases do not take any account of the enormous number of individual factors involving time and living space, which are of decisive importance to the animal in the wild. The condition of oestrus in the wild animal is very often linked with a particular seasonal breeding cycle, which according to circumstances depends on the animal's country of origin and not on the local conditions (emu). In the free-living animal many factors are involved which may affect success or failure in breeding: there are individual factors such as compatibility and antipathy, as well as social relationships; factors such as light, temperature, diet, the type of shelter available, the substrate and other ecological conditions may all play a part. Depending upon these factors, fertilization may or may not be possible, the period of gestation may be interrupted or lengthened, parturition and the subsequent rearing of the young may all be influenced in a positive or negative fashion. In many wild animals it is necessary for there to be a particularly fortunate interplay of numerous factors for breeding even to take place (Hediger, 1965). This is the norm and the automatic sequence followed by laboratory animals is the result of a schematic situation arranged by man; the latter should in no way be regarded as the normal situation. The simplification of conditions in the laboratory affects not only the behaviour

50

during reproduction, but also the habits, social behaviour, flight behaviour, feeding behaviour and so on, in fact the whole background of behaviour. The natural behaviour should be the only criterion; it alone is vital for every comparative study (Hediger, 1964).

It is true that with zoo animals we are not dealing with the original stock in its purest form, but it is significantly a much more pure source than that of the domesticated, overbred laboratory animal.

The importance of the study of behaviour in wild animals to the phylogenetic discussion of human problems is shown for instance in Konrad Lorenz's pioneering work *On Aggression* (1963). In this book he gives a natural history of aggression, a phenomenon on whose analysis and control depends nothing less than the fate of mankind.

It is well known that a basic knowledge of the human blood circulation can be obtained from the study of the conditions in less highly developed organs; every medical student has to start by acquiring a detailed knowledge of the circulation of the frog, lizard, pigeon and so on. That similar procedures must be followed not only in the fields of morphology and physiology but also in the discipline of psychology, curiously enough, is still not generally recognized today. With his comparative investigation of aggression Konrad Lorenz has undoubtedly contributed quite significantly to recognition of this fact which is long overdue; he begins with fish and progresses step by step through the animal kingdom to man.

Many other problems of human behaviour should be approached from a similarly fundamental point of view. Comparative methods should be employed, using wild animals as a basis for working out a solution to such problems. It is only possible to draw attention here to one of these, namely that of homesickness. This is an eminently biological phenomenon, which in man may give rise to the highest poetic achievements and also to serious crimes such as arson and murder. There is no doubt that its roots are primitive in origin and that these can only be exposed by comparative studies. The zoo can make a significant contribution to this problem because many of its animals have been removed from their familiar surroundings and into a strange environment. This transplantation is also the crux of the problem of human homesickness. We are not clear about the effects of transporting an animal or of the journey which involves the change from one geographical area to another with a different type

51

of climate; other factors about which we are not clear are the lack of familiar fellow creatures or the presence of strange ones, the new surroundings including their detailed features and the view from the enclosure, the diet of the animals and so on. All these changes in their home background have an effect about which we are uncertain.

The human form of homesickness may be related to the most improbable details of the familiar background, for example, even the chirping of house-sparrows may be significant. In his fascinating monograph on the spread of the European house-sparrow in North America W. B. Barrows (1889) gives the precise years (beginning in 1850) when sparrows were imported into the New World at great expense and for sentimental reasons, particularly by the English, German and French settlers. To every settler the familiar chirping of the sparrow meant a piece of the mother country that he did not want to be without.

Considering the great importance of homesickness in human psychology and psychopathology it is astounding how little work has hitherto been done on this phenomenon. In the nineties Karl Jaspers devoted his thesis to the subject "Homesickness and crime" (included in his collected writings which appeared in 1963). This classical investigation, in accordance with its period, contains characteristically not the slightest reference to the animal kingdom.

In a new work on *The Nostalgic Phenomenon* C. Zwingmann (1962, p. 315) makes an attempt at investigating at least one basic difference between human and animal behaviour. Admittedly the comparison appears to have been forced upon him by his reference to examples which are largely fanciful. He argues that tropisms and instinctive actions—such as the return of salamanders to their distant breeding-places, the return of a dog to its master, the suicide of falcons after capture or the destruction by a merlin of its own claws in a similar situation—could be interpreted as signs of nostalgia unless this difference did in fact exist.

A detailed comparative study, such as that undertaken by Lorenz in his approach to the nature of aggression, is of far greater importance than the examination of such borderline subjects which are biologically so grotesque. One certainly cannot get at the crux of human homesickness, without studying the importance of the home from its most primitive forms onwards; this primeval phenomenon is also eminently important to zoo biology. The same can be said of numerous other matters which come under the heading of human psychopathology and psychiatry. The exclusion from such investigations of the vast majority of organisms of the animal kingdom, which is so rich in variety and form, must necessarily lead to wrong conclusions; at the best such results would be incomplete.

Homesickness is also a phenomenon which can effectively contribute to the clarification and definition of the nature of zoo biology. Around the turn of the century the homesickness of animals played a prominent part—as a catchword—in zoological gardens. It was regarded as the most likely and most important factor contributing to death among zoo animals—even when, e.g. faults in diet, infections or parasites, must have destroyed the animals. At that time zoological gardens found themselves in the convenient position of being able to explain all cases of death among the animals in the simplest terms. Homesickness constituted the main cause of death which was always plausible; it also obviated the need for making a detailed pathological investigation which—if conscientiously performed—can be a very laborious and complicated procedure.

In so far as homesickness—or more primitive forms of it—occurs as a factor influencing zoo animals, it constitutes a subject which is now being dealt with in greater detail by zoo biology. The human psychologist may merely glance at the zoo in order to round off and supplement findings derived from the study of man, but in principle this is actually outside the field of zoo biology in the narrower sense.

This example not only illustrates the extremely wide field covered by zoo biology, it shows also the difficulty or the impossibility of establishing sharp dividing lines in this relatively young discipline (Hediger, 1942) which is typically a borderline subject.

2

What is Zoo Biology?

Zoo biology is a borderline subject which is concerned with questions that extend from zoology to human psychology and from ecology to pathology. The subject matter included in these disciplines covers such a wide field that it is not easy for one individual to give an overall view. This was the gist of the outline which I put forward in 1942, when I attempted to show the interplay of the most important disciplines.

The subject of zoo biology can also be briefly described thus: it embraces everything in the zoo which is biologically relevant (Hediger 1953). It is therefore that science which concerns itself with all those phenomena "which occur in the zoological garden and—in the widest sense—are of biological importance". From this it follows that the science of zoo biology immediately identifies itself not only as a borderline subject but as a definite mixture of many different disciplines, embracing them all to some extent and also seeking to synthesize them into a whole (Hediger 1956, p. 6). The whole is achieved by the uniqueness of the confrontation of animal and man in the zoo, taking into consideration optimal function, organization, improvement and exploitation.

On the one hand zoo biology provides the scientific basis for the maintenance of wild animals in the zoo under optimal and appropriate conditions and on the other hand it investigates and formulates the special biological code of practice which applies to man and animals as a result of keeping animals in captivity. Zoo biology therefore has a twofold objective and for this reason it concerns

54

itself with biological phenomena in both animals and man.

Zoo biology is still a very young science and today many zoos are still run without the faintest idea that it exists. In some places no thought is given as to what the present role of a zoo either is or should be. The criteria on which a zoo is judged vary correspondingly from place to place; the zoo may be evaluated according to its rate of profit, the number of visitors, or the sale of peanuts, sausages, postcards and other comparatively paltry souvenirs. Also when assessing values the size of the animal stock, the rarity and costliness of the animals exhibited are used in a biased way, no regard being paid to the scientific evaluation, the efforts in the service of popular education and training, the promotion of conservation and so on.

There are only very few cases where zoos have been regarded in their entirety as a biological phenomenon and treated as such. Here, zoo biology has to be fitted in amongst many other disciplines to which it can make a contribution; these extend well beyond zoology, animal psychology and veterinary medicine into human psychology, psychiatry, sociology, criminology, architecture, technology, landscape gardening and so on.

Even chemistry, pharmacology, and botany can play a part in zoo biology, as for example in connection with the preparation of artificial sea water, the compatibility of helminthicides or the use of bamboo for decorative purposes. The emphasis in all this is always placed on the special conditions in a zoo.

For example in the case of phenothiazine, a drug used to combat nematodes, it is not really the chemical composition or its effect on domesticated animals that is important, but of much greater significance is the fact that even in the smallest amounts it has a paralysing or even lethal effect on kangaroos, similar to that of derris root on the lesser panda or of yew on perissodactyls.

Bamboo—to cite but a single example from botany—is particularly suitable for the decoration of vivaria, aviaries and cages, but it possesses the unfortunate peculiarity that cut stems—even when cut under water and carefully protected from air embolism—do not take up water and thus in a short time the bamboo withers and becomes dried up. So far there has been no effective help from plant physiologists towards solving this small but irritating problem in zoo biology.

It is obvious that the veterinarians with all their special knowledge

—from bacteriology to radiology—have an enormous part to play in zoo biology, particularly where wild animals are concerned. Comparative pathology is of even greater importance, because it can provide the zoo biologist above all with extremely valuable pointers about faults in animal husbandry (e.g. incorrect diet, parasitization, accommodation etc.).

Certain findings of the pathologist may indeed even have a specific zoo-biological aspect, which extends beyond pathology. An example will illustrate the point in general: Herbert Fox, the former pathologist of Philadelphia Zoo, published in 1923 a comprehensive work on the diseases of wild animals and birds in captivity. In the section on skeletal injuries (p. 343 *et seq.*), based on the vast amount of material available to him, he states that among the mammals it is particularly the Cervidae (deer), Bovidae (cattle, antelopes etc.) and Camelidae (camels, llamas) which show the most numerous fractures, when they chase each other and fall down on the slippery floors of the cages. Fox also mentions cases of broken pelvis in antelopes from doing the splits. Drawing on his wide experience as a pathologist he ends significantly with the words: "animals with long extremities, especially when the bones are quite near the skin, have a rather high incidence of fractures . . . "

The zoo biologist is in complete agreement with Fox's findings, but takes the argument a step further. He uses the pathologist's statistical survey for the purpose of working out prophylactic measures for these long-legged ungulates which are liable to this kind of injury and he takes steps to guard against this happening in three particular ways: first, by avoiding sharp angles in the ground plan of the paddock so that as far as possible chases can follow a curved (not angular) course, secondly, by using a sufficiently roughened surface for the ground on which the animals can pull up and not skid, and thirdly by preventing the animals from becoming excited and aggressive.

It is not unusual for newly born ungulates to come to grief even as early as their first attempt to stand, by doing the splits with their hind legs on a ground surface that is too smooth. At such times, the failure to spread sufficient straw or put down an adequate layer of sand can rightly be regarded as a case of neglect in the technique of husbandry.

Nevertheless it is not always the ground surface which is primarily to blame in the case of those animals that are particularly prone to leg fractures. Such injuries can also be caused in other ways as for example, in the servaline cat, a long-legged carnivore. I have been told in several zoos of numerous leg fractures among these attractive spotted cats from Africa; in the wild they live on the ground but in captivity casualties occur when they climb up high wire-netting and then fall down. Fractures of this type can be avoided by removing opportunities for this kind of climbing activity (for example by fixing strips of transparent plastic, which is not noticeably offensive, to the wire about 30 inches from the ground).

Again, the frequent leg fractures in ratite birds come from quite different causes; in young ostriches and rheas, for instance, they may occur as a result of the birds suddenly rushing about and even spinning around as though in a fit. They often get caught up in the wire-netting but even if this does not happen, this seemingly mad larking about can lead to fractures. The leg of an ostrich is an extremely specialized organ and a fracture usually results in death.

These three types of leg fracture from quite different causes are mentioned simply as an example to throw light on the nature of zoo biology: under certain circumstances, the zoo biologist and the pathologist read quite a different meaning into a leg fracture. The same phenomenon is seen by both of them but from different points of view. The task of zoo biology is to apply this specific interpretation, so far as this is possible, to all phenomena and occurrences in the zoo and to codify them.

Naturally, zoo biology welcomes any information which comparative pathology can provide from the zoo that is of interest to its work and which contributes in so far as it can to the advance of such work. Zoo biology itself however only calls for a small part of the findings of pathology; it only makes use of that part which is directly related to the particular situation in which humans and animals encounter each other, such as occurs in every zoo.

All natural science disciplines tend to clutch at mathematics and make use of it for their own purposes; similarly zoo biology not only makes use of certain aspects of mathematics but also of all relevant branches of science, in order to clarify its own field of work and to develop it further. It can borrow material from various disciplines and draw comparisons, for example, from the fields of biology,

57

medicine and psychology, thus bringing about a fruitful synthesis and symbiosis.

In this context it is worth mentioning the lessons to be learnt from the anthropozoonoses, diseases that attack man as well as animals, such as tuberculosis, ornithosis, foot-and-mouth disease, cancer, malaria, anthrax and so on. The outbreak and course of such diseases among zoo animals are of interest to human medicine; zoo biology for its part is extremely interested in investigations of this kind, in order to protect the animals, the visitors and the staff from such infections. Far-reaching basic research is involved here as well as the application of results for practical purposes. In his pioneering work on *Changes in animals during captivity: phenomena parallel to the casualties of civilization in man*, H. Nachtsheim (1949) refers to these points. Aggression and homesickness have already been mentioned as further examples.

For the rest I can only hope to convey in this book the scope of zoo biology by mentioning such diverse subjects as parasitology and criminology. Within the restricted framework of this book only part of the immense spectrum can be revealed by indicating a few examples of the many forms and far-reaching aspects of zoo biology.

Nevertheless it is to be hoped that future colleagues will be in a position to show the importance of what is meant by zoo biology and to present the extent of its scope with the necessary forcefulness at a time when it is still opportune. By opportune I mean a point in time, at which there is sufficient "material", that is, adequate populations of wild animals, still available to work with. The "material" in this case is both precious and irreplaceable and is of incalculable cultural value to the whole of mankind.

Elspeth Huxley (1963) has given an outspoken and serious warning that it may soon be too late to get to know the living world as it is today; that it is possible that whole species may disappear from the face of the earth before we have even discovered them. She also made the point that we are the poorer for everything that we have lost in the natural world, and poorer also in knowledge. Ignorance, of course, leads to dangerous slips and errors.

Already many human races (Red Indians, Tasmanians and others) have been completely exterminated in historical times, some of them even as recently as in the time of our parents. Important roots and

Fig. 27 Children humanizing a footstool. The humanization of animals by adults can lead to serious misunderstandings, amounting to cruelty to animals.

Fig. 28 The Capuchin Monkey Boby greeting a human friend (Photo Jurg Klages).

Fig. 29 The animal as an article of merchandise. A part of the bird-market held every Sunday in Paris. To increase their commercial value, certain drab birds are dipped in garish colours so that they will fetch a higher price from unsuspecting customers.

Fig. 30 On the premises of a Marseilles animal-dealer thousands of Java Sparrows (*Padda oryzivora*) are treated as goods in transit, destined for dispatch to retailers in central Europe.

Fig. 31   On an air transit flight from Brazil, the Zurich Zoo was
expected to perform what was in many respects a most repugnant
task; they had to care for 28 possible survivors out of a total consignment of 138 Marmosets (*Hapale jacchus*) which had been
crowded together.

Fig. 32   In a fish market: marine animals on sale have a particularly strange look about them, particularly when they are
from deep-sea fisheries.

Fig. 33 The South American Pacarana (*Dinomys branickii*) is of exceptional interest to zoologists and to students of animal behaviour. In spite of its rarity, its exhibition value is practically nil.

Fig. 34 The daily promenade of the King Penguins is a great attraction to visitors and provides a very popular subject for photography.

Fig. 35   Even in early spring considerable crowds of people gather to watch the apes.

Fig. 36   The monkey terraces draw big crowds of spectators in every zoo.

Fig. 37   In 1964 there was only one Giant Panda (*Ailuropoda melanoleuca*) in the Western world, namely the one in the London Zoo (this picture however was taken of the one in Brookfield Zoo, Chicago, in 1951).

Fig. 38   Giant Pandas are exceptionally valuable as exhibits, doubtless because their soft fur and rounded heads have such an appeal for children.

branches of our own ancestral tree have thus been finally chopped off and lost. A long, macabre list of animals, which have been exterminated only in the last hundred years by irresponsible and ignorant men should be appended here. Zoos have given sanctuary to the very last specimens of various animal species—from the passenger pigeon to the quagga—that have been exterminated; today zoos are the last place of refuge for other species that are dying out, such as the Arabian oryx, the blesbok, the white-tailed gnu, the common mountain zebra, to name only a few examples. And funds for conservation work still have to be raised by *begging* for them. These sums are ludicrously small relative to the work that needs to be done to conserve species that are in immediate danger and for studying living phenomena that still share our planet but which may have disappeared for ever by tomorrow.

The serious conservationist is driven to the brink of despair by the arguments put forward by competent but pitifully ignorant authorities who turn down even modest requests for help. It is true that there are also projects on a more generous scale but nowadays these are the exception.

In this connection the historical origin of many zoological gardens from cabinets of curiosities and from the menagerie linked with the annual fair, constitutes a serious hindrance; this is a point which I have already referred to in Chapter 1.

It so happens that in many cases zoos convey an image that is reminiscent of the circus or amusement park. This is due amongst other things to the fact they are directed by non-academics and that their advertising, e.g. in posters, lends support to this image.

For this reason the large American zoos, for instance, no longer make use of advertisements; in fact, these zoos are always full of city-dwellers, hungry for nature, particularly at the weekends, a point to which I will return later. But the majority of European zoos have to achieve the highest possible numbers of visitors for reasons of finance and therefore they seek to attract as many people as possible into the zoo by posters and other methods of propaganda. No botanic garden is run in this way. Every university department of botany possesses automatically, as it were, a botanic garden; its support by the university, that is by the relevant state or city, is equally taken for granted. In botanic gardens visitors are so to speak tolerated. Some directors of botanic gardens make no concealment of the fact that visitors are not welcome. The garden is required to provide material for teaching and research purposes. Any advertisement is unnecessary and unacademic.

By contrast I do not know of a single university department of zoology which has a zoo with material at its disposal, in a similar fashion to a botany department. It is only in Amsterdam—as already mentioned—that the Zoological Institute of the University lies in the centre of the zoo, but both organizations are run quite separately from each other.

Normally, therefore, zoological gardens stand completely apart from the university; they use advertising methods and are sometimes under non-academic direction. By this fact the remoteness between university and zoo, or between science and menagerie management, is often widened in a fatal fashion and indeed it becomes a yawning gulf. For their part some zoo directors give a more or less distinct impression of having an aversion to scientists. As zoo practitioners they often feel superior to scientists and rightly so within their own profession when the scientists know nothing about zoo management.

It would be in accordance with the pressing needs of our time if every zoo were to be closely linked with a university for the purpose of achieving optimal scientific exploitation; a liberal supply of zoologists and other scientists should be available in every zoo. There would never be any lack of interesting work and the basic biological research could be promoted to the greatest advantage in this way.

When practical management is permeated by scientific activity, difficulties naturally arise particularly at the outset; these can be avoided however, providing there is mutual respect, a careful delineation of authority and above all by harmonious personal relations. There are well-known examples which can be enumerated both of friction and harmony—antagonism between the commercial and the scientific director, and easy cooperation with one director working under the other.

Naturally zoo biology has first and foremost to do with zoology, primarily with systematics; in the first place one must know the animal species that one is dealing with and for this reason care must be to provide correct labels for the public. The zoo is hardly the appropriate place for systematics that involve detailed work over a long period; this kind of work is more properly done in a museum. Distinguishing characters such as dentition or skeletal peculiarities can often only be investigated on the dead animal, and the necessary comparative material for this work is usually found only in the museums.

As has already been mentioned, there are zoos which take a particular pride in first importations; others point out with emphasis that they even "discover" species or races and make available the first scientific description. To the uninitiated this usually suggests adventurous searches through jungle and steppe, leading finally to the capture and importation of the long-sought after animal. In fact such discoveries usually take place in a very much less dramatic fashion *after* the arrival of the animal in a zoo, namely by the trained eye of a specialist who looks at the animal and is struck by some more or less insignificant deviation from the species or races already known.

L. Zukowsky (1929, p. 207) gives some examples of such animals which were imported by the firm of Hagenbeck and named after Hagenbeck by the competent systematists, such as a mandrill from the hinterland of Lagos which bears the name *Mandrillus hagenbecki* Zukowsky. Sometimes such zoo discoveries do not have a very long life in scientific systematics; the differentiating characters subsequently show themselves to be insufficiently constant and pronounced to justify the establishment of a new species or race.

The converse also occurs, however, namely that certain animals in the zoo are assigned to the best known species and it is only after a considerable time—in some cases years—that one becomes aware that one is dealing with a completely new species. This happened, for example, with the bonobo or dwarf chimpanzee, *Pan paniscus* Schwarz, which was first described as a separate species in 1929 by E. Schwarz, but which had already been living as a specimen in the Amsterdam Zoo from 1911 to 1916 as reported by P. J. H. van Bree in 1963.

Zoo biology is not directly interested in discoveries of this kind; it is grateful to zoological systematics for its valuable assistance and is delighted—if this expression is allowed—when for its own part it makes a contribution to systematics; on the other hand the description of new animal species basically belongs more properly to the museum world. Zoo biology must restrict itself above all to biological problems which arise in the zoo from the confrontation of the living animal with living humans; it is concerned primarily with the discovery, formulation and consideration of the principles arising in the zoo and the basic research connected with this animal-man confrontation.

At this point I must deal with a certain attitude that is widely held but basically erroneous regarding the management of animals, namely the disastrous confusion of domesticated with wild animals.

"A comprehensive literature exists on how to manage domestic animals, dealing at length with every conceivable detail. Feeding, breeding, transmission of hereditary characters, pedigree, distribution, market value, pathology, training and so on have long been the subject of basic research and have become the specialized departments of an impressive science. On the other hand, the study of how to keep wild animals in zoos can hardly boast of even the most general outlines; all it has to show is a collection of more or less disconnected pieces of advice and some facts. In this book, therefore, an attempt will be made to sketch out a few essential lines for preliminary study. It is neither possible nor advisable to discuss at length individual species; that would furnish the subject matter for an exhaustive textbook on zoo management; our concern is rather to lay the foundations and nothing else."

For various reasons I have allowed myself to repeat verbatim this passage from the introduction of my book *Wild animals in captivity*, published in 1942, to which I referred in the Foreword. In the first place this is because the long-awaited comprehensive textbook on keeping wild animals in zoos actually appeared while the present book was being written; I refer to the magnificent and truly comprehensive work of a much respected colleague, Lee S. Crandall, *The management of wild animals in captivity* (1964). Secondly, because in spite of all the progress in the keeping of individual species of wild animal the fundamental guiding principles which are essential to the maintenance of wild animals in the zoo have received too little attention; perhaps this is just because of the many individual successes in some places but in any case the fundamental principles are in danger of disappearing altogether from the mental horizon of people in responsible positions and there is a growing threat that the work of zoological gardens will develop in a false direction.

At that time (1942, p. 46) I enlarged on the subject thus: "A fundamental problem of zoo biology is how to neutralize as far as possible all modifying (non-hereditary, externally conditioned) and mutative (hereditary) degeneration phenomena in captivity." This statement put forward almost quarter of a century ago must be reiterated today and given fresh emphasis.

The processes by which domesticated animals are bred have become confused to some extent with those by which wild animals are bred and the way in which these processes have become mixed up gives cause for alarm. In fact the breeding aims in the one case are diametrically opposed to the other: the breeding of domesticated animals for economic purposes must be directed above all to the service of human nutrition, to the production of meat, milk, eggs and so on; it must therefore step up the effects of domestication to the greatest possible extent; in other words this means that the natural development of the species in the wild must be combated. Breeding for economic ends requires early maturity, fast growth, fattening, therefore hypertrophy of sexual behaviour, of the ovaries (e.g. in fowls), of the milk glands (e.g. in cattle), deposition of fat, and with it a minimal expenditure of energy during movement, optimal utilization of food and so on.

In the zoo, however, we must take care to counteract all these domestication phenomena; the wild animals loaned to us from nature must be kept in the most pure and original condition. We do not want to keep good utilizers of food, efficient fatteners, domestic tigers or domestic monkeys that are incapable of moving; on the contrary we want to keep the species as true to nature as possible. The zoo animal must therefore be given the most natural food possible, not the most nutritious, as well as sufficient space to move in. Nature knows nothing of early maturity, artificial fattening, sexual hypertrophy, the degeneration of the sense organs and the loss of the ability to move.

The selection of the domesticated animal works towards diametrically opposed ends to that of the wild animal; with wild animals in the zoo our sole aim is to keep to the rules of nature as far as possible. The zoo must be the opposite of a profitable farm; it must work in nature's direction, and according to natural tendencies and not towards maximal production of protein and fat. In this context the original stock must be safeguarded.

There is a danger which already exists in some places that man in his naïve fashion will try to emulate his ancestors and repeat the ancient experiments of domesticating new animal species by applying modern techniques. The approach of the veterinarian, trained only in domesticated animals, evidently plays a disastrous role in this field, for example on the subject of nutrition; this will be referred to again in a later chapter.

In contrast to the production of animals for economic purposes, there should be no zoos which are profitable, rationalized or auto-mated. Staff difficulties, which are usually basically financial diffi-culties, ought not to lead us in the zoo towards regarding a press-button system with the director at the controls as the ideal solution to these problems. In farm animal production automation may bring astonishing successes in the sense of profitability; in the zoo we must keep right away from it on principle because it is necessary to main-tain not only the animal itself but also its behaviour in the purest, most natural state possible.

If we bear in mind the methods of feeding, fattening and breeding which are already commonly practised in farm animal production— for example artificial insemination, artificial fertilization, artificial twin-formation, artificial rearing and so on in cattle—it is not difficult to imagine going in for tissue culture on a large scale for the rational production of protein, perhaps in conjunction with the utilization of the substances which settle on purification plants. The domesticated animal would then be unnecessary as a production unit or at most it could be kept in farm reserves, as a "renewal stock" for the tissue cultures; its role would be similar to that played today by the big game reserves in relation to the zoological gardens.

The zoos, however, are not there for this purpose and in the future they ought not to be misappropriated to provide protein for human consumption; as cultural institutions of mankind they must provide adequate surroundings in which non-domesticated animals can be maintained.

There are numerous examples of this type of confused enterprise where the mixing up of zoo and economic animals is clearly undesir-able. Thus, for example, the animal park of Lange-Erlen in Klein-Basel, which has been going since 1870, runs a profitable poultry farm alongside the real zoo park with deer, monkeys, parrots etc.

As P.-A. Pichot (1873, p. 10) has recorded there was a particularly remarkable piece of equipment for fattening poultry in the Jardin d'Acclimatation in Paris. In a kind of merry-go-round over 100 young poultry were kept singly in narrow, numbered cages that were arranged in five rows one above the other. From his fixed position the keeper could operate the merry-go-round which was constructed on the principle of a circular conveyor belt. He could bring one chicken after another in front of him thus enabling him to introduce the desired amount of food into the crop by pressing a pedal. By a light turn of the merry-go-round the next chicken followed on. A simple hoist provided with a counterweight moved the keeper from one row of chickens up to the next, so that in the shortest time with the least expenditure of energy a maximum number of chickens could be crammed with food, namely 400 chickens per hour. After 18 days of this regime each chicken had doubled its weight. Visitors to the Jardin d'Acclimatation could buy these fattened poultry. Furthermore this zoo was well stocked with zebras, tapirs, elephants, kangaroos and so on. Automatic feeding and this confusion with the production of farm animals was already in existence therefore about 90 years ago. Now there is a new threat of this fundamental error threatening from Philadelphia (cf. Chapter 7).

3

The Zoo as a Place for Man
and Animal

This title is not intended as some kind of allusion to certain novels which describe the rare cases of men who manage to get into a zoo in circumstances that are always highly fantastic. These deal with the fate that overtakes such men when forced to live inside a cage usually in the monkey house, thus completing the collection with the species *Homo sapiens*. (For example, see Richard Garnett's *A man in the zoo*, 1924). The intention here is to show the increasing importance to modern man of the zoological garden and to counteract the impression that zoological gardens are purely zoological concerns or luxury establishments—as they were formerly regarded—which one or other city can afford as a special feature.

We are dealing here with a subject that is typical of zoo biology. It shows clearly that this discipline also touches on anthropology, questions of civic architecture, sociology and social hygiene; it does not merely impinge on these subjects but overlaps and delves right into them. Taking zoos today as a whole they are the expression of a worldwide phenomenon: they are the concern of every man, at least of every large-city dweller.

The concentration of enormous numbers of humans into the smallest possible space in skyscraper complexes is a special feature of the times in which we live. This is happening on every continent and during the last few decades a radical change has been taking place in the type of human dwelling in urban areas. Abroad, the population count of every large city is equivalent to or even double that of the total population of Switzerland and the many side-effects of these large concentrations of people are much more gross and obvious than in Switzerland. However, even in some Swiss towns there are already clear symptoms of a hunger for nature, a disease of civilization that is still scarcely recognized. It is a kind of psychical deficiency, a phenomenon which is not to be cured with pills but only by leaving humans open to the influence of nature; this applies particularly to the big-city dweller, who must be provided with access to secondary forms of nature such as parks and zoos.

From the public health point of view the importance of the open spaces and parks, the well-known "lungs of the big city", has already been recognized for a long time. In some places these green oases have been used so intensively that many of them have lost their original character as small cameos of nature and in this sense they have become almost sterile. Nevertheless the stocking of them with animals that could be seen was an important characteristic of these open spaces.

Increasingly the city-dweller lives in an environment which is a far cry from nature, surrounded by abstract forms in synthetic materials, devoid of animal life and subject to artificial conditions of light and temperature; caught up in a tangle of electric wires the human population is assailed by the humming or reverberation of noisy machines.

Weekend trips into the country are becoming more and more difficult on account of the big distances involved and the increasing risks of accidents on the road. Nowadays it is only the favoured few who can get away from it all and enjoy the peace and seclusion of a day in the countryside under blue skies in the absence of jet planes, and feast their eyes, ears and noses on the innumerable treasures offered by the edge of a forest with a view over green meadows. These people have no need of a zoo, they still have direct and immediate contact with nature in its purest form. To some extent our great-grandparents spent their lives in simple houses made of wood, that is in parts of the forest. Light and warmth were derived immediately from nature and the water was pumped from the earth. In many cases people lived under one roof with cattle, horses and a number of other domestic animals. There were all kinds of wild animals living in the fields and woods of the immediate vicinity; the smaller ones took up residence in storehouses and cellars. At that time nobody suffered from a hunger for nature, and indeed many activities, often the most important ones, took place under the open sky. Hunger for nature is a modern phenomenon, the seriousness of which is still underestimated. Like crime it grows proportionally with the concentration of humans per unit of area and becomes evident when we take into consideration the development of zoos as a whole.

Just as it is not possible to include here more than a glimpse of veterinary medicine in the zoo, equally it is not possible to go into any detail on social ethnology or the science which is concerned with the big city as a biological organism. Whereas everyone can see that veterinary medicine and zoos must be closely connected there are only a few people today who even suspect that a zoo is of importance to a big city.

It is precisely for this reason that this point must be dealt with, even if we restrict ourselves to a single example. It is well known that there is a close association between crime and large concentrations of humans and that the crime rate is highest in densely populated areas. It is also noticeable that juvenile crime and delinquency flourish in the fertile environment of the big city. These problems are almost unknown in rural areas. Doubtless the underlying factors are of a very complex character, nevertheless it may safely be assumed that the degree of contact with nature, or the absence of any such contact, plays some part and possibly a role that is decisive.

At this point one should draw attention to the work of the social-ethnological group of the Centre National de la Recherche Scientifique in Paris, in particular the study of Y. M.-J. Chombart de Lauwe (1959) on the social psychopathology of the maladjusted child. Although this work might appear to have no connection with zoo biology the concept, for example, of the big city as a special biotope in the ecological sense (p. 36) is given serious attention; mention is also made of the fact that even individual districts may have quite different biotope characteristics, and that young people in particular may be upset by all sorts of unnatural processes and thrown off balance.

Further light can be thrown on the general situation by mentioning the fact that it is a common experience to find the youth of urban agglomerations with more and more free time at their disposal

68

and increasingly cut off from wild life. Isolated from nature, in a vacuum with nothing to do, young people are forced to find compensation in all kinds of activities such as sport, scouting, adventure games and so on. Evidently all this is not the final answer.

The zoological garden can help with this problem, not only by supplying a form of nature at secondhand but also by filling the vacuum in spare time activity with intensive contact with nature, by providing significant things for people to do with animals and plants, thus bringing the modern generation into contact with living things in a way that was familiar to our ancestors day by day in their houses, fields and gardens.

A visit to the zoo undoubtedly represents a welcome diversion to many people but it is also beneficial in a more positive sense; as an important part of the big-city habitat, however, a zoo has yet other tasks to fulfil, which extend beyond its perimeter fence. But when anything arises that touches on this dividing line, it is precisely at this point that people who are narrow-minded and lacking in vision issue a warning about finance; they put a stop to every kind of initiative, raising a wall of red tape.

It is a shameful and regrettable fact that most zoological gardens are still not yet as well organized as they should be for educational work with schools and with people who are looking for spare time activities; this is particularly important today as the teaching of biology in schools is having to give way increasingly in favour of technical subjects. Innumerable schoolchildren are put at a disadvantage in this respect and the ignorance of sixth-formers in relation to knowledge of the simplest living processes in the animal kingdom (elementary zoology) is sometimes shattering.

Shouts from youngsters "look at the animals" are frequently heard in most of the zoos all over the world but particularly in the zoos of large cities. Young people have a passionate desire to make direct contact or to have "something to do with animals". We hear remarks of this kind from all sections of the populace and this is symptomatic of the modern disease which stems from an ever-increasing alienation from nature, leaving people with a sense that something is lacking.

Every zoo is a mine of information about nature and this storehouse of knowledge should be made available to all, particularly to school and youth groups; the information should be disseminated through the relevant organizations, by means of organized courses, club activities, staff training schemes, lectures, information services and so on. Before this aim can be achieved, ways must be found of breaking through the jungle of red tape but instead of this being done the frustrating welter of rules and regulations is currently being strengthened. Teenage problems are dealt with piecemeal, by introducing police regulations and other measures; admittedly such steps are taken with some reluctance because one is aware that these methods do not get at the root of the trouble which has many ramifications. Experts have also stated that "the main problem is boredom" and that "the greatest problem lies in the organization of leisure time" and so on. Bearing in mind the above statements, one of the most accessible sources for making use of leisure in a sensible and satisfying way is the zoo with its wealth of highly interesting animals; the contribution which the zoo could make, however, is often deliberately overlooked, due to ignorance, pedantry or for reasons of convenience. The healthy desire for information, for instruction and for active participation assumes giant proportions, but the opportunities in zoos for satisfying this urge for knowledge, participation and investigation are usually very poor or are completely lacking in some zoos; this is because the appointment of staff with talents for this purpose might affect the budget unfavourably. Some governing bodies still believe that their job is concerned with feeding animals, removing manure and keeping the paths clean. Some of those who are in responsible positions frequently ignore the present position in which the zoological garden is assuming the significance of a place where youth, particularly the young people in the big city, can be encouraged to contemplate the wonders of nature and to respect the living animal and thus be guided towards a respect for life in general.

Police regulations and laws will certainly not make any impression on boredom which hangs like a heavy and ominous cloud over some of the youth in densely populated areas. There is no doubt that inspired and inspiring educationists, trained in natural history and appointed as teachers in the zoo, would have remarkable opportunities of capturing the interest of a considerable number of groups of young people; their attention could be drawn to facets of animal life, particularly of animal behaviour that are of absorbing interest and really exciting. It would even be possible to devise simple research projects. In every zoo as well as a vast number of biological questions there are also a number of technical ones which crop up, such as the creation of the habitat in the widest sense which includes problems of lighting, irradiation, temperature, automatic timing devices and so on; there is also the measurement of respiration rates, duration of diving, sleep and activity rhythms. This means that it would be possible to keep young people interested in technical matters busy in the zoo with tasks that are absorbing and worthwhile.

A few central European zoos have moved ahead in this field by setting up zoo schools, e.g. Frankfurt-am-Main, Cologne, Hanover and London. There have also been establishments of this type in America for a long time. Nevertheless for the majority of zoos there still remains a great deal to be done. But let us return now to the zoo as a necessary constituent part of the human habitat of the big city.

From Peking to Los Angeles and from Johannesburg up to the north of Canada new zoos are continually being built or, where they are already in existence, they are being significantly enlarged. Many capital cities now have more than one zoo: London, Detroit, Berlin, Paris and others already have two, and so has Chicago, which in addition has the largest public aquarium so far in the world. New York has five zoos, and also the new Aquarium on Coney Island which is still in course of construction, where amongst other things whales and walruses are kept.

The first installation of this type, with gigantic pools for toothed whales, was set up on the east coast of Florida in 1938 when Marineland Studios was established. At that time these oceanaria were tied to sites near to the sea-coast, as for example the Seaquarium in Miami and Marineland of the Pacific south of Los Angeles. Since then it has been shown that it is possible to run this kind of establishment quite independently of the sea using artificial sea water. The opening of the Seven Seas Panorama far from the coast in Brookfield Zoo, Chicago in 1961 has already been mentioned. These oceanaria have already become popular in Japan and Australia, and Europe ought not to delay building them any longer.

America's National Zoo in Washington, D.C., is at present being completely rebuilt, enlarged and modernized, and in 1962 a grant of ten million dollars was approved for the construction of an aquarium in this city.

This list could be considerably longer, but these examples must suffice to demonstrate the irresistible spread, enlargement and enrichment of zoos and public aquaria throughout the whole world—and all this is taking place in spite of the usual miserly outlook of financiers everywhere. How can one explain this paradoxical state of affairs! The answer can be reduced to a very simple formula: zoos and large aquaria were formerly considered to be optional luxury establishments but today they are widely regarded as a constituent part that is absolutely essential to every large city; they form irreplaceable elements of the big-city habitat, that is of the environment of modern man. Man cannot do without them just as he cannot do without parks and open spaces. Stated more precisely, they are emergency exits to nature, secondary natural places where the city-dweller can appease his hunger for nature, a hunger which cannot be sloughed off from one generation to the next but which is deep-seated and must be satisfied.

The further that technology spreads into our lives, taking possession of the private spheres of activity as well as pervading our working life, the stronger the need becomes for man to occupy himself at least in his spare time with non-technical matters, that is, with living animals and plants. In the irresistible spread of the zoological garden throughout the world, and also in the growing numbers of those nature-lovers who keep aquaria, vivaria, birds and other animals at home, we cannot fail to recognize a reaction against the alarming penetration of technology into our everyday lives.

If one regards the keeping of domestic animals and the cultivation of plants as the oldest, the most widespread and grandiose example of experimental biological activity, then the establishment of the zoological garden must certainly be regarded as the second oldest and second largest biological experiment of mankind, and therefore a phenomenon of great significance (Hediger 1956).

For all too long zoos were regarded solely as local concerns, chiefly as places of local entertainment. In fact however factors of quite a different order of magnitude are involved. In this field, as with domestication, man's role is not only that of the practical experimenter, but he himself is also involved in the experimental process. Almost all domestication starts from simply maintaining animals in captivity and for this reason it is not always easy to distinguish between the effects of domestication and the effects of captivity; these two factors are closely involved and the question arises as to how much they come into contact with each other and to what extent they overlap. Within the framework of a compilation on casualties of civilization (Zivilisationsschäden) in the work already cited, H. Nachtsheim (1944, p. 2) stated the following: "Just as we can establish parallel changes in the hereditary characters in man and animals under conditions of domestication, a parallel can also be drawn between the injurious effects which can be observed in primitive man when he encounters civilization and the changes which the wild animal experiences when it is kept in captivity."

More information on this subject has since been obtained as the result of numerous investigations carried out by various people including W. Herre (1959). According to the latter the parallelism of domestication phenomena in animals and man teaches us also that the man who has been moulded by civilization still remains under the influence of the whole of nature. Konrad Lorenz already saw in 1940 (p. 5) a number of noteworthy parallels between the conditions under which modern man lives in the big city—conditions which man has brought upon himself more or less voluntarily—and the conditions into which he has transplanted his domestic animals. Above all he found indications in both of them of a retrogression of specialized attributes and abilities, as opposed to an evolution—in short he found a decline. It has already been stressed earlier that it is one of the primary tasks of zoo biology to recognize such reactions and to counteract them by suitable measures, that is, by keeping animals in the most natural condition possible; this is because it is not the duty of the zoo to raise new domestic animals, but to maintain the wild stock and its behaviour in the most natural form possible.

We are not concerned here to enter into a discussion about individual characters affected by captivity or domestication, but to draw attention to indications of a much more comprehensive phenomenon which has hitherto received virtually no attention from the biological side, namely what one might briefly describe as a change in the environment.

The zoo has already been characterized as a constituent and essential part of the big-city habitat; this applies to the large cities of all continents. A more distinct relationship is already beginning to emerge: the larger a city, the larger and more numerous its zoos. At the same time news is increasingly coming in, supported by documentary evidence, of the extinction of animals in the previously untouched areas of Africa, America, Asia, Australia, even of the polar regions and of some zones in the sea. The worldwide decline in the original habitats of large animals runs parallel to an increase of zoo animals in the large cities. When we count up the total animal inventory of all the zoological gardens in existence today (about 500), the result is a fauna of truly imposing richness: about 200 gorillas, about 300 orang utans, thousands of chimpanzees, tens of thousands of other primates, enormous herds of elephants, hippopotamuses, rhinoceroses, immense zebra herds, prides of lions, flocks of ostriches etc.

Wildlife habitats are now partially occupied by humans and technical installations; on various continents the animals now live in conditions which are far removed from their original environment, in neo-habitats and reserves. Zoo biology must stress the importance of this "reversal in the disposition of man and animals in the available space" because the biological process involved is of truly gigantic proportions and requires *urgent* investigation. Urgent by reason of the fact that both animals and man are involved and also because the original environment is disappearing at an exceedingly fast rate; the process is irreversible and therefore opportunities for comparing the original environment with the new conditions vanish overnight.

Fig. 39 All animal groups contain examples of food specialization. Among the reptiles, for example, the Gila Monster (*Heloderma suspectum*) has a partiality for birds' eggs.

Fig. 40 The food of the Keas bred in the Zurich Zoo in 1964 consisted not of a uniform mash but of wide selection of items, including carrot, lettuce, groundnuts, sunflower seeds, willow twigs, millet, sprouting barley, veal and so on.

Fig. 41 Walter Hunziker the Senior Keeper of Zurich Zoo succeeded in breeding the Kea in 1964. It was found that the provision of a suitable nesting-hole and complete freedom from disturbance were just as important as the diet.

Fig. 42 The method of offering food to animals in a zoo must be compatible with humane attitudes on this subject. This Jaguar in a South American zoo is being offered a live pigeon on a kind of fishing-rod.

Fig. 43 In this way the big cat allows itself to be lured into the water (for example, for filming). In Europe this method is rightly regarded as unacceptable.

Fig. 44 The Koala (*Phascolarctos*) is regarded with affection everywhere. These marsupials feed exclusively on eucalyptus leaves and so far it has not been possible to find any artificial substitute which will serve as an ideal diet. At present, outside of Australia, they can only be kept in California for this reason.

Fig. 45 A eucalyptus wood in the vicinity of San Francisco.

Fig. 46 Mealworms, the larvae of the beetle *Tenebrio molitor*, form an important food in zoos for many fish, amphibians, reptiles, birds and insect-eating mammals.

Fig. 47 The faeces of lions and other large cats living in zoos is of an ointment-like consistency; in the wild it has not the same appearance and often contains large masses of hair from prey animals such as antelopes and so on.

Fig. 48 Feeding is not only a physiological matter. To many animals, including the Reticulated Giraffe, the grass growing outside its paddock tastes better. This is an obvious subject for detailed investigation which is overdue (Photo K. H. Winkelstrater).

Fig. 49   Since 1937 large numbers of flamingoes have been bred on Infield Lake at Hialeah Racecourse in Miami. This was the first breeding of flamingoes in captivity.

Fig. 50   In spite of following old-fashioned feeding methods, flamingoes were bred for the first time and in large numbers in the artificial conditions of Hialeah.

4
What Does Man Mean to the Animal?

This cartoon illustrates better than any long dissertation one of the fundamental problems of zoo biology, namely the significance of man to the animal and of the animal to man.

It goes without saying that animal psychology has come to occupy a prominent place in zoo biology; I am referring here to animal psychology as distinct from ethology. I have tried to show elsewhere (Hediger 1963) that objective research on comparative behaviour, in which individual and subjective assessments have no place, serves no purpose in the zoo. Within certain limits it is possible not only to describe animal behaviour objectively but also to understand it

F
75

subjectively. In the zoo it would be senseless, unscientific and also in a certain sense irresponsible if one were intentionally to ignore everything which seemed to the observer to affect the natural behaviour pattern of the animal. In fact it is one of the first duties of the zoo man to take the trouble to understand as much as possible about the animals in his charge.

This statement has nothing to do with sentiment nor is it lightly made: years of experience in making careful observations, together with a sympathetic feeling for biological problems makes it possible eventually to predict precisely the behaviour of an animal according to the rules that apply in given situations. Where would we be in the zoo if we had to do without these shades of interpretation? It is legitimate to ask what is clearly an opposite question in this context: what is the significance of man to the animal? In my opinion the answer to this is quite clear: every day in the zoo one has literally thousands of animals, representing hundreds of species, in front of one and the animal's reactions to man are certainly something which cannot be overlooked. Their reaction to man is easier to assess the more closely they are related to man and the more explicit their expressions are. In the zoo this applies essentially to the vertebrates, particularly to the higher vertebrates.

Basically our question is concerned with the problem of the systematics of animals. It seems completely natural to us as humans to subdivide the animal world into a certain number of different groups—classes, orders, genera, species etc. We differentiate between vertebrates and invertebrates and among the vertebrates between the mammals, birds, reptiles, amphibians and fishes. This scientific division and naming of the animal kingdom, known as systematics, was founded by the famous Swedish naturalist Carl von Linné who lived from 1707 to 1778; in his great work *Systema naturae* he named and described all the animals and plants then known.

We now come to the question as to whether there are animals which also divide up the living things around them into groups; in other words is there a form of systematics among animals? In a certain sense one must acknowledge that this takes place among higher animals. There is no doubt, for example, that some predators distinguish different categories of prey animal according to size, appearance, smell etc. They do not attack everything they see at random; they avoid dangerous or unpleasant prey such as the porcupine or the North American skunk, at least after the first painful encounter. It is also certain that many prey animals are able to distinguish different kinds of enemy because the latter have different warning signals and different methods of flight or avoidance of predators, dependent on the circumstances and according to whether the enemy is on the ground or in the air. In the presence of a goshawk a hare behaves differently from when a fox is around. The prey may be instinctively aware of the characteristics of a given predator, or it may acquire the knowledge by individual learning. Here however we are concerned solely with the problem of whether man is classified by animals into various groups and if so on what basis. Fundamentally it must be accepted that this is possible for some animals; they are able to distinguish different kinds of humans, such as the harmless passer-by from the armed hunter. Many animals in the zoo distinguish their keeper from the visitor, the keeper being of importance to them and the visitor of no consequence; and so on.

Here there is a wide field of animal psychology and zoo biology in which little work has been done. Every zoo offers a wealth of opportunities which have fortunately still not been exploited. M. Spindler and E. Bluhm (1934) were the first to investigate the characteristics by which zoo animals recognize their keepers; they did this with Californian sea-lions. Zoo biology still needs this type of investigation on a large scale because it provides a valuable approach to the understanding of animals.

Returning to the earlier question of the significance of man to the animal, particularly to the zoo animal, it is accepted that man can be regarded as significant by the animal in at least five ways: according to our present knowledge he may be regarded as an enemy, as prey, a symbiont, a piece of inanimate environment or a member of its own species. This theory can easily be supported on the basis of everyday observation.

1. *Significance as an enemy* is by far the commonest. Wherever man chooses to put in an appearance he causes the wild animals to take flight; he is the focal point of the animal flight reaction and he is virtually regarded as a universal enemy. Animals which have lived in surroundings free of man for thousands of years—such as certain seals and penguins in antarctic regions, the endemic animals of the

Galapagos Islands and so on—behave rather like tame animals and provide the exception in that they do not take flight. But it is as difficult for man to get near enough to stroke a wild animal, like a hare or deer, that lives near built-up areas as it is for him to touch a chimpanzee in the tropical forests of West Africa or a black rhinoceros in the savannah. To all of them man has the significance of an enemy; biologically they are forced to escape from him as soon as he has overstepped their flight distance (Hediger 1961).

2. *Significance as prey*, by contrast, is the rarest of all and in any case can only apply to the large carnivores, especially the big cats. Normally even lion, tiger, bear, hyena and so on react to the approach of man by a flight reaction. They all follow the law of flight. Deviations from normal behaviour only occur rarely in individual man-eaters; in these cases, which are very exceptional and occur in quite definite circumstances, man is no longer regarded as an enemy but as prey that is relatively easy to catch. Among the most famous man-eaters were the two lions of Tsavo which killed and ate most of their victims, a total of 135 African and Indian workers, during the construction of the Uganda railway inland from Mombasa before the first World War. These two man-eaters are now in the Natural History Museum in Chicago.

After an arduous and dangerous chase the lions were eventually killed by a man who has described his experiences in a monograph (J. H. Patterson 1958). The book describes this exciting hunt and is a mine of information for biologists and students of animal behaviour. There is an Indian counterpart to this in Jim Corbett's (1957) account of the man-eating temple tiger, although more comparable perhaps was the man-eating leopard of Rudraprayag which killed no fewer than 125 people (J. Corbett 1949). All these accounts are absolutely reliable and of the greatest interest to the animal psychologist, as is also *A book of man-eaters* by R. G. Burton (1931). There is no question that to the animals described in these books man had the significance of prey; it should be borne in mind however that these accounts deal with abnormal and not normal behaviour.

There are few people who have in effect been human guinea-pigs and gone through the experience of being treated as prey by a man-eater but one of them is no less a person than the famous missionary and explorer Doctor David Livingstone (1813–1873). As R. G. Burton (1931, p. 58) has put on record it was the rare fate of Livingstone to be seized by a lion, released and then left lying on the ground: "Growling horribly in my ear, he shook me as a terrier does a rat. The shock produced a stupor, similar to that which seems to be felt by a mouse after the first shake of the cat. It caused a sort of dreaminess in which there was no sense of pain or feeling of terror, though quite conscious of all that was happening. It was like what patients partially under the influence of chloroform describe, who see all the operations but feel not the knife. This singular condition was not the result of any mental process. The shake annihilated fear, and allowed no sense of horror in looking round at the beast."

However another explorer, Inverarity, who was attacked and injured by a lion in Somaliland, felt none of the dreamy stupor described by Livingstone but, "on the contrary felt as usual." He remained absolutely motionless, which is certainly the most intelligent thing to do in such a situation, because every movement stimulates attacks involving fresh bites and blows from the paws. He added that the claws and teeth entering the flesh did not hurt as much as one would think; the only really painful part was "the squeeze given by the jaws on the bone".

The behaviour of a man-eating baribal is described in the new eight-volume edition (1953) of Ernest Thompson Seton's classical work on the wild animals of North America (Vol. 2, Part 1, p. 167). The accident occurred in a lumber camp on the Red Deer River, about 30 miles south of Etiomame in northern Canada. While two men were busy felling trees in front of their log house they saw a baribal or American black bear (*Ursus americanus*) on the opposite bank of the river; they shouted to their companion who was busy cooking in the hut to come out and see the animal. The bear swam across the river, shook the water off its fur and rushed straight at the astonished men, who fled as quickly as they could into the hut which was only about ten yards away.

The cook, named Wilson, ran so fast towards the hut that he missed the door and ran round the back; his two companions were able to save themselves by getting into the hut. As Wilson got round to the door the bear caught up with him and delivered a blow with its paw which evidently broke his neck. The two men inside the hut pelted the bear with cans of food and bits of wood, but this did not prevent the bear from dragging its victim away. Later, when ten revolver shots were fired at the baribal, even then it did not release its prey, but moved slowly off into the forest, where it escaped from an organized hunt. This tragic incident was satisfactorily investigated by the Canadian Mounted Police. It was accepted—certainly correctly—that this truly extraordinary behaviour was a case of abnormal reaction.

However it is by no means necessary to travel as far as Africa, India or the north of Canada to meet man-eaters. These occur in the form of the brown rats (*Rattus norvegicus*) in large cities in Europe and America. C. Richter (1945) has shown that even in the immediate vicinity of John Hopkins Hospital in Baltimore, children and adults have frequently been bitten and eaten by rats while asleep; he says the rats regard them literally as food. Between 1939 and 1943 at least 93 persons were attacked by rats within an area of two square miles surrounding the hospital. Sixty-five of these patients were taken to John Hopkins Hospital for treatment. In most cases the rats were content to lick the blood flowing from the wounds made by the bites; in a few cases however parts of the face had been eaten. As is well known rat bites are extremely dangerous because they carry the dreaded rat-bite fever, which in fact occurred in 10 per cent of the patients mentioned.

Without doubt rats are the most dangerous animals in zoos all over the world, a fact every keeper should constantly bear in mind. It is not even necessary to be bitten by a rat to receive a fatal infection; it is sufficient if a drop of urine from an infected rat—dead or alive—gets into a small wound or an abrasion of the human skin. Occasionally even the white laboratory rats which are generally regarded as harmless turn out to be carriers of infection.

Naturally it is not possible to refer here in detail to the blood-sucking and disease-carrying insects, ticks and other arthropods that are dealt with comprehensively in medical literature. On the other hand, it should be noted that the true vampire bats (*Desmodus* and others), distributed in central and south America, occasionally attach themselves to sleeping humans and lick the blood that flows from very small wounds made by their bites. For zoo biologists the fact that such vampires can cause trouble is important; animals in zoos within range of these bats are liable to suffer from wounds to the skin and so on which can be dangerous.

When I paid a visit to Rio de Janeiro Zoo at the time that I was planning the zoo for São Paulo, I was struck by the fact that the lights were left burning at night in the stalls of rhinoceros, hippopotamus, elephant etc. They found it necessary to keep the lights on in order to keep the vampires away.

3. *Significance as a symbiont.* If by symbiosis we understand a partnership between species that are not closely related, which does not provide much practical advantage to either partner, then man as a symbiont of the honey-guide (*Indicator indicator*) must be mentioned. It is an impressive example of this kind of partnership, in which the honey-guide, a small African bird, leads people to colonies of wild bees in the expectation the human being will get at the honey. The honeycomb is inaccessible to the bird until it has been opened up; the bird can then get to the wax and the brood, which it finds exceptionally attractive. Baboons and honey-badgers also enjoy honey and the bird likewise guides them to colonies of bees.

This example of symbiosis sounds like a lovely fairy-tale but it has been confirmed as fact on a great many occasions. There is an extensive literature on the subject which has been summarized brilliantly and examined critically in the monograph written by H. Friedmann (1955). The author was himself led to colonies of bees on twenty-three occasions and there can be no doubt about the importance of man as a symbiont to the honey-guide.

True examples of the importance of man as a symbiont in relation to animals are rare. One reckons among them perhaps also the relationship of the gun dog to its master or that of the trained falcon to the falconer. The help given by the animal is doubtless of value to the human hunter and the animal receives its reward for the help given, thus making it a mutual enterprise. In neither case, however, can the assistance from the animal world be described as entirely voluntarily: in the case of the gun dog a domesticated animal is concerned and the bird of prey is a trained animal, both of them having become dependent upon man. In this sense one could also speak for example of symbiosis in the case of a draught horse which draws a cart for man, for which it receives food in return.

4. *Significance of man as part of the inanimate environment.* When birds

are reared under artificial conditions the human keeper is often treated as a perch or even as a nest. Young birds will perch on the keeper's head or even on his outstretched arm as though it were a branch. Young swallows that have been reared in captivity will occasionally fly into the open mouth of a man, doubtless because this opening has a certain similarity to the nest entrance for the bird.

One of the tricks performed by some snake-charmers makes use of the marked visual acuity of venomous snakes: by means of appropriate movements made with one of his hands, the charmer holds the attention of the snake and at the same time he pushes the other hand carefully under the animal from the rear so that eventually the dangerous reptile can be carried around freely. The snake is aware of the hand and arm supporting it as a substrate or as a piece of the inanimate environment.

When I was a student I used to let bats (*Rhinolophus*) fly freely in my bedroom; sometimes on waking up in the morning I would find a bat hanging from my hand which dangled over the edge of the bed. The bat had included this part of my anatomy as one of the places that was suitable as a hanging site for the day's sleep, that is, part of its inanimate environment. House-mice disturbed by someone in a cellar where there is no shelter occasionally flee under the person's shoes or up their trouser legs; F. Brock (1934) has observed that even the hollow of a human hand can be treated as a refuge by mice, i.e. as a small part of the inanimate surroundings.

The same kind of behaviour has been observed by O. Heinroth in the sparrows (*Passer domesticus*) reared by him. These birds however also regarded him as an "old wall" suitable for nest-building: "it chirped persistently in my ear, as though courting me and then it crept into my outside coat pocket or in between my knees under a table napkin that lay over them and turned itself round in this cavity as though building a nest; in short, it took me both for a mate to be courted (as a member of its own species) and for an old wall which provided a suitable nest-site." Although the expression of the male sparrow's sexual drive was both endearing and amusing, it was not entirely pleasurable for Heinroth. "On the one hand the persistent chirping hurt my ears and on the other hand this bold champion was a danger to everyone who approached me as he insisted on

82

defending me furiously. When the servant girl came into the room he tried to bite her lips and eyes, and as she had her hands full, with a loaded tea-tray, she had no defence of any kind. The sparrow only attacked my wife when she was sitting beside me and when we drew too close together; however, we had only to offer him a hand over the edge of the table for him to bite her finger and we always wondered how he managed to distinguish between our hands, even when they were clasped together. F. von Lucanus observed similar behaviour in parrots."

In certain circumstances the larger mammals may also regard humans simply as a place for climbing and make use of them accordingly. In his excellent book *The call of the koala* A. Pratt (1937, p. 101) reported that when koala bears (*Phascolarctos cinereus*) are on the ground and want to climb up, as a flight reaction, they have been known to grasp a human leg and climb up it, evidently taking it to be a tree-trunk.

The stories of tropical snakes seeking the warmth on a cold night of a person's chest as they lie asleep are by no means all invented.

The parasites and their relationship to man need not concern us in detail here. It is sufficient to point out that the different organs of the human body provide an extremely varied series of habitats for parasites. Depending upon the species parasites live in those most suitable for the relevant stage of their development. In other words ecological principles apply to parasites just as they do to free-living animals.

5. *Significance as a member of the same species.* Together with the significance of man as an enemy this is the most important aspect of all from the viewpoint of zoo biology. Ignorance of this may lead to serious incidents, indeed to fatalities, as a wealth of experience unfortunately confirms. When the zoo animal regards a person, particularly its keeper, as a member of its own species, there are two possibilities: the animal sees the keeper as a rival of the same sex and this leads to aggressive behaviour, or it sees in him a potential mate and this may present a danger to the keeper owing to importunate attempts to mate with him.

Even the entrance of the human into the animal's enclosure (cage or paddock) may be regarded as an intrusion by a member of its own species into its own territory and thus treated as a challenge. Strongly aggressive behaviour is stimulated and unless the keeper is aware of the general principles regarding defence of territory against members of the same species, he will be taken by surprise and regard the animal as suddenly malicious or unreliable.

Fortunately, however, the fact that the animal in the zoo quite frequently regards man with the significance of a member of its own species does not always lead to unfortunate incidents; on the contrary, providing the behaviour patterns are understood, there are some such as greeting ceremonies and marking, which would otherwise remain obscure or liable to misinterpretation.

In those male animals which regard humans as sexual rivals, aggression will often occur only during the mating season; in some of them however mating behaviour may last throughout the year. Deer of the temperate and northern zone (red, fallow, sika, wapiti, roe and others) in which the mating and antler cycle is closely correlated with the time of year, may be as gentle as lambs outside the breeding season; and then suddenly, literally overnight, when they have cleaned their antlers they become dangerous. It is essential that inexperienced keepers should be warned of these radical changes in behaviour which are astonishingly rapid.

When a lioness is on heat male lions which normally allow their keeper to stroke them as he passes by, may suddenly spring up and rage against the bars; their aggression may die down again in the presence of the lioness. Such extreme jealousy of man as a rival is characteristic of lions; this form of sexual rivalry however does not occur in the tiger and the leopard which are closely related. When members of the public see a lion raging at its keeper as he passes the enclosure, they think that the lion is trying to eat him; in fact this is not so because lions will mutilate rather than attempt to eat a rival of the same species and same sex during the few days that are critical.

The tiger's characteristic reception of a familiar human is expressed in a much more pleasant way. Because it regards the keeper as a member of its own species, it greets him in tiger fashion, by a snort or a violent sneeze; this is the form of greeting which takes place between tigers when they meet in a friendly fashion. Greeting ceremonies, some noticeable and others less obvious, also occur in many other animals. Among the birds one of the more impressive perhaps is the shoebill (*Balaeniceps rex*); it lowers its head and greets the keeper with lively claps of the bill that are often followed by peculiar gulping movements. G. Steinbacher (1937) has described them as follows: "these movements resemble those with which adult herons regurgitate food to their young. They should be regarded as ritual movements such as occur in many birds. They are an expression of sociability, particularly between pairs. The bird acts as though it were feeding a member of its own species, in this case the keeper . . . "

The transfer of species-specific ceremonies—whether fighting, greeting or courtship—to a human that is familiar can only be explained by the animal in question no longer regarding the human as a creature of another species, but as one of its own species.

Where this takes place in the zoo care has then to be taken to see that the human accepted into the animal species also occupies a high position in the social hierarchy, indeed the dominant social position. This is particularly important in every case where the human has to deal directly with the animal with no intervening barrier, that is inside the enclosure and therefore inside the territory. In other words, the keeper must occupy the Super-Alpha position, otherwise he would be exposed to all the moods, social aspirations and aggressiveness of the animal or animals in a hazardous manner. New or temporary keepers usually have to take particular care; they are in much the same position as inexperienced teachers who are faced with disobedient schoolchildren; admittedly the children will neither bite nor hit out but in an atmosphere where authority is lacking they will be impudent and get up to all kinds of mischief, profiting by any sign of weakness.

The tendency to assimilate a member of another species is known as zoomorphism when it is the animal that makes the approach; when the initiative is taken by the human this is known as anthropomorphism. Further details on this subject can be found in Hediger (1961, 1964). The process of assimilation involves building an animal of another species into the social organization of its own species with all that this implies. This may happen quickly or slowly but there is no hard and fast division and it is only a matter of degree.

O. Heinroth (1941, p. 54) expresses it thus: "if man rears mammals or birds when they are quite young, so that they never have the opportunity to get to know a member of their own species, a so-called imprinting on man, particularly a keeper, readily takes place in these animals. They therefore accept him so to speak as being of the same species and behave accordingly."

The concept of imprinting has recently been defined and clarified by K. Lorenz (1961), W. H. Thorpe (1956) and R. A. Hinde (1962), and it is still under active discussion today. It is not possible to go into this in more detail here. It is only necessary to mention that some authors—such as W. H. Thorpe—do not regard imprinting as a special phenomenon but rather as an extreme case of learning, indeed of very rapid learning during a specially labile phase of post-embryonic development.

It seems to me that imprinting has a certain similarity or relationship to what one usually calls a psychic trauma. Like imprinting, the trauma is also an indelible experience, which may take place in a matter of only a few seconds or minutes. The process of imprinting is one of the phenomena where it is quite possible that comparative studies in the zoo may yield significant advances. Certainly the psychic trauma—such as homesickness, aggression, subjective space requirements and many others—is among the phenomena which are by no means the monopoly of man.

Let us now turn to the process of assimilation that works more slowly and which is even more significant from the viewpoint of zoo biology than the more rapid process of imprinting. In considering this the terminology of von Uexküll may be of use and also the concept of tameness which some people regard as old-fashioned. It is a commonly observed fact that young wild animals, which thrive in captivity under the influence of sympathetic care and understanding, will become tame relatively quickly; they lose their flight reaction when faced with humans. Man is then no longer regarded as an enemy to be avoided, his significance as an enemy is lost and he becomes a familiar fellow-creature. Finally he is accepted as a member of their own species with all that this entails with regard to the behaviour patterns described earlier, such as greeting ceremonies, fights between rivals and attempts at mating.

During this gradual process of becoming trusted, which may take months or even years, the man undergoes a "change in significance" in the sense of von Uexküll's Umwelt theory (1928). Naturally the

86

range of species with which man may be involved in this way is not unlimited; nevertheless it is an astonishingly wide range extending for example from the robin to the elephant. The age of the animals is one of the limiting factors; adult individuals are already set in their ways and can no longer adjust themselves. Furthermore the chances of assimilation are also restricted by the following factors:

a) body size and sense organs;
b) systematic position;
c) the nature of the medium in which the animal normally lives (e.g. land or water)

It is not to be expected, for example that a mole would ever be in a position to regard a human as a member of its own species. Its underground habits, the organization of its senses and the small size of its body constitute definite obstacles. Taken on its own, the smallness of its body would certainly not be prohibitive. O. Heinroth (1941, p. 54) has observed that even a bird as small as a robin may regard a human as a rival of the same species, to be driven out of its territory by flying aggressively at his face. (Similar behaviour in a sparrow has already been mentioned).

Very small animals will often treat one part of the human body so to speak as *pars pro toto*: examples include a tortoise which may react to the shod foot in this way, a pigeon that reacts to the human hand, a dog that reacts to the human leg and so on. A completely tame otter (*Lutra lutra*) totally orientated on humans treated the leg of its keeper exactly as if it were a female of its own species and used the crease of the trousers, in order to execute the bite on the nape of the neck which is typical of the species.

As far as systematics are concerned the relevant position of the animal also limits the extent to which man can achieve significance as a member of the animal's own species. I still do not know of any case in which an invertebrate animal has regarded man as a member of its own species. There may be a few examples among fish, if in fact they occur at all. On the other hand for anurans (frogs and toads) the human hand may have this significance and thus stimulate amplexus in males. In some circumstances the vocalizations of tame male frogs may also be evoked by trusted humans. There are more frequent examples of reptiles accepting man as a member of their own species but it is among the homoiotherms that this significance is usually found. A high degree of intimacy between man and animal is a prerequisite in all cases for the achievement of this type of human significance. It scarcely ever occurs in the wild although there are cases in which capercaillies suddenly display to man or attack him and crocodiles have been known to challenge certain types of small boat with outboard motors, apparently taking them to be rivals (P. B. M. Jackson 1962).

As already mentioned, in some circumstances the limitations imposed by different kinds of medium, such as land and water, may form an obstacle to assimilation; however this can often be overcome by appropriate technical equipment, as for example enclosing marine animals in large oceanaria. The latter have rapidly achieved popularity, particularly in America, and in these huge exhibition tanks it is possible for man to come into close contact with large animals of the sea which were hitherto inaccessible; these include dolphins and other toothed whales. Artificial conditions have provided the opportunity for these species to accord to man the significance of a member of their own species (cf. Hediger 1963). There are well-authenticated cases of drowning men being assisted by dolphins. The transport of members of their own species to the surface of the water is a characteristic way in which dolphins are known to help each other. There is no doubt that the rescue of drowning humans by dolphins can be interpreted as a transfer of the typical behaviour pattern under conditions in which assimilation with man has taken place.

This short review has already given some indication of the extensive range in which opportunities may occur for the inclusion of a trusted human in the social structure of a wide variety of animal species. Therefore a knowledge of this phenomenon—both theoretical and practical—is extremely important to zoo biology. In dealing with such animals the human keeper must know the precise role expected of him as an animal and consequently play his part in the ritual behaviour patterns according to the rules of the species concerned.

Individual cases involving the inclusion of humans in the ritual behaviour of animals have been observed in every zoo. Many examples could be given here but the main point of interest is to establish the basic principle underlying such behaviour. A paper by

K. M. Schneider in the professional journal *Der zoologische Garten* (1928), on the breeding of emus (p. 29), serves to illustrate the point: "in the spring of 1928 the widowed male also built its nest again in the usual way. During the month of May a craftsman had to carry out certain work in the paddock which involved working in a squatting position; it was most amusing to see the emu continually pushing the man in the back in an unmistakable attempt to mate with him." Corresponding behaviour in large ungulates however, is not a matter for amusement because life may be endangered when these animals become importunate. This demonstrates once again the importance of the rule that repair work must never be carried out in enclosures that are occupied. (There are additional reasons which are mentioned in Chapter 8).

In the zoo avoidance of accidents often depends on the finest interpretations of the way in which the rules of behaviour should be followed in practice; the relevant theoretical knowledge is of importance in this respect. With large primates the incorporation of the human keeper into the social structure of the group sometimes has its amusing aspects, but occasionally it has fatal results. The following is an attempt to illustrate this point:

In the Monkey House in Zurich Zoo from 1929 to 1962 there lived a capuchin monkey (*Cebus*) which reached the exceptionally great age of 36 years. This capuchin, named Pfyfer (or Piper) supervised every human who entered the house or, when it was in its outer cage, everybody that came into the wide area surrounding the monkey house. Among the hundreds of thousands of zoo visitors Pfyfer had some friends, whom he was in the habit of greeting in the manner characteristic of the species, namely with a penetrating whistle or a series of high-pitched screams.

Pfyfer was the undisputed Alpha animal of the whole capuchin group (Alpha signifies the highest social rank within the particular animal group). The Beta animal, inferior to Pfyfer, was a younger male which scarcely came into the picture. Pfyfer died at a great age and as soon as this happened the hitherto Beta male, named Boby, moved up into the Alpha position. This was not only apparent in his behaviour towards the members of his own species but also in his behaviour towards humans, firstly towards the keeper and secondly towards the friends of his predecessor.

As already mentioned, as a rule keepers in the zoo play the role of a Super-Alpha animal, particularly the primate keepers. This even applied when Pfyfer was alive. After his death, however, his successor immediately tried to subordinate the keeper; Boby attacked the keeper who was Super-Alpha to himself at the first opportunity and bit him so severely in the hand that the keeper was unfit for work for more than a month. In spite of his injuries he did not go for medical treatment until he had clouted Boby to make clear to him that he had stepped above his social rank, so to speak, and that Boby could occupy the Alpha but not the Super-Alpha position. This clarification of the position was biologically absolutely correct—and after that no further difficulties were experienced between Boby and the keeper.

Boby, the successor to the former Alpha capuchin, behaved in a highly surprising way to the human friends of his predecessor: immediately after Pfyfer's death Boby took over and greeted these friends in the same striking manner; the people were naturally very impressed by this because, like myself, they had expected to be greeted by silence in the Monkey House when they walked in after the death of Pfyfer.

There are two significant points about this astonishing transfer of friendship which need to be stressed. First the offering of titbits played no part in it. I was regarded as one of their friends by these two capuchins and I had never brought them any kind of food. The greeting reaction therefore had nothing to do with the expectation of food, but evidently depended only on the event of seeing a family acquaintance again who was the equivalent of a social partner. Also the former Alpha capuchin and his successor showed a clear tendency, during or immediately after the greeting, to search for something edible in the cage and to eat it—as a quasi-demonstration.

The second point, involving a detail that was regularly observed, was very significant: human friends were never greeted if the keeper, the Super-Alpha, was present. If therefore I wished to demonstrate the greeting behaviour just described to, for example, students, I always had to—and still have to—get the keeper out of the house, or at least out of the range of perception of the capuchin.

This behaviour is in accordance with a remarkable rule that has also been confirmed for example in gorillas by G. B. Schaller (1963,

Fig. 51   Example of an external foreign body, that is, one which penetrates the body through the skin; a camel lay down on a piece of wood with a protruding nail and could not free itself.

Fig. 52   Even ladies' handbags may contain foreign bodies which can be dangerous if they get into the apes' cage, especially mirrors which are bitten into fragments.

Fig. 53   Example of a 'biological' foreign body: a corroded stone from the stomach of a sea-lion.

Fig. 54   The smooth, round fruits of horse-chestnut can be dangerous to many animals. This one was removed from the throat of a Llama at the last moment.

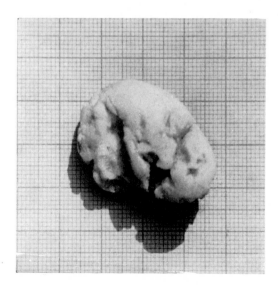

Fig. 55   This piece of wire—three inches long—from a rusty boundary fence ended up in the stomach of a bison cow and penetrated the heart cavity, causing the animal a very painful death (Zurich Zoo).

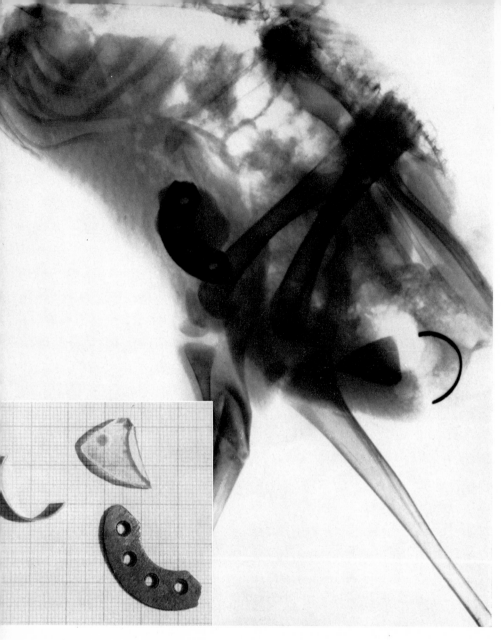

Fig. 56   Foreign bodies in a Rhea chick in Zurich Zoo (1962): a piece of glass, an iron shoe ferrule and half a gold wedding-ring (X-ray photograph by zoo veterinarian Dr P. Weilenmann).

Fig. 57 Another example of a dangerous foreign body which killed a Bison on 10 September 1964. This piece of wire had pierced the stomach, diaphragm and heart of the animal.

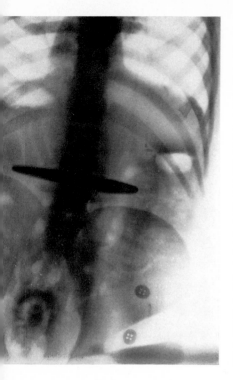

Bedenkt
die Fremdkörper-Gefahr!

Magen eines Kamelhengstes † 6. II. 1945

Fig. 58   A ballpoint pen five inches long in the stomach of the Gorilla *Achilla*. X-ray photograph 17 May 1952 (from Hediger 1953).

Fig. 59   Internal staff notice hung up in all staff rooms in order to remind keepers of the danger of foreign bodies. Untouched X-ray photograph of a camel's stomach.

Fig. 60   The wooden capital has been gnawed by giraffes and for this reason upholsterer's nails, which are among the most dangerous foreign bodies, have been driven into it.

Fig. 61   Remains of a purse swallowed by an elephant: parts of bank notes and coins bent by the molars.

Fig. 62   Angular stone (natural size), drawn in by an elephant through its trunk and later removed from the same organ by careful massage.

Fig. 63   Another example of a 'biological foreign body': every two years or so elephants shed pieces of molar the size of a hen's egg or a man's fist, sometimes weighing a couple of pounds. Normally these pieces of tooth are spat out.

Fig. 64   Remains of a purse with parts of the zip-fastener which had been swallowed by an elephant and passed out in the faeces.

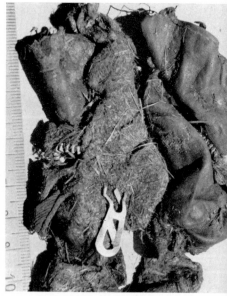

p. 239) and in chimpanzees by R. Schenkel (1959). Schaller describes the behaviour of a gorilla group when it was split into two sub-groups. In one of the two sub-groups the Beta male naturally took the lead and occupied the top social rank. When the two sub-groups were later re-united, the females of the group led by the Beta male no longer paid any attention to it. The Alpha animal then counted as the leader for the whole company.

It appears to be a general rule—in any case among primates—that in the presence of the Alpha animal individuals of lower status lose their social position and are scarcely noticed, if at all, and in some cases they are threatened or attacked. For this reason R. Schenkel (1959, p. 133) characterized the primates as social opportunists. One of the female chimpanzees, with which he was on familiar terms, was being stroked by him through the wire when she bit him badly on the hand at the very moment when the dominant keeper appeared. On the basis of such experiences he states: "opportunism and lability in intimate relationships are typical characteristics of primates—and they are also not unknown in mankind."

A large number of examples of this kind could be cited from experiences gained in zoos. From analysis of such cases the facts force us to assume that man—and certainly the man that is well-known—can be incorporated into the social structure of animals that are widely different, and consequently can be regarded and treated as a member of the species concerned. From the scientific point of view it would be a major sin of omission to disregard these facts which have been confirmed on so many occasions.

6. *Significance of man in a motor-car.* The centaur-like fusion of man with his motor-car should be mentioned if only as a supplement to complete the picture. Although it is not of much importance in the zoo, it may be of the greatest importance in animal reserves.

The terminology and the approach adopted by von Uexküll in his Umwelt theory (Theoretical Biology, 1926) is useful both here and in the general field of zoo biology. In an animal's environment—the actual part of the surroundings in which the animal lives—only those things are noticed which are biologically important to it. From the sum of these observations the animal builds up a subjective world which is its environment.

PRIMARY SIGNIFICANCE:

UNFAMILIAR = NEGATIVE

SECONDARY SIGNIFICANCES:

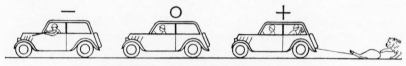

— STRONGLY NEGATIVE (hunter = enemy)
o FAMILIAR—NEUTRAL (harmless creature)
+ POSITIVE (food supplier)

In order to avoid the possibility of serious accidents in nature reserves it is of the greatest importance that the motor-car should be regarded as part of the animal's environment, in fact as a large and harmless animal. Nowadays visitors in the Tama Zoo in Japan are conducted round the large lion paddocks, for instance, in motor vehicles.

For example, when motor-cars suddenly put in an appearance for the first time in the habitat of the African big game, the animals do not know how to classify this phenomenon. At first the motor-car has a somewhat negative significance like everything else that is strange. This attitude can be considerably strengthened if negative stimuli are received from this new object in the environment. For example if shots are fired from vehicles the motor-car can then become a definite enemy that stimulates flight reactions at great distances; unfortunately this was what happened in some areas where unscrupulous hunters were at work and doubtless this practice will continue in the future.

On the other hand in the early days of the so-called camera safaris, the motor-car achieved a positive significance, through the animal being lured as near to the camera as possible with bait; in the habitat of the lion, for instance, a haunch of zebra was dragged behind the car, thus enticing these big cats to come within camera range. In this way the animal associated food with the car; as a purveyor of food the car was an object of positive significance in the lion's environment.

If the car was then used not for photography but for some totally different purpose, such as a tour of inspection, it could happen that the lions would approach the car and proceed to search for the bait that was no longer there; this search might be carried out at very close quarters with uncanny thoroughness, thus making it decidedly unpleasant for the person in the motor-car. It is well known for instance that in the nature reserves of North America the bears have gone so far as to tear off car roofs and rip the upholstery apart in the hunt for the accustomed titbits.

Man must lose no time in making-up his mind about the effect and importance of new objects when he first introduces them into the environment of animals. In nature reserves the motor-car must acquire a significance that is neither negative nor positive; it will then be regarded by the animals as of no consequence, a neutral being which is not worthy of any further attention. Knowledge of this kind is important in nature reserves because mens' lives may depend on applying it correctly or incorrectly (Hediger 1951).

It is however of particular importance that the big game in the national parks should not associate the motor-car with man. People ought not to make themselves conspicuous against the background of their motor-cars in the neighbourhood of the animals; humans should not be associated with cars. It is only thus that the motor-car can retain its significance as a neutral being and accidents be prevented as far as possible. To avoid associating man with the motor-car, it is necessary, for instance, to get into the car or alight from it out of the limelight so to speak; this should only be done well outside the range of the animal's perception, and naturally feeding in any form must be prohibited. All this may sound obvious now but it was by no means obvious at the beginning of mass tourism in the big game reserves. It needed a considerable number of serious incidents before this simple fact of animal psychology came to be taken into consideration and generally accepted.

From the viewpoint of zoo biology the significance of the motor-car ought to be mentioned as in the zoo it should definitely be entirely positive. There are already large zoos, in which the visitors are conveyed past the paddocks in vehicles, e.g. in San Diego. In these zoos the driver of the vehicle usually adds to his commentary given over the loudspeaker by calling certain individual animals by name and throwing them bits of food, thus encouraging the animals to approach the vehicle as it arrives; this not only contributes to the entertainment of the visitors, but also adds to the enjoyment of the animals. Everything of a suitable nature that enriches the animal's life is welcome from the angle of zoo biology.

This short reference to the motor-car is of general interest to zoo biology as it underlines the fact that man has the power to introduce into the animal's environment not only himself but also a number of strange objects with definite signs (positive, neutral, negative).

When the motor-car achieved the significance of a neutral being or creature, in contrast to an object, this was regarded as a practical solution to be aimed at in the reserves. A complementary development has taken place which is worth mentioning. Although it has not yet been possible to prove statistically, everything appears to confirm that in the African countryside for instance, the motor-car is now regarded by big game as merely another large animal.

To elaborate on this we must start with the tendency to assimilation which is deeply rooted in every higher animal. There are even humans who swear at their car as though it were a human being, when it does not react according to their wishes. Motor-cars are often provided with human faces in advertisements and cartoons; this gives them a humanized significance. If this takes place in *Homo sapiens* with his highly developed brain the possibility of animals accepting the motor-car as another animal is not so unlikely.

From the point of its size the average African truck falls within the category of elephant, rhinoceros, hippopotamus. It carries two head-lamps like eyes at the front and the radiator is often shaped like a mouth; the bonnet represents a kind of head and the rest of the truck looks like the body of the animal. A motor vehicle has a specific smell, leaves a specific scent behind and makes characteristic noises. It not only moves but mostly follows well-worn tracks (primitive roads) which to some extent are identical with the routes used by big game; in short the vehicle behaves according to a certain pattern.

The damage or "injuries" inflicted on vehicles by big game animals in involuntary encounters or as the result of provocation, are of interest in this connection. So far as I can ascertain, the records of vehicle maintenance in repair shops in central Africa indicate that damage is almost exclusively to the front or the side of the vehicle; this corresponds to the places which are most exposed during fights between game of a comparable size.

5
What Does the Animal Signify to Man?

In the zoo many people meet a large number of animals and the question inevitably arises as to what significance the animal has for man. This question has practical and theoretical aspects which touch on fundamental issues and extend well beyond the confines of the zoo. To a large extent the animal has the same significance for man as man has for the animal. To man, the super-predator, the animal is regarded in general as prey, even though man's life is based on the domesticated form of animal from the point of view of food. There is not a city that could exist without the continual flow of meat, fats, eggs, milk and so on. It is tempting to go into this state of affairs in detail here but this is not the place to do so; instead, a few examples will be given to show the main ways in which the animal is of significance to man.

As well as its overriding importance as prey, in rare cases the animal may have the significance of an enemy. It should be noted however that nearly all accidents that take place in zoos and circuses or while hunting, do not fall into this category; strictly speaking only the rare cases of man-eaters come under this heading. Zoo keepers and trainers involved in such incidents are attacked as social or sexual rivals, but not because lions, chimpanzees, deer and so on want to eat them. The so-called critical reaction is involved in hunting accidents when the hunter becomes the victim of the game animal—which has usually been shot at; this reaction is a specific form of self-defence in an animal whose flight has been hindered for some reason and in all such situations the enemy is the man and not the animal. Bolting horses which claim many human lives every year are also not enemies of man from the biological viewpoint. These accidents are caused by the animals taking flight which is a fright reaction.

In the biological sense neither the hordes of parasites and disease vectors nor the pests of stored food and noxious plants belong to this category; the enemy of man remains—as already stated—the man-eater.

The importance of the animal as a symbiont of man occurs as rarely as does the converse.

The idea that a man will mistake an animal for part of the inanimate environment is only to be found in fantastic adventure stories, like when the hero, exhausted in the jungle, sits down on a tree-trunk lying on the ground and then realizes that it is a giant snake.

On the other hand the animal plays a supreme role as a fellow member of the human species in every case where we allow ourselves to be guilty of humanization; this is something which almost every human being does quite often. There is no reason why people should not indulge in this in their private lives but from the scientific point of view it is inadmissible; it is no exaggeration to say that over considerable periods of time the history of animal psychology is exactly the same as the history of the fight against the humanization of the animal (Hediger, p. 231).

The mania of anthropomorphism is generally widespread and unbelievably deep-rooted in the public; it is one of the most important and worthwhile tasks of the zoological garden to counteract this attitude to animals because it leads to a total misunderstanding of the animal and thereby quite frequently to animal torture. There can be no animal protection without knowledge of animals and humanization is a main obstacle on the road to this knowledge. The struggle against humanization is therefore a service to the animal, an elementary part of animal protection—if not always a simple one.

Two examples will illustrate this point. In spite of all the warnings that have been issued on the subject people unfortunately still persist in the bad habit of bringing live animals back as souvenirs from their travels in the tropics; these are often affectionate little monkeys, which soon turn out to be unattractive and troublesome inmates in the home, particularly as they are not house-trained. In disgust the owner then usually applies to the zoo for a simple and effective formula on how to train a monkey as quickly as possible to be clean in the house. One then tries to explain to the impatient enquirer that there are two types of defaecation in mammals, namely the localized and the diffuse, and that the monkeys by nature belong to the diffuse type; therefore, this makes it impossible to train them to be clean in the house. This information naturally comes as a disappointment and the member of the public then thinks that people in zoos know nothing about animals and cannot even say how a monkey should be house-trained. Not infrequently the person then tries out his own method which has no chance of success and also involves torture to the animal.

The fact that the animals most like humans, namely the monkeys and even the anthropoid apes, practise the diffuse type of urination and defaecation is significant from the biological point of view; it is also significant however to the medical professions. There are psychiatrists and child psychiatrists (O. Meyerhardt 1945), who believe that the fouling and the uncleanliness of schizophrenics and enuretics rests on an instinctive weakness or on a degeneration of instinct. This surely cannot be right because our closest relatives in the animal kingdom have never possessed such an instinct of cleanliness; primitive races of man also do not have it. Localized urination and defaecation in man is a completely modern phenomenon of of civilization; the seeking out of a particular place for this purpose rests on quite recent advances in hygiene. It is an invention of the brain and in no way the functioning of a primitive instinct.

Another example which shows how fatal humanization can be for the animal is provided by the case of a young lioness which was sent to Zurich Zoo in 1959 by a South African animal protection society. The lioness which was then about one year old had been found in the Kruger National Park as a helpless cub and had been reared by animal lovers; finally the police refused to allow the carnivore to be kept privately any longer and so suitable accommodation had to be found for it. A well-wisher financed its transport by air to Zurich. After the arrival of the young lioness we became anxious because it was obviously suffering from a persistent stoppage. Vigorous treatment finally brought to light a dangerous tangle of fine shavings and torn material: the people who regarded themselves as animal lovers had indulged in a grotesque form of humanization and had provided the young lioness with a pillow against the fatigue of the journey. But animals do not know what to do with a pillow; nature has so endowed them that they can be comfortable without this human invention.

As this example shows, human ideas of comfort may cause suffering to animals. Humanization of animals often leads also to pampering and thereby to torture—the very reverse of what the true animal lover intends. In every case humanization leads to dangerous

'What fun it is to be a rhino'

by Robärt

In December 1964 a Lucerne newspaper thought fit to criticize the newly-opened Africa pavilion for rhinos and hippos at Zurich Zoo because they found it too luxurious. They did this by means of a cartoon which as well as being extremely anthropomorphic also showed gross zoological ignorance: the "rhinoceros" is in fact a hippopotamus.

The real purpose of this new house was to give the public a chance to seeing the rhino and the hippo—the largest land mammals after the elephants—before they are exterminated.

misunderstandings. One of the most frequent misconceptions which is constantly met in the zoo is the business of regarding the animals as prisoners. This is as false and old-fashioned as if in these days everybody still thought that radio and television sets contained little men who talked, sang and danced inside the sets. People are always more open-minded about empirical results in the technical field than

Charles H. Wilson

Man and Animal in the Zoo: Zoo Biology

in biological matters. It is precisely in this field that zoos have a particularly important contribution to make by acquainting the public with biological knowledge; they should aim to give the public an all-round education in biological matters, and to achieve the same level of education in this as in technical subjects.

Zoo animals do not regard themselves in any way as captive, but on the contrary they are more like "property owners", as I have shown in detail in 1950. They enjoy "the freedom of captivity" as E. G. Boulenger (1937, p. 56) so aptly expressed it. Equally pertinent is the statement that the so-called free-living animal certainly does not live free in fact, but is restricted by spatial, temporal and personal relations. It is confined in a strict time and space system and by an unrelenting social hierarchy; it is also subject to the continual pressure of avoiding enemies and seeking food and water.

As with everything else, one can also go too far in the fight against humanization, as C. W. Hume (1962) has rightly pointed out. In his profound book on man and animals, which is full of ideas, he devotes a fascinating section to the praise of humanization. He first expressed his conviction that some people who watch animals professionally may have an intuitive understanding of animals, whereas others, who lack this intuition, do not think that this can be done.

When anyone with sound professional experience of animals interprets animal behaviour intuitively, this is very similar to the reading of the facial expression of our fellow-men. On this Hume points out that Darwin's efforts have already shown how extremely difficult it is to analyse human facial expression objectively. Finally the nervous system of the higher animals is homologous with that of man. Within certain limits the electroencephalograms of the most varied mammals—from mouse to monkey—are analogous. Also, in animals fear may have psychosomatic results, that is, it may lead to such disorders as stomach ulcers. In many respects the processes of learning are so similar in man and animal that knowledge gained from animals has thrown a new light on learning processes in children and thus influenced the methods of teaching.

In Hume's opinion the animals are not so basically different from man as to exclude the possibility that claims by man to understand animals intuitively are well-founded. Some extreme opponents of

100

anthropomorphism do not admit that intuitive understanding is even possible within reasonable limits. Hume makes the same rebuke to these exaggerated opponents of anthropomorphism as to the opponents of vivisection. The anti-vivisectionists hold all animal experiments to be completely meaningless, because the results achieved on animals may not be directly applicable to conditions in the human body—and the anti-anthropomorphists regard it as unscientific and therefore inadmissible to apply psychical characteristics of man to animals whether by homology or even only by analogy. They therefore always write hunger, pain, fear, joy and so on in inverted commas, in so far as these are used with reference to the animal; they also regard the possibility of subjective interpretation as out of the question.

Another vivid illustration given by Hume should be mentioned here: a normal man can imagine quite well what the world of a totally colour-blind person is like, whereas the reverse is not true; and a man cannot know exactly how a mother feels towards her new-born baby but in spite of this, the expression maternal love is not printed in inverted commas.

In this book humanization (anthropomorphism) is understood to be the adoption of an attitude which treats animals as though they were humans; this attitude involves the approximation of animals to the species *Homo sapiens*. Hume on the other hand gives his anthropomorphism another meaning. He understands by it the employment of the human's own subjective experiences as a method of visualizing by analogy the subjective experiences of animals of another species.

In my opinion however the intuitive understanding of animal behaviour may definitely be increased over and above this by a precise knowledge of the behaviour of certain animal species and of their environment; thus a subjective empathy does not waft through the air but can be reinforced by factual material. The accuracy of the feeling specially directed at each animal species and each individual must be put to the test of the behaviour prognosis, to see if it comes true in a given situation for a certain animal. In the case of the pillow for the lion the assumption that the pillow would be appropriate to meet the needs of the situation was a hundred per cent wrong. On the other hand if by a carefully calculated biological manœuvre I can get an antelope to move to a place chosen by myself in advance, then such tactics are not based on my own subjective experiences but on hundreds of observations. For instance quantitative and qualitative observations on the flight behaviour of many antelope species and many individuals in various situations enable one to predict where an antelope will go in certain circumstances. Similarly it is possible to get a chimpanzee to enter a transport cage by showing it a small tortoise; it is well-known that chimpanzees and other primates regard a tortoise—also a snake in certain circumstances—as something sinister. The word sinister ought to be written confidently without inverted commas according to Hume, otherwise the anti-vivisectionists quoted by him would be correct in their thesis that none of the findings obtained from the animals should be applied to man, not even the pharmacological results.

Both man and animal have a common tendency to associate together; so far we have only considered the importance of the animal as a companion, in the context of humanization. We now come to the other aspects of the problem.

It would be wrong to think that man would be in any way less forthcoming in this respect than the animal, indeed astonishingly enough man goes even further. As mentioned in Chapter 6, animals may see man as a rival of say, the same species or the same sex; in certain circumstances man also does this. I could tell at length of the consultations I have had on this subject in my capacity as zoo director; these would fill a book on their own. Amongst other things, mention would be made of the cases of men in tears who had to hand over a monkey to the zoo because their wives had finally declared that it must be the monkey or the wife but not both! Cases of animals seen as sexual partners would also find a place in such a book.

Here we can only deal with one special case concerning the significance of one species for another which has often been confirmed in animals but never established with any certainty in man. It is now well-established that young animals imprinted on or hand-reared by man regard the latter as a parent, usually as the mother; it has also been established that human mothers accept animals as children in the truest sense of the word, including suckling them at the breast; this has even happened with baby elephants. As well as elephants however the most varied babies are accepted as their own by woman; this applies not only to native people but also to highly civilized ones. Viki Hayes, a three day-old female chimpanzee was adopted by a married couple K. and C. Hayes who were psychologists; the young chimp was bottle-fed and treated as a child for six years, unimaginable sacrifices being made in the interests of a scientific experiment (Hediger 1961, p. 269 *et seq*). In addition to numerous scientific publications, C. Hayes (1952) has also published a very interesting popular book.

In contrast to this are the cases of so-called wolf-children, that is, human children which are alleged to have been reared by wolves as parents. There is also a book on this subject (J. A. L. Singh and R. M. Zingg 1942), the contents of which were taken seriously by many scientists, particularly by psychologists and psychiatrists, but not by all. This book was discussed critically by O. Koehler (1950) and B. Bettelheim (1959); the latter's work is of interest and will be referred to later.

Claims are repeatedly made that it is possible for human babies to be reared by wolves. At Zurich Zoo we have had plenty of opportunity to make observations at close quarters on the rearing of young wolves in their dens; anyone who has had experience of this, or who is familiar with wolves from direct observations on their behaviour, will be of the opinion that it is not possible for the human baby to be reared by wolves, even if it is conceded that children of native peoples are extraordinary robust and hardy.

The so-called wolf-children are accepted by Bettelheim as being the result of extreme emotional isolation; they are children which grow-up in the total absence of love and under continual threat of death. Such youngsters do not turn into wolf-children because female wolves behave like human mothers but because human mothers treat their children in an inhuman way.

Two fundamental fallacies lie at the root of all reports on so-called wolf-children. The first is concerned with the initial encounter between the wolf and the human baby. Newly born or very small children are relatively often abandoned in India, and in many other countries inhabited by native people who are scarcely civilized and who hold certain social and religious ideas; these young children are put outside the human settlements, usually at night, into the habitats of large wild animals in the expectation that carnivores will regard them as prey, carry them off and eat them. In Africa alone hundreds of cases of this kind occur every year. I personally know of one case which occurred in 1960. On one occasion the wife of a European official, a white woman who often indulged in the dangerous habit of going for nocturnal walks by herself, found a black baby which had been exposed in this way on account of the death of its mother in childbirth; it would doubtless have become the victim of hyenas had the official's wife not found it and reared it in her home where I saw it in the best of health. In the vast majority of cases carnivores arrive before humans can come to the rescue; this applies also to the uncivilized regions of India.

According to the opinions of animal behaviourists when a carnivore encounters a human being at night in the wild for the first time, the possibilities of what may occur are only twofold: either the helpless little human is treated as prey by the carnivore, or, because it is human and enemy scent is attached to it, it will be avoided by the carnivore. In both cases death is certain; it will die quickly from being bitten or slowly from hunger and exhaustion.

People who believe in wolf-children, accept a third possibility: they believe that the human baby may have a significance to the carnivore as a member of its own species, namely as a young animal. This is particularly likely to occur when the carnivore is a female that has accidentally lost her own young and is therefore suffering pain from the pressure of milk, with the consequence that the female feels an exceptionally strong urge to adopt another young.

It is not only asking a lot that the chance meeting should take place (if it ever actually does so) but it also presupposes that the baby finds its way on its own, without any assistance, to the atypical nipples of the carnivore and that the carnivore happens to be suffering from an excess of milk. Also why has no one ever observed a female carnivore that has adopted a newly born member of another species, such as a monkey, bear, a wild piglet or an antelope? It always has to be something rare, a human baby.

In fact the "agonizing pressure of milk" occurs only in domesticated animals, particularly in the cow, in which the mammary glands have become grotesquely overdeveloped as a result of hundreds of years of selection by man, and in man himself where similarly unnatural conditions are present. As a rule the women of native races and the female anthropoid apes suckle for three whole years; in highly civilized women the period of suckling is shortened in an unbiological way, and has to be induced often to a minimum by all kinds of means.

Amongst wild animals we find that conditions are different. In the wild, infant mortality is remarkably high; in some animals it is over 50 per cent. To a certain extent therefore the loss of the one or more young is a normal phenomenon. In the over-riding interest of the maintenance of the species the loss of the rising generation ought not to prejudice the life of the mother. It is more important that she should remain fit and become pregnant again in the shortest possible time. For this reason the production of milk in wild animals decreases as soon as the stimulus of suckling disappears.

In 1963 in Zurich Zoo the two-year-old offspring of the female chimpanzee Lulu died; three days after its death, the mother was already showing renewed signs of oestrus with much regressed breasts.

In his research on mountain gorillas living wild in the area of Kabara G. B. Schaller (1963, p. 101) found a mortality of 40 per cent to 50 per cent during the first six years of life; the mortality is highest in the first year of life. In this connection it should be remembered that gorillas only have a few enemies apart from man. On the basis of his observations on the vicuna (*Vicugna vicugna*) in southern Peru C. B. Koford (1957, p. 164) assumed that the mortality of the young shortly before, during and after birth was about 50 per cent. A mortality of 50 per cent of the young in the first year of life has also been given for a European wild ungulate, namely the red deer (*Cervus elaphus*). Fraser Darling (1937, p. 43) considered this statement of Cameron to be exaggerated, but was forced to confirm it in the course of his own investigations on red deer in Scotland.

In East Africa L. M. and M. H. Talbot (1963, p. 80 *et seq*) established a mortality of 50 per cent shortly after birth in the young of the white-bearded gnu (*Gorgon taurinus*). Under exceptional conditions this juvenile mortality rises even higher. Thus in the extremely dry season of 1960–1961 practically the entire population of young of the year died.

Many similar examples could be cited. These all show that the loss of half of the young in the first year, usually before weaning, is fairly normal. Also all the experience in zoos shows that in those mammals that have suddenly lost their offspring, the "pressure of milk" does not occur in any way that would make the mother specially ready to adopt the young of another species. It is sometimes very difficult to put newly born mammals artificially to wet nurses and in some cases all sorts of tricks have to be employed such as applying the scent of the wet nurse to the young.

As well as the fallacy of the alleged pressure of milk factor, which is said to work in favour of the adoption of the human baby, there is a second fallacy which concerns abnormal children. Why should it always be the wolf that accepts children that behave like animals, e.g. walking on all fours, feeding off the ground, refusing to keep clothes on, not speaking and so on; why is it never a dog, cat, lion, tiger, hyena or some other four-legged animal? Many physical defects such as certain inborn heart conditions, persistent gill slits and so on are usually considered by medical men and anatomists to be disturbances of the embryonic development leading to the retention of ancestral stages.

In contrast to this the erect posture, the wearing of clothes, articulated speech, eating with utensils and so on are the most recently acquired characteristics of man, which each individual normally has to acquire for himself during his development. If these newly acquired characteristics do not appear on account of serious physical disturbances, this does not automatically mean a regression, but simply the retention of an earlier stage in development, through which we all have to pass for some time. There is no need however to drag the wolf into this.

A great deal more could be said on this subject. Thus it used to be thought that female anthropoid apes—which are not carnivores and which of all animals are the closest to man—would adopt an exposed human child or even abduct one, if for example they had lost their own young; there is a significant absence, however, of any serious report of such an event even though many adventurers with an eye for the main chance have zealously looked for cases of this kind. Thus on the basis of zoo biological considerations and facts, we are forced to the conclusion that J. A. L. Singh and R. M. Zingg must have been the victims of a hoax with their alleged wolf-children.

Indeed no incontestable evidence can be submitted today on this

Fig. 65   Water bucket of light-weight zinc, used as a drinking-trough in the transport cage of a lion, from which extremely sharp-edged pieces have been bitten.

Fig. 66   Many lethal foreign bodies come from neglected wire-netting.

Fig. 67   Wire-netting, used to protect trees, always provides a dangerous source of foreign bodies.

Fig. 68 In one sense the yew (*Taxus baccata*) can also be regarded as a dangerou
foreign body because it is poisonous; for this reason it should not be allowed to grow
in the grounds of a zoo.

Fig. 69 Lungs of a tubercular elephant. The section shows extensive caseation of the
lung tissue.

Fig. 70 An example of intraspecific intolerance: male African Porcupines (*Hystrix*
make a frontal attack on each other and bite out the spines attached to pieces of
skin and muscle about the size of a walnut.

subject; there can only be circumstantial evidence and a consideration of the matter on biological and psychological grounds, as was rightly emphasized by J. Lutz and Emil E. Kobi in their latest expression of opinion (1964). Just because it is not possible to set up experiments in this field, it would at least be worthwhile perhaps to elucidate exactly what is open to investigation, namely the habits of the Indian wolf in its natural habitat and under suitable conditions of captivity. Considerable sums of money have already been spent on less important expeditions, for example, on the search for the yeti, the alleged snowman of the Himalayas which surely only exists in the realms of fantasy.

In view of the great differences in brain and environment, the ways in which the animal may be significant to man are much more numerous than in the reverse case; only five categories in which man is important to the animal can be found. As we have seen, the significance as a companion is reciprocal; we have dealt with this at some length and it is now time to discuss the many other ways in which the animal is significant to man.

These are so numerous however that even their simple enumeration is out of the question in this book. We must be satisfied with taking a look at both ends of the spectrum which attracts animals to man in his environment, and with mentioning a few particularly striking examples between these extremes. The two extremes are indeed poles apart: at one extreme the animal has the significance of merchandise and at the other extreme it has the significance of a deity. Both these attitudes which are in incredible contrast to each other are still very actively held today.

Let us first consider the animal as merchandise, both live and dead. This dubious significance occurs primarily in situations in which man has to deal with large numbers of animals that have a market value and thus become objects of trade. One has only to glance at a fish, poultry or meat market, the trade in cattle and other animals, the transport of such animals and so on to appreciate this.

In deep-sea fisheries the contents of the net which may weigh several tons is lifted on board by a winch, and the crew climbs over the mountain of floundering fish as though it were a pile of sand or gravel. The fish are left to die as it is neither practical nor even possible to kill them individually. In the poultry market—at least in

H

many areas—live chickens are tied together by their legs and sold with their heads hanging down, to be carried home in this way by the customers. These animals can only remain alive until they reach the kitchen; similarly cattle will be killed when they arrive at the slaughterhouse.

Until a few years ago edible tortoises and turtles were stored as living conserves like rocks on board ship for weeks and months; often they were roasted alive. Until two hundred years ago black slaves were exported from Africa, closely chained to one another; about a quarter of this cargo of "black ivory" died on the voyage. Man has therefore regarded even his fellowmen as merchandise, almost within living memory.

Nowadays the treatment of other humans as merchandise is regarded as criminal, but this is still permissible to a surprising extent in relation to animals. Often this is a matter of blind spots as C. W. Hume (1962, p. 18 *et seq*) expresses it; one does not notice obvious enormities, because one is accustomed to them or does not think about them. It was not until 1962 that the use of the gin-trap for wild animals, one of the worst instruments of torture, was forbidden in Switzerland as a method of hunting. But the use of living fish as bait is unfortunately still widespread today. Even children, who like to fish, can witness the way in which a minnow squirms as its body is impaled on a hook as bait to catch larger fish. If the fish does not take the bait then the minnow dies slowly. Naturally the minnow is not so sensitive to pain as man, but one cannot however deny it all feeling of pain; according to zoological classification it is after all a vertebrate animal, just as man is. Moreover it ought to be an offence to allow such methods to be used, particularly as a pastime or for sport.

Although it is tempting to go into this subject in greater detail these few examples should serve as an indication of how closely certain of the various kinds of significance which we attach to animals are mixed up with animal torture, animal protection and the humanitarian approach. A further reference to C. W. Hume (1962) may suffice; here we must restrict ourselves to some zoo-biological aspects of the significance of the animal as merchandise, an attitude which is obsolete today.

The purely commercial view that wild animals are a business

proposition—which has already been condemned in my Introduction —still persists in one form or another in some zoos. This old-fashioned attitude presupposes that animals are a form of merchandise, whereas in the modern approach the emphasis is much more that animals are valuable gifts on loan from nature, entrusted to zoos. While attempting to get agreement to a rule forbidding the feeding of animals by the public, I had a long battle with the members of the governing body of the zoo; one of the arguments put forward, by a member who reckoned to be a zoologist, was that as feeding was so popular with the public we should at least allow one species of "cheap" monkey to be fed. The death of one or two animals would be neither here nor there.

A similar mentality is found in certain zoological gardens which run a so-called children's zoo for profit. In German the term Kinder-Zoo is ambiguous because it does not state clearly whether this is an enclosure for human children or for young animals. Usually a mixture of both is involved: in the enclosure human children can meet non-dangerous and defenceless young animals. In these children's zoos some of the animals that I have come across have included quite young elephants, rhinos and gorillas alongside rabbits, guinea-pigs, lambs and kids.

The recommendation or justification of such children's zoos in my opinion stands or falls according to the quality of the supervision. One serious mistake that is frequently to be seen is the presentation of living animals as toys to human children. Animals however are neither merchandise nor toys but in fact are living creatures with feelings, often sensitive beings, which ought not to be treated as inanimate objects. With properly trained supervisory staff, the animals can be presented to the children in a suitable manner that also shows consideration for the animals; where this is done a children's zoo can be an important institution both from the educational and zoo-biological points of view and it can be run in the interests of the child as well as of the animal. Good and conscientiously run children's zoos are centres where valuable contact can be established between man and animals, encouraging a healthy love for animals and true animal protection. The running of this kind of children's zoo however is by no means cheap; nevertheless it should not be run for profit.

Unfortunately this kind of serious children's zoo is rare at present and in the meantime there are a great many children's enclosures in which all kinds of helpless young animals, and even older ones, are rendered defenceless and submitted to a form of prostitution; animals are put at the mercy of human children who because there is no risk attached are not subjected to any form of restraint. Thus the children are not given the opportunity of learning to approach animals with respect, by holding back and allowing the animal to take the initiative in making close contact.

In children's zoos that are inadequately supervised or without any form of supervision, defenceless animals are often literally tormented to death; the prices charged for admission include a rate of "replacement" and thus the deaths of animals do not encroach upon the profits. Old-fashioned undertakings of this type that are biologically backward even go so far as to hire out animals from the children's zoo for all sorts of occasions. This is an additional and particularly evil consequence of the commercial attitude which still persists in some places.

Animal dealing, from which some zoological gardens also expect commercial profit, is considered to be only a necessary evil from the viewpoint of zoo biology; its aim primarily should be to meet supply and demand among zoos, in order to avoid unnecessary collecting activities involving casualties among the natural populations.

The use or more properly the misuse of certain animals as capital investment is based on the same attitude of regarding animals as a form of merchandise. Around 1960, after the catastrophic collapse of the chinchilla industry in North America, the breeding of chinchillas was the subject of a high pressure advertising campaign in Switzerland that was also fraudulent to some extent. The advertisements were directed at small savers and investors; exceptionally high profits were forecast for people buying one or two pairs of these fine-furred rodents, naturally at an inflated price. Anyone who was not able to keep these animals at home was given the attractive offer of leaving them in the care of the seller, at a price.

After I had received numerous and somewhat disturbing letters from chinchilla breeders who had been cheated in this way, I ventured to issue a warning against this kind of capital investment; I pointed out the great drop in price which chinchillas had suffered in recent years and that this kind of thing had happened previously with many other fur animals. On the other hand I recommended chinchillas as attractive pets; they are quiet, clean and odourless rodents which are easy to keep, somewhat similar in style to the golden hamster. These comments however were not appreciated by one of the more vociferous chinchilla gangsters; I received somewhat violent threats and was favoured with anonymous telephone calls at night, until the shady chinchilla dealer was arrested and convicted.

It is virtually only a short step from using live fur animals as a capital investment to using live animals for personal adornment. In 1962 Zurich Zoo received some beetles (about $1\frac{1}{2}$ inches long) from a lady returning from Mexico; they belonged to the family Tenebrionidae and the genus *Zopherus*. The whole upper side of these beetles was studded with small flashing stones; a small screw ring had been inserted into the hard wing-covers and a glittering gold chain was attached to the ring. As was described in Brehm's *Tierleben* of 1914, in Mexico and Yucatan elegant women have the habit of pinning these hardy beetles on to themselves as crawling forms of adornment. In the instructions on how to keep the beetles alive it simply said that from time to time they must be put into damp, decayed timber; in this way these undemanding pieces of adornment would remain alive for months.

There are countless ways in which animals may have a significance to man but only a few further examples will be given to illustrate the attitude of research workers and specialists. These people are sometimes no longer able to see the wood for the trees or the whole animal for one of its organs. To exaggerate slightly: for the geneticist some animals are virtually nothing more than mere carriers of chromosomes; the research worker on venoms sees his specimens only as walking phials of poison; to the brain specialist the external appearance of an animal is lost behind its brain structure.

The extent to which this lack of proportion may in fact affect specialists was once made clear to me while I was being conducted through the animal rooms of a big pharmaceutical firm. After we had visited the rooms with white rats and mice, rabbits and other laboratory animals, we reached a room with several fine guinea-pigs. The laboratory technician assistant corrected me, they were not guinea-pigs but carriers of testes, the guinea-pigs were all in the next room. To him the animals which I had called guinea-pigs were only carriers of a given experimental organ and the rest of the animal did not exist for him in his particular surroundings. Probably zoo people are also not exempt from corresponding professional distortions, they too suffer from a certain occupational blindness, from which it is always worth trying to free oneself.

Finally at the other end of the broad spectrum regarding the significance of animals to man, there is the category in which animals are regarded as sacred. The attitude of Indians to zebus can be mentioned as a case in point. This attitude is still prevalent in India today and a sacred zebu lying in the middle of a road may bring the traffic to a standstill. Even today millions of people still revere their totems or animals which symbolize their ancestors and which must therefore be preserved. In this totemism we can see what is probably the most ancient form of nature protection.

The attitude of man towards animals which is furthest removed from that of the commercial point of view is doubtless the worshipping of animals by man as deities. The most impressive examples of this are found in the civilizations of ancient Egypt and ancient Greece.

6

The Exhibition Value of Animals

In the previous chapter we examined some of the ways in which the living animal, not necessarily in the zoo, may have general significance for man. Let us now consider the particular ways in which animals on show in a zoo are significant to man. No secret has ever been made of the fact that the earlier show-booths were the ancestors of the modern zoo; these included travelling exhibitions as well as those that remained in one place. The exhibition of "living curiosities" has always played a prominent role and even today the provision of zoological and natural history displays is still the most important function of the zoo. Zoos must therefore take the trouble to present their animals in the best possible way, both from the point of view of the public and of the animals on show. Technical installations, buildings and so on, also play an important part in this. The central point of interest however is the animal itself, and the question of its exhibition value will now be examined.

Animals with high exhibition value attract visitors; they arouse general interest and in the final result also affect the takings of the zoo. On the other hand, animals with small exhibition value are not noticed by the public; they exist in the shadows so to speak and are often regarded by the governing body as useless makeweights in the animal stock. In framing policy on an animal collection the exhibition value must be taken into account but it is only one among many other factors.

In the heyday of the show-booths all sorts of tricks were tried in an attempt to enhance the exhibition value or to conjure one up where none existed. In my own youth at annual fairs I remember seeing men dressed up to look like gorillas and seals presented as mermaids. The exhibition value of donkeys was increased by painting them with stripes to look like zebras. During the twenties of this century at San Diego Zoo, which today is a model scientific organization, they still played at making two sacred white elephants out of two ordinary Indian elephants, by spending vast sums of money on powder; although this was done for amusement it nevertheless brought in 7,500 dollars (H. M. Wegeforth & N. Morgan 1953, p. 100). Moreover it was established during this procedure that the usual practice of oiling the whole body of an elephant could be harmful to the animal.

The particular zoological characteristics of the species do not determine the exhibition value of the animal; this arises from the special relationship of man and animal, which itself can vary according to nationality and race. The exhibition value has less to do with the actual value of the animal than with the public's attitude to it and is not necessarily related to the scarcity value of the animal, although the two may sometimes be related. The exhibition value can be assessed quite simply by statistical methods: taking into account the area of the exhibit it is only necessary to count the spectators who stand in front of an animal for a given period of time. In brief, the public congregates in the largest numbers for the longest periods of time in front of the paddocks or cages of animals which possess the highest exhibition value.

Another method is to ask direct questions of large groups of visitors, but this method does not bring to light certain characteristic fluctuations which are caused by temporary peaks of activity amongst the exhibits. An animal that is largely ignored and regarded as "boring" may attract crowds of spectators in a very short time by suddenly rampaging around or by producing a startling noise, associated perhaps with play or aggressive behaviour. Thus when the big cats are asleep they do not attract much attention but when they are fed they immediately acquire maximal exhibition value; feeding time for the lions is undoubtedly one of the major attractions to the public and, together with other feeding times, it is therefore well publicized in various ways.

"Savageness" and "predatoriness", are characteristics which

Fig. 71   This picture (after John H. Kaufmann, 1962) demonstrates how so-called free-living animals may be 'imprisoned' in their own territory: the lines represent all the observed movement of a group of free-living Coati, *Nasua narica*, during nine months. The loop, top right, shows how the group once ventured briefly over the boundaries of its territory 'in error'.

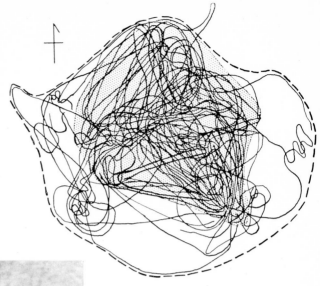

Fig. 72   Foot-and-mouth disease is a constant threat in European zoos: a male bison with foot-and-mouth.

Fig. 73   An Eland (*Taurotragus*) suffering from a catarrhal infection, caught from a sheep. Note the secretions running down from the eyes.

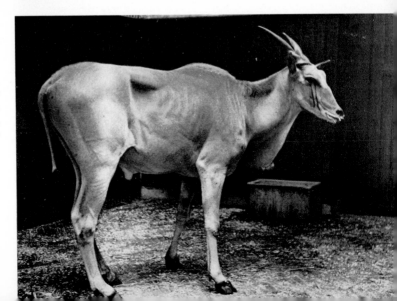

Fig. 74 Zebra faeces with nematode worms (ascarids) which indicate the need for a worm cure.

Fig. 75 Rhea faeces, with a massive content of the parasitic worm *Chapmania tauricollis*. This parasite, shaped like a collar-stud, climbs up grass stems and can then be taken up by other animals.

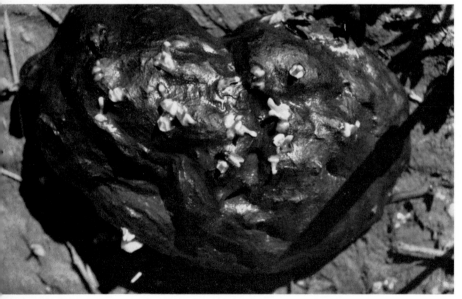

Fig. 76   Fish also have several parasites to contend with. Pike (*Esox lucius*) with gill parasites (*Henneguya*).

Fig. 77   Polar Bear trailing a length of tapeworm (*Dibothriocephalus*) behind it. Parasites play an important role in zoo animals, not infrequently even causing death.

Fig. 78   Inadequate fencing has been responsible for fatalities in many zoos. Example: a Stanley Crane killed by a marauding fox.

Fig. 79   A female Roe Deer killed in Zurich Zoo by a fox that had broken in. Since the installation of a fox-proof fence eight feet high set in concrete, with an acutely angled overhang facing outwards, these surprise attacks have stopped completely.

impress many people and these can be seen in a dramatic fashion before and during the act of feeding, thus providing the spectators with a display that has a special fascination. The interest aroused, for example, by the feeding of the sea-lions or anthropoid apes is motivated in quite a different way. The intense activity and the spectacle of maximal mobility of the sea-lions are doubtless important; in the anthropoid apes the primary attraction is their human-like behaviour at meal times.

Despite the immense attraction to the public of seeing the big cats being fed, there are biological reasons why this cannot be carried out every day but only on six days in the week. Although Sunday would be an administratively convenient fast day, it is not usually chosen on account of the large crowds of visitors who come to the zoo on Sundays and who would be disappointed at missing the feeding of the big cats. It is for this reason that as far as possible the day chosen for the fast day is the day on which there are fewest visitors.

As already indicated, the traditional fast day for the big cats, which is now observed in almost all zoos has a biological basis: a lion or tiger living in the wild does not make a kill every day or night; a deer, a wild pig, an antelope, a zebra or some other animal is killed only every few days. On the basis of their long experience in Africa various British authors maintain that in one year a lion kills on average only 40 to 50 head of big game. E. Hubert (1947) who had considerable experience with lions in the Albert National Park and managed to get to within 30 to 50 feet to photograph them, considers even this apparently modest figure to be still excessive. Most of his observations were carried out in the plains of Ruindi-Rutshuru, south of Lake Edward and he reckoned that at this rate of decimation the prey animals would have soon been exterminated.

Large vegetarians such as eland, gnu, zebra and so on are completely absent in this area and on the basis of a great deal of evidence he came to the conclusion that his lions only killed about 20 animals each per year; the prey were relatively small species such as topi, kob, reedbuck, warthog etc. Precise figures are of course difficult to obtain; the information available however was sufficient to estimate the order of magnitude and above all to establish with certainty that a lion in the wild does not make a kill and eat every day. In any case the inclusion of one fast day per week for big cats is biologically completely justifiable because overfeeding of wild animals in captivity may have just as fatal an effect as undernourishment. It should also be noted that zoo animals usually move about less than those in the wild, and that in some circumstances they eat to pass the time rather than to satisfy physiological requirements. (Animals are not necessarily alone in this). Obesity in wild animals is unknown under natural conditions and it occurs in captivity only when the level of activity is too low and at the same time the supply of food is too abundant.

Of the animals which have high exhibition value at feeding times, next to the big cats, come the monkeys; the latter's exhibition value is partly on account of their puzzling likeness to humans but there is no doubt that it is also due to the fact that their activity graph seems to correspond with that of man. Monkeys like man are by nature diurnal animals which sleep at night. The siesta which plays a certain role in *Homo sapiens* has even been observed in several monkeys in the wild; apart from their siesta monkeys are usually very active throughout the day and they are always doing something.

In addition to the characteristics mentioned above monkeys have other attributes; for example their free and easy sexual behaviour undoubtedly has an attraction for the public even if individual visitors may find it somewhat repulsive. Nevertheless the view that the sexual curiosity of the public constitutes the main motive for a visit to the zoo is undoubtedly exaggerated. There is no doubt however that every zoo has a quota of cranks of this kind but fortunately they are the exception and not the rule. These people usually have plenty of spare time and are normally well known to the zoo staff; they are given nicknames and are often under much closer supervision than they suspect. Sometimes they are useful to the zoo, because they may wait for important mating events which even a competent keeper may happen to miss.

It is interesting to note in this connection that in certain zoological gardens the keeping of monkeys has been known to be forbidden on principle and that in one of the largest zoos in the world a spacious open-air enclosure for baboons had to be pulled down because its inmates had behaved "indecently"—as though there could be such a thing as an indecent animal! This is yet another example of adopting a moralizing attitude to animals and judging them according to human standards—a case of the most crass anthropomorphism.

At this point it is worth mentioning that in some monkeys there may be behaviour patterns that are apparently sexual (erection, mounting of anoestrous females) but which are not associated with the sexual cycle; these have purely social functions, such as greetings or demonstrations of social superiority (H. Hediger & F. Zweifel 1962).

In addition to the monkeys and to other animals showing a high level of activity, exotic animals are also an attraction to the public. We have repeated evidence of this in zoos. What exactly is meant by exotic? Exotic is not synonymous with foreign, as one might at first think. Systematic questioning of large groups of research workers in Switzerland has shown, for example, that the polar bear, although certainly foreign, is not regarded as exotic. Earlier on, by exotic, people meant animals that were more "southern", but this did not include penguins, of which the largest species is the most southerly animal in the world.

In central Europe exotic animals are taken to be those which are not only foreign but also tropical: lion, elephant, giraffe, humming-birds, giant snakes etc. are exotic animals and accordingly of high exhibition value; by contrast, species that are endemic have much less drawing power with the public. This theoretical statement corresponds completely with what is found in practice.

A study of the history of many zoos, particularly of those in Europe, shows that having started with the exhibition of endemic or European animals, many were soon forced to turn to exotics because the native species had insufficient exhibition value. Basel Zoo which was opened in 1874 is a perfect example of this: the prospectus issued at its foundation stated: "as far as possible the visitor shall be offered a complete display of the splendour and beauty of our Swiss fauna in its most natural groupings, particularly the alpine fauna; in addition European animals of interest, in so far as these are suitable for a zoological garden, should be given full recognition and representation".

Within two years of its opening the new undertaking found itself in difficulties and the government had to give financial help. The Basel report for 1875 contained the following statement: "the high mortality among endemic and alpine animals is to be deplored, and as a result even the keeping of ibex has had to be given up because of continual failures".

As Fritz Sarasin, the famous naturalist and historian of the Basel Zoological Gardens states in his Festchrift (1924): "in 1888 further interest was aroused and attendances were increased by a hippopotamus exhibit and by the organization of a 'Nubian Nights' concert in conjunction with a Nubian caravan". In 1886 Fritz Sarasin and his cousin Paul had brought back the first elephant from Ceylon to the zoo, and finally the original aim—the keeping of endemic animals—was virtually abandoned in favour of the exhibition of exotic animals with high exhibition value. As already mentioned, several zoological gardens have developed along similar lines.

Hummingbirds are among the exquisite exotic animals listed earlier. The Bronx Zoo in New York devotes a special room, the so-called Jewel Room, to keeping these tiny sparkling aviators. To Europeans, just as to east coast Americans, these small colourful, nectar-sipping birds have a particularly exotic appeal and a correspondingly high value as exhibits.

But we have only to go to the west coast of North America, perhaps to San Diego Zoo in southern California, to find a change in values, namely a devaluation of these fascinating birds. In this region hummingbirds can be seen flying freely around the flowers in the open and their exhibition value is scarcely greater than that of a chaffinch or a blackbird in Europe. It would never occur to anyone in that part of the world to exhibit endemic hummingbirds in cages. On the other hand K. C. Lint (1965) has recently reported that a very beautiful aviary for hummingbirds from South America has been opened in San Diego Zoo.

It would be extremely interesting to find out which animals in American zoos are regarded as exotic by the *coloured* populations there. Do Indians regard elephants as exotic animals or are tigers exotic to Africans? These simple and obvious questions show once again the extent to which the exhibition value of the animals is rooted in the humans concerned, and how many are the problems of a human psychological nature which repeatedly crop up in the field of zoo biology.

The geographical origin of the animal however forms only one

118

factor in the total assessment of its exhibition value and other criteria are involved which have nothing to do with it. Thus, for example, it is an everyday zoo experience that young animals have greater exhibition value as a rule than adult specimens of the same species. It is for this reason that publicity of births is one of the most effective advertising methods adopted by those zoos which still go in for this type of thing. The effect which young animals have on man is probably fundamentally a matter of instinct.

In 1940 Konrad Lorenz showed that positive reactions, connected with protecting the young, are released in man by those animals which correspond to the so-called "child schema". "In young animals, as in small children, we all respond to a well-defined combination of characteristics accompanied by specific feelings and emotions, which are associated with the equivalent experience in rearing and caring for our own species. Animals which have this combination of characteristics are designated as 'sweet' or 'nice'. To produce this specific effect the object must have the following: 1. a forehead that is prominent compared with the outline of the face as a whole (domed head, short nose), with the eyes positioned below the centre of the head; 2. relatively large eyes; 3. a generally rounded form of head and body; 4. short extremities; 5. a certain soft elasticity of the body surface."

Pretty well all these characteristics are found, for example, in the giant and lesser pandas. There are few animals which have such a universal and irresistible appeal as these two species; pandas are *a priori* attractive to everyone and as a result they have a high exhibition value. In the giant panda its extreme rarity is an additional attraction. In the years 1938–1945 every Londoner was so to speak in love with his "Pandy", which for many years was the only specimen in the zoos of the western world. After its death London made great efforts and spared no cost to acquire another giant panda. On 5 September 1958, to the delight of Londoners, another representative of this fascinating species arrived at Regent's Park. In December 1963 the giant panda was bred for the first time in captivity at Peking Zoo.

The foxy-red, lesser panda with its long tail also has a singular appeal, which is doubtless linked with the "child scheme" of Lorenz. The pandas are also examples of those animals in which the juvenile characteristics are in no way confined to the young but are also retained in the adults.

There is no doubt that the positive impact of young animals on the public is also dependent on other factors; behaviour is no less important than the external appearance of the body, the sounds produced by the animal and so on also play some part. It is not possible to give a detailed analysis of all the factors involved but that of relative size must be mentioned here. The impact of size was made particularly clear to me on one occasion before the "no feeding" rule was generally enforced. During rebuilding operations in the Basel Zoo a cart horse had to be given temporary accommodation with some ponies. While the public were feeding the animals in this enclosure the wretched cart horse was offered nothing because the small, young-looking ponies were nearly always favoured and made a fuss of by the public.

At the time when the public was allowed to feed the animals one frequently noticed how visitors went to every conceivable manœuvre to cheat the larger inhabitants of a paddock, so that the smaller ones could be crammed with as many titbits as possible. To the public the smaller animals were regarded as youngsters whereas in fact the larger ones were not necessarily the oldest. The really young animals are often not capable of digesting solid food—at least not in such quantities—whereas the total food requirement of the adult animals is much greater. The public however usually judges the animals on a sentimental rather than on a rational basis.

The division of the animals into likeable and unlikeable groups is closely connected with this; the purely subjective impact made by an animal is linked with but not directly related to its exhibition value, as will be shown shortly. Among the animals which enjoy universal popular appeal, at any rate in Europe, are the penguins; these birds are accordingly used or misused as trade marks.

When advertisers make use of animals for commercial purposes it is obvious that they can only use those that make a pleasing impression; we are concerned here with an interesting psychological aspect which is also important from the viewpoint of zoo biology. It would be wrong for instance to show on the title page of a prospectus a gelada baboon making an angry grimace; it is not an attractive sight with its mouth wide open, exposing its sinister looking canine teeth and showing the paler inner side of its upper lip curled half-way back to its eyes. However interesting and unique the picture of this extreme grimace may be to the professional zoo man and to the student of animal behaviour, it is quite unsuitable for advertising purposes. It is also clear that zoo advertisements ought not to threaten with the repulsive, so to speak, but to entice with the attractive.

As already mentioned, animals such as penguins and pandas are clearly very appealing even though in completely different ways. If in addition to their popular appeal such animals also have an easily reproducible black-and-white pattern with clear outlines, then they are ideal subjects for advertising, including everything from sweets to underwear and refrigerators. Zebras are among the favourite zoo animals chosen by artists and advertising men on account of their striped pattern. It is significant that the giant panda, which only occurs in the remote west Chinese province of Szechwan, has been chosen as the badge of the World Wildlife Fund on account of the appealing characteristics mentioned; it also decorates the cover of the international journal for professional zoo staff, *Der Zoologische Garten.*

Nevertheless, both the penguin which lives in the far south and the zebra which comes from central and southern Africa can also be used in Europe for advertising purposes. The zebra has an aura of the exotic based on its land of origin, but what about the penguin? It certainly has nothing of the "child schema" about it, apart from its short legs: the eyes are by no means large; the face is noticeably pointed, running down into the long bill and the skin in fact is spiky. Here the popular appeal evidently rests on quite different characteristics, and in this case the penguin's erect posture (on the land) is the decisive factor.

As a rule it is those animals, which—like man—are marked by an erect posture that make a particularly pleasant impact. Indeed the following rule can be postulated: the degree of attraction decreases in proportion with the deviation from the vertical posture towards the horizontal. It is indeed quite traditional that man regards the bear as a remarkably likeable character. As child psychologists have established many small children far prefer teddy bears to dolls made in the human likeness. The bear is the first large animal which Stone

Age man in Europe kept in captivity; the most impressive constellation of the northern skies is named after it. It is the heraldic animal of Bern, Berlin and numerous other cities and communities. The story of the foundation of the town of St Gallen is very closely tied to this animal through the encounter of St Gallus with a bear. Bern and Berlin also keep their heraldic animal outside their zoos in municipal bear-pits. The Ainus in eastern Asia still practise their archaic bear culture today and so on. Doubtless this positive evaluation depends, amongst other things, on the erect posture which in general is so rare among large animals but typical of the bears.

Dogs and cats are quadrupeds in which the longitudinal axis of the body is normally held horizontal; but these domestic animals are never so appealing as when they sit up and beg. What is the significance of this begging posture? The vital point is that the erect posture of man is adopted. And are not men who hold themselves erect regarded as the personification of uprightness and honesty, and therefore much admired? A man that crawls on all fours makes a poor impression; it is as though he is deviating 90 degrees from the upright. The most extreme examples are provided by the snakes; the revulsion which these arouse in the greater part of mankind is too well known to labour the point.

The "law of angles" which is so important in determining the attitude of man to animals may even be applied to fish: no other fish has achieved such worldwide popularity as the sea-horse (*Hippocampus*); this is even true of areas far from the sea and many women wear ornaments representing sea-horses. They are one of the very few fish in which the orientation is usually vertical—with the head at the top. At the same time it is diverting that the closest and commonest relatives of the sea-horse, the pipefishes, such as *Syngnathus*, should have remained generally unpopular and unknown. The German name for pipefish Seenadel, translated literally means sea-needle, a name which suggests that it might be suitable as a brooch. However the pipefishes are horizontally orientated snake-like fish, although otherwise very similar in structure and habits to the popular sea-horse.

Why should the bats, which include the disease-carrying vampire, generally be regarded as sinister? When in the resting position bats are indeed vertical, but they are orientated head downwards, not

Fig. 80   In a zoo in Florida a wire is installed above the three foot high fence around the duck lake. At night it is electrified to keep raccoons out.

Fig. 81   A group of Crested Pigeons killed by a Beech Marten *Martes foina* which had entered through a hole in the fencing.

Fig. 82 Mice, like sparrows, may also be dangerous vectors of disease.

Fig. 83 An example of the retention of long outdated grotto style from the last century. Even birds from the tree-tops of the tropical rain-forest, a completely different habitat, are still put on display in a grotto, even if only a symbolic one.

upwards. Their deviation from the acceptable angle is therefore not just 90 degrees as in snakes, but 180 degrees.

Parrots and owls are vertical birds; added to this parrots are among the most intelligent of birds, and in some circumstances they can be taught to talk. The canary has a less erect posture than the budgerigar and it is for this reason perhaps that it has largely supplanted the canary in spite of the latter's beautiful song. In many places—as formerly in ancient Greece—the owl is a symbol of wisdom. If this bird does not arouse popular feelings everywhere as might be expected from its vertical posture, this must surely be on account of its noctural and therefore "sinister" habits. Man does not want any such deviation from his own cycle of activity. Evil men, witches and demons are creatures of the night and all nocturnal animals are unattractive as far as man is concerned.

As already indicated, favourable impact and exhibition value are not the same thing. The relation between the two still remains to be investigated in more detail. At this stage it is worth drawing attention to an example of the human attitudes to exhibition value in terms of what creates a sensation, even though this is completely outside the field of zoo biology: a criminal for example is usually at the focus of public interest and in some respects he can be described as having exhibition value; at the same time that he is the focus of interest, there may be no public sympathy for him. Lack of sympathy can be an element in determining exhibition value. Snakes for example, particularly the large and venomous forms have a definite exhibition value, as anyone in a zoo will confirm; this is precisely because most people regard them as repulsive. The comparison between snakes and criminals obviously cannot be taken very far in that snakes have nothing to do with crime. Many men can however even get enjoyment from looking at something gruesome. The creepy or the sinister exercises a specific attraction on quite a few people, as witness crime novels and horror films.

Another factor which contributes towards exhibition value is the extent to which the animal actively responds to the zoo visitor; high exhibition value is usually attached to animals which show a lively response, immediately going up to members of the public and accepting food from them where this is permitted. This applies for example to monkeys and deer although, fortunately for the animals,

I

this is no longer permitted in the majority of zoos. The average person who visits a zoo, more properly described as someone with a simple outlook, sometimes regards it as an insult when the animal does not take any notice of him. He makes up his mind quickly that the animal is stupid and boring, and does not take into consideration that it is impossible for any animal to pay special attention to each individual of hundreds or thousands of visitors, even if he attracts it with titbits.

As a zoo director one unfortunately has to admit that there are times when pressure of work forces one to hurry past cages and enclosures and some animals do not like this. One would gladly linger with them and have a short chat, allow them perhaps to snuffle at one and encourage them with a pat or have a short game with them and stroke their beautiful coats, and so on. Unfortunately this is usually reserved for the keepers and some of them recognize it is a great privilege. The animals in the zoo are not the only ones to take offence when the zoo director is in a hurry; there are some visitors who show a lack of understanding, taking it as an insult or as a sign of arrogance when the director does not stop to chat with them in the zoo. It does not occur to them that he might perhaps be hurrying to answer an overseas telephone call, to get to a lecture or to talk to someone in the office who has already been kept waiting; and, what is more important, he may be on his way to deal with some urgent matter such as a birth, a sick animal or an accident.

There are few occupations in which a senior member of staff is so exposed to chance meetings with people as in the zoo. In almost all other professions he is protected from casual visitors by the machinery of appointments, secretaries and so on. In the zoo however when he takes a walk in the course of his duties (see Inspection) the director is completely accessible. The zoo director is never off duty even at night when he can be telephoned for instance to settle some point which is being debated over a drink, such as the gestation period of the elephant (21 months) or the number of humps in camel and dromedary (Bactrian camel two, dromedary or Arabian camel one); the query may even concern the answer to a crossword puzzle if the word still missing at a late hour is a bird with three letters (emu, kea etc.).

Although the feeding of animals by the public has now been

abolished in most major zoos, the following remains to be said on the subject. It has already been emphasized that this dangerous practice rests basically not on a real love of animals but on human egoism. The visitor enjoys getting an animal to feed out of his hand. Surely there are many people of a certain type who get a special satisfaction from having someone—so to speak—eating out of their hand? Some expressions used in everyday speech are directly linked with zoo biology, such as looking "sheepish", "mulish" or "hangdog".

In some animals that appear to be holding their heads at an angle this actually denotes suspiciousness, alarm or a threat preparatory to showing aggression. In the black-footed penguin the angle to which the head is turned can be regarded as a definite indication of mood (Hediger 1961, p. 136 with illustrations). Expressions such as "sheepish" or "hangdog" certainly have nothing to do with animal behaviour.

Given that animals which show lively reactions towards the public have a high exhibition value, then it is easy to understand that animals which are inactive or asleep will have the opposite effect; foolish visitors often try to rouse animals by making a noise, shouting, clapping their hands or throwing stones at them and so on. Many people hold the anthropocentric view, that having paid their entrance money, this gives them the right to expect every animal to be ready to give them a special reception. They do not think of the fact that each animal species has its own cycle of activity which bears a close relationship with the demands of nature and that certain hours of the day or night must be spent either in activity or at rest. Some unusually interesting facts about the sleep of animals have recently come to light; these will gradually be investigated in relation to our knowledge of sleep in man. In the densely populated areas the number of people who suffer from insomnia and who have become dependent on sleeping tablets is known to be increasing at an alarming rate. In cases like this the problem can be tackled by examining the equivalent behaviour under the most natural conditions possible; in the case of insomnia the sleep of animals can be investigated (Hediger 1961).

For the zoo visitor the ideal animal is one which has a cycle of activity that corresponds with the opening hours of the zoo and which is therefore continually active during these hours. Animals only fit in with this anthropomorphic concept relatively rarely. Many animals may be active for only part of the day or none of it according to their biological constitution.

A certain amount of change in the activity rhythm of an animal can often be achieved by arranging feeding times so that periods of activity may be synchronized with the time when the public are in the zoo. But it is not possible suddenly to change animals that are typically nocturnal into completely diurnal animals. In various zoos (Bristol, Bronx and others) attempts have been made to simulate a reversal of night and day, by giving the animals a very bright light by night and a very subdued blue or red light by day. In all these attempts however success can scarcely be regarded as a hundred per cent. In animal houses with a reversed rhythm of day and night the public also has to be kept in semi-darkness and this raises problems of human behaviour.

The exhibition value of an animal may reach impressive proportions. The story of the famous polar bear cub Brumas is a case in point. This cub was born in the London Zoo on the 27 November 1949 and was found dead there on the 18 May 1958. The rearing of polar bear cubs is largely a matter of chance. Some mothers rear their young without mishap; others, in spite of every care, take no interest in their young and may even eat them. The London Zoo had had particularly bad luck with their polar bears. For some 120 years, it had never succeeded in rearing young polar bears to the adult stage.

The luck did not change until after the Second World War when the London Zoo had obtained a good breeding female polar bear from the Hanover Zoo. In spring 1950 this female was exhibited with the first polar bear cub to be shown in the London Zoo. The cub was named Brumas and excited unprecedented enthusiasm, not only amongst Londoners but throughout the whole of Britain. The snow-white, soft-furred cub showed all the characteristics of the "child schema" and caught the imagination of the whole country in a way that had never happened previously. Hours before opening time the crowd was jammed in front of the zoo gates, and at the polar bear enclosure a special queue had to be formed. Anyone who lingered in front of Brumas for more than a few minutes was hailed by the overseer through a loudspeaker and asked to move in order to make room for the crowd streaming in behind. Brumas became the subject of innumerable newspaper stories, radio and television broadcasts, pamphlets and books; toys were modelled on her and the polar bear cub image in one form or another was used over and over again as an advertising theme in all branches of commerce. The public enthusiasm was on an unprecedented scale and a total of over three million people visited the London Zoo in 1950, making an all-time record. The cash takings were equally successful, bringing in a clear surplus of over £12,000.

Polar bears grow very quickly and by the following year the irresistible ball of fur had developed into a half-grown polar bear which was nothing like as attractive in appearance; the exhibition value of the cub dwindled in proportion with the speed of its growth. The three million visitors of 1950 had sunk to below two million by 1951 and instead of a surplus there was a deficit of £13,000. Naturally other factors may have played a part but the *Financial Times* of 17 December 1952 regarded the waning attractions of Brumas as the decisive factor in the steep drop in the number of visitors and the consequent loss of gate money. In short, as Brumas grew up she lost the "child schema" characteristics and also much of her exhibition value.

7
Food

In Chapter 5, on the significance of man to animals, it was pointed out that research workers who specialize in a narrow field, concentrating perhaps on one particular organ of the body, often lose sight of the animal as a whole. This kind of thing has happened to a remarkable extent during the last two decades on the whole subject of feeding animals in zoos. It has occurred in both theoretical aspects and in the practical techniques of giving food to zoo animals.

One of the theories that is gaining more and more support may be described as the "retort theory" (Retorten-Auffassung). It is based on the view that due to the nature of the digestive system of a wild animal one has only to fill it up with carefully balanced amounts of protein, carbohydrate, fat, minerals, vitamins and trace elements for it to remain alive and healthy.

This retort theory is based on false principles and must therefore be rejected from the standpoint of zoo biology. It has a legitimate application to the rearing of domestic and farm animals where the pressing problems of feeding an ever-increasing human population have to be met. In rearing animals as food for humans the following principle is valid and worthy of support: animals carrying the maximum protein and fat should be reared in the shortest possible time at minimal cost. It is completely misleading, however, to suggest that this has any validity with regard to animals in zoos. Every care must be taken to preserve zoo animals from the effects of domestication and every effort should be made to provide them with living conditions that are as near to nature as possible—this aim is completely opposite to that of any undertaking that rears animals for profit.

Fast-growing protein suppliers, economic food producers and animals for fattening are not wanted in zoos. Abstract races of animals reared for domestic or agricultural purposes, bred artificially, may be the stockbreeder's ideal animal but from the point of view of zoo biology these "higher" breeds are little more than grotesque caricatures of their ancestors in the wild. It is the fate of domestic and laboratory animals to be reared in unnatural conditions; animals in zoos, however, must be reared in conditions that are as near as possible to those in the wild. A knowledge of domestication and its manifold operations is undoubtedly of importance to zoo biology because it indicates the necessity for constantly being on the watch for early stages of domestication. It is the sole purpose of zoological gardens to keep their animals as near to the purely wild form as possible; if it were otherwise zoos might just as well be run on the lines of animal husbandry enterprises.

It is clear that quite dangerous domestication effects are involved in feeding. This is why feeding techniques are regarded as vital in the rearing of farm animals. In the interests of zoo biology, therefore, great care must be taken to ensure that these influences do not creep in through feeding techniques. The retort theory virtually opens the door in the zoo to domestication effects that are totally undesirable and for this reason it must be rejected. The only principle on which the feeding of zoo animals should be based is that the food must be as natural as possible.

This applies not only to quantity and quality but also to the method and time of feeding; consideration must be given to the various types of feeders (continuous eaters and occasional eaters) and social factors may also be involved. Above all, one must remember that animals do not live by bread alone (Hediger 1950, p. 120).

It is not possible to achieve a completely natural diet in the zoo, neither is it possible to provide a completely natural enclosure. Substitutes have to be provided for the most part, to a greater or lesser extent, but the basic principle holds good: the food should diverge from the natural to the least possible extent. Lions, for instance, cannot be fed live zebras, antelopes or warthogs, nor is it possible to give them other live animals as a substitute e.g. horses, goats and dogs. Portions of dead carcasses, mostly of horse and cattle, which have been skinned and gutted can be supplied; these are virtually carrion since they have lost all their blood. Animals such as lions and tigers also eat carrion in the wild, i.e. prey which has been dead for some time. The habits of the big cats in returning to their kill the following night can be turned to good account by big game hunters who wait near the kill, preferably perched high above the site.

In any case a hunk of meat (horse or cow), which has to be broken up by using teeth and claws, is more akin to natural food than minced meat with all its trimmings. If the atrophy of these organs is to be countered they must obviously be kept in use. There is also a hint of the excitement of overthrowing prey in the wild as the animals wait to leap on the food thrown through the bars by the keeper. It is certainly more exciting than waiting for a piece of "cake". By contrast a joint varies in taste and consistency according to the carcase; similarly the solubility of the bones varies. It takes some time for a zoo animal to tackle a rib or a shoulder, thus ensuring that it exercises its teeth, jaw muscles and claws. Tackling food of this kind also breaks up the monotony of existence for a predator in captivity.

Monotony in any form is unnatural because life for animals in the wild is full of variety and change, especially in regard to food. Psychological factors often play a prominent and decisive role as I described in detail in 1942 (p. 126 *et seq.*). There is no need to repeat this material here except to draw attention to the theme of the behaviour scientist W. Fischel (1938, p. 275) which is in particular need of emphasis today: "The assimilation of food by animals serves not only as a means of procuring materials for metabolism but it also brings psychical experience with it." Fischel conducted many experiments on the preference of various animals for certain kinds of food and amongst other things he found direct preferences—mostly of a temporary nature—in which one kind of food is excessively favoured. This often corresponds with special needs which in the wild, for instance, might fluctuate according to the time of year. Food available to animals out in the wild is not constant throughout the year but changes in quantity and quality with the seasons.

In his valuable research into the hunger and appetite of zoo animals, the ethologist and animal psychologist D. Katz (1948, p. 185 *et seq.*) states: "The appetite of nearly all free-living animals is subject to a daily rhythm and in many to an annual rhythm." Furthermore, he states (p. 197): "It is possible to reduce the appetite of an animal for one of many approximately similar foods by only offering it this particular food over a long period of time. But even in the course of a short meal an increasing saturation can be established. In the first place we would speak of a chronic conversion and in the second place of a temporary conversion."

Rations that are "complete" in the physiological sense are now supplied to animals in a number of zoos. Details of these will be given later in this chapter together with such results as are available. The latter should serve as a warning against monotony in feeding wild animals and against the retort theory. Food preferences still exist but they can become displaced by experimental conversions. By offering so-called complete rations in the form of "cakes", the animal is deprived of any chance of selecting food that is favoured temporarily; only a monotonous physiological repletion is achieved. It is well known that man also resists stereotyped forms of diet. It is only domesticated animals, with their blunted sense organs and their standardized needs that have become accustomed through successive generations to monotonous and uniform diets.

In his monumental work *Disease in captive wild mammals and birds*, Herbert Fox (1923, p. 4) states that captivity causes numerous physical and mental disorders; unaccustomed, unnatural and unvaried food, amongst other things, reacts harmfully on captive animals. Muscles which are not used may degenerate, as for example the maxillary muscles of the lion. "He gets his food regularly with awful monotony—twelve pounds of meat at 3.30 p.m. day after day; there is no alteration of feasts and fasts, with consequent change in the balance of the body reserves . . . Gastro-intestinal disease is the commonest disease of wild animals in captivity."

Fox is referring here to the circumstances which prevailed at the Philadelphia Zoo in 1901 when as pathologist he performed autopsies on every mammal and bird that died, and on all the large and important reptiles.

Many changes have taken place since this date. For example nearly all zoos have introduced fast days for carnivores. Animals are given rabbit or poultry as a change from horsemeat and cattlemeat. Many American zoos are in a position to provide horsemeat from carcasses killed immediately before feeding time; the carnivores are given parts of the animal which are still warm and steaming, together with blood, skin, bones and viscera. This method is ideal from the standpoint of zoo biology, but it cannot be adopted in all zoos; in Switzerland, for example, zoos are forbidden by law to do their own slaughtering. Since Fox's time gastro-intestinal diseases have declined in importance. On the other hand, the "awful monotony" to which Fox rightly objected has become even worse owing to the feeding methods adopted in some zoos today. These methods are, in fact, the result of the retort theory which was developed in the Philadelphia Zoo by Herbert Fox's successor, namely Herbert L. Ratcliffe who was responsible for formulating the theory and putting it into practice.

In Ratcliffe's first publication on food reforms for zoo animals, he postulates that much could be gained from applying advances in the nutrition of humans and domestic animals to zoo animals. Although the zoo biologist can certainly have confidence in the scientific principles as applied to the feeding of domestic animals and civilized man, nevertheless this raises a fundamental point: modern man in his urban environment is far removed from a state of nature and his animals, as a result of domestication, are unrecognizable distortions (morphologically, physiologically and mentally) of their wild ancestors. As such, these animals cannot be used as a norm for evaluating the wild animal. In fact, the opposite is true: it is the wild animal alone that provides the fundamental standard and not the secondary form fabricated by man in his domestic animals.

It is worth stressing once again that zoo biology has the task of seeing that animals in zoos are kept as free as possible from the effects of domestication and captivity, and it is only when this aim is being strictly followed that one can afford to take a look on the side at the secondary, domesticated forms. The greatest care should also be taken when making comparisons of physiological nutrition between such animals as man and apes, cattle and antelopes, dogs and sea-lions. The feeding behaviour of related species can be surprisingly different, as for example within groups such as the whales, deer, geese, tortoises and turtles. The feeding habits of different races of man also differ widely: the Eskimos, the Watussi and the Melanesians all feed fundamentally in different ways.

Ratcliffe, however, classifies mammals and birds into only three groups in relation to his diet reforms: omnivores, herbivores and carnivores. He gives an ideal diet for each one of these extremely simplified categories; each diet is made up of a crushed mixture, standardized and homogenized. These uniform "cakes" are supplied to zoo animals at regular intervals in pre-determined quantities. From the standpoint of zoo biology this technique of feeding exaggerates the potential monotony previously censured by Herbert Fox.

According to Ratcliffe (1956) the new feeding methods, which were introduced in the Philadelphia Zoo in 1935, achieved astonishingly successful results. He believed that these results were supported by indisputable evidence, based on his own statistical material together with that of his predecessor Herbert Fox. I am somewhat doubtful about the deductions made from the statistical data and quite apart from any question of fundamental principle, the reasons for my scepticism will perhaps become apparent from what follows. Lee Crandall, who had more than 50 years' experience of feeding animals in one of the largest zoos in the world (Bronx Zoo), adopted much the same attitude as myself. In his latest comprehensive work he remains quite politely aloof from Ratcliffe's ideal "cakes". Crandall (1949, p. 109) wrote: "We have not fully adopted this method here because we have felt that supplemental natural diets, under close supervision, permit adjustment to the needs and vagaries of individual animals." This experienced zoo man recognized not only individual animals but also individual needs and vagaries; as a conscientious curator he regarded these as of sufficient importance to be taken into consideration with regard to feeding. This point of view is in direct contrast to the impersonal standards of the retort theory which fills animals up with stereotyped uniform "cakes".

Ratcliffe (1954, p. 4) based his arguments on the autopsies mentioned earlier which were carried out on all animals that had died in the Philadelphia Zoo since 1901; he rightly pointed out that this was a unique achievement, covering 16,000 mammals and birds. However, it must be pointed out here that methods of performing post-mortems have changed and been improved over a period of fifty years; when comparisons are made today with earlier findings this must be borne in mind. In the second place one must take into consideration the fact that many other changes besides feeding have taken place since the introduction of the new feeding methods in 1935. The Philadelphia Zoo, which is proudly named America's First Zoo and which brings out a publication under this title, has been repeatedly forced to move with the times since it opened to the public in 1874. In view of its venerable age buildings have been restored, the fight against vermin intensified, improvements in hygiene made, drugs (sulphonamides, antibiotics etc.) administered; as a result of all these changes, the living conditions of animals have been improved not only in the field of nutrition but in every other respect. These complex conditions must be taken into account when evaluating the mortality figures before and after 1935. It is wrong to regard the new feeding methods as solely responsible for the decline in mortality.

Nevertheless these particular errors are made throughout the relevant publications of H. Ratcliffe, as for example, in a paper published in 1956 in which he again recommends his feeding methods to the "traditionalists". The following heading is used for his figures in Table 1: "The value of improved diets to the Philadelphia Zoological Garden in terms of annual death rates during 20 years before diets were improved and 20 years thereafter." The average annual percentage mortality for 1916–1935 is given as 18·8% for mammals, as against 11% for 1936–1955; for birds, over the same period, 20·7% as against 13·9%.

In actual fact these figures give no clear indication of the advantages of the new feeding methods because food was responsible for only a relatively small proportion of the mortality. In this sense the table is misleading, as also is the statement on the reduction in replacement costs (p. 12): "Thus, on the average, these diets have reduced replacement costs by about one-third." Here it is important to know whether, for example, less costly animals, such as monkeys and geese were involved or more expensive exhibits such as rhinoceros and giraffe. No information is given on this point.

In his bulletin (1956, pp. 11, 12), Ratcliffe only gives averages of "number exhibited" for the 20 years before and after the diet reforms: from 1916 to 1935 it was 592·6 for mammals and 1267·0 for birds. From 1936 to 1955, however, it was only 520·0 for mammals and 1009·9 for birds. After the diet reforms therefore, the average number of individuals kept was considerably lower than before. We must remember these figures when reading the contents of the pages that follow.

In a later publication on arteriosclerosis amongst mammals and birds in the Philadelphia Zoo, Ratcliffe and his colleague M. T. I. Cronin (1958, p. 41) make a startling statement: "arteriosclerosis was markedly rare before the diet reforms were introduced." From 1901 to 1932 it was found in less than 3 % of autopsies but thereafter its frequency increased to about 20 %. This statement was amplified as follows: "But in 1935 the traditional and often inadequate diets then common to zoological gardens were replaced by controlled diets. Under these conditions arteriosclerosis has developed much more frequently."

It is not clear in which year the increase in arteriosclerosis started. Many passages of the Ratcliffe-Cronin publication, as for example the one quoted, suggest that it could have been the year in which the diet reforms were introduced (1935) but in other places (p. 48) it is clearly stated that the first outstanding rise of arteriosclerosis conditions started within the fourth five-year period (1931 to 1935), after the change in feeding methods, in association with decreases in the number of animals exhibited. Unfortunately individual years are not quoted in these tables, but five years are grouped together. In the five-year period 1926 to 1930 arteriosclerosis is found in only 1 %; the next five-year period, 1931 to 1935, it is found in 14 %. It is a pity that the data for the individual years are missing.

The substantial increase in arteriosclerosis—approximately ten to twenty times—in the Philadelphia Zoo, correlates closely in time with the diet reforms; because of this, one is tempted to assume that this increase was caused perhaps by the new diet—more particularly since no increase in arteriosclerosis was noted in zoos where animals were fed in the traditional manner. In his report for the year R. E. Rewell (1949, p. 492), pathologist of the London Zoo stated explicitly: "cardiovascular disease is as usual, a rare cause of death in our animals". No case of arteriosclerosis was found that year. Also, no increase in arteriosclerosis was observed in Paris, Berlin, Frankfurt, Rotterdam and so on. For years these zoos with their rich collections of animals recorded no case of arteriosclerosis. In their extensive report on the causes of death at the Rotterdam Zoo for the years 1959 and 1960, van Bemmel, Zwart and Peters did not name this disease directly but particularly mentioned an agouti (*Dasyprocta aguti*) which died as a result of severe haemmorhage in the chest due to a torn artery. Deposits of calcium were found on the walls of the *aorta* and *truncus caroticus*, but these could scarcely have been caused through social pressure (due to being confined in too small cages) since the agoutis in Rotterdam are allowed the free run of the zoo.

Ratcliffe and Cronin (1958, p. 49) expressly emphasize that the new diet was not a major factor in the marked rise in arteriosclerosis in the Philadelphia Zoo. They give a totally different explanation. In their opinion, the diet reforms introduced in 1935 led to a much healthier life for zoo animals and consequently to greater longevity; this of itself led to a greater frequency of arteriosclerosis which in a certain sense is known to be symptomatic of old age. Moreover the "improved" diets in Philadelphia resulted in breeding successes which had not previously been achieved; a larger number of individuals were on exhibition and this resulted in social pressure or direct stress. Both authors see evidence of this in the increasing frequency of injury as a cause of death, especially in breeding groups, and the loss of young through failure in lactation. They therefore regarded social pressure as the main factor in the increase of arteriosclerosis in the Philadelphia Zoo.

It should not be forgotten, however, that the total number of individuals in the period 1936 to 1955, compared with that of the previous 20 years, did not increase but declined significantly. The population pressure should therefore have been noticeably less and consequently arteriosclerosis should have declined. In fact the opposite took place and the statistical evidence refutes the case made out by these authors.

In 1956 H. L. Ratcliffe made a substantial improvement in the recipes based on his retort theory as compared with those given in 1940. He renewed his claims that the reformed diets were superior to the old-fashioned feeding methods of those professional zoo people whom he described as: "traditionalists who vaguely prate of 'natural foods' when actually they mean man-made fruits and vegetables that are available commercially" (1956, p. 2).

Perhaps it should be stressed here that during the past few decades the zoos which had not subscribed to the diet reforms introduced by the pathologist into the Philadelphia Zoo had in fact made their own improvements in feeding methods, by approximating the diet as far as possible to natural food instead of following the retort theory. In Zurich Zoo, for instance, carnivores were given meat with bones and some freshly killed rabbits including the skin and entrails; the traditionalists had also heard of certain other essentials such as minerals, vitamins and trace elements, and these were naturally included in the diet.

The big cats were given the freshest and most lean meat; the polar bears, because they eat oily seals in the wild, were provided with the fattiest meat; the hyenas and the jackals were supplied with meat that was the least fresh because they are accustomed in the wild to eating carrion, even stinking carrion.

Tainted fruit, withered lettuce and decaying vegetables which were unsuitable for human consumption were enjoyed by tortoises equally as well as if they had been of the best quality. Among the wildfowl, the Australian Cereopsis Goose, for example was offered more lettuce than other geese because they graze plenty of fresh green stuff in the wild. The beavers were given the opportunity to gnaw the bark off bits of willow and to fell lengths of softwood stuck into the ground, thus keeping their growing incisors in good condition. American tapirs, Sarus cranes, peccaries and others, were occasionally given fish for a change, as also were the big cats. Duikers (*Cephalophus*) liked fresh pigeons (F. Kurt, 1963). Care was also taken to see that all the ratite birds received sufficient grit which they utilize in their stomach like many poultry and game birds. The secretary bird (*Serpentarius*) was given a freshly killed snake whenever, for example, an injured or sick specimen was available; the tegus were served with snails and all the monkeys were given sausages— also appreciated by the Director—several times a week.

And in spite of this diet all these animals lived; indeed many of them which were not commonplace breeders were successfully bred e.g. mandrill, gibbon, Capuchin monkey, radiated tortoises from Madagascar, beaver, Cereopsis goose, emu, rhea and so on. I have the firm impression that animals prefer changes in their diet to the "awful monotony"—rightly denounced by H. Fox (1923, p. 4)—

which is brought about by the reformed diet with its uniform "ideal cakes".

I may, perhaps, be permitted to mention here that in 1964 the Zurich Zoo was the first zoo in Europe to succeed in breeding the New Zealand kea (*Nestor notabilis*), which I reported in detail in *Vogel Kosmos* (August, 1964). It must be admitted that the food offered (near an appropriate nesthole) by Keeper W. Hunziker to this rare and costly bird was a decisive factor in the success of this achievement. The kea favoured meat from time to time—up to 600 grams of calf's meat per day—and then green clover or carrot, peanuts, germinated barley, lettuce, sunflower seeds and so on.

The screamers (*Chauna torquata*) which hatched young in the Zurich Zoo in 1963—the first in Europe—showed that traditional feeding and general management, of which feeding is only one element, did not "ruin everything". H. Hediger and F. Bucher (1964) reported on this first success which could well be repeated, given favourable weather. In our climate the weather is a very important factor.

In 1956 the improvement in the Ratcliffe diets, mentioned earlier, were characterized by a more detailed division into groups than those contained in the rough divisions of 1940. The divisions in 1956 were as follows:

Diet A	omnivorous mammals and birds
Diet A-1	debilitated monkeys etc.
Diet A-2	cage birds
Diet A-3	flamingoes
Diet B	herbivorous mammals
Diet C	carnivorous mammals, birds and reptiles
Diet D	ant-eaters and aardvarks
Diet E	cats (Felidae)

According to Ratcliffe (1956, p. 8) the introduction of this feeding system into a zoo demands nothing more nor less than "a willingness to break completely with the past". This sounds rather like the latter-day evangelists for the nutrition of man: up until now man has done everything in the wrong way.

The Basel Zoo according to Ratcliffe's paper (1956, p. 9) was the first to undertake the reformed methods of Philadelphia; this took

Fig. 84   Typical structural fault. The wire used to hold the netting in place is thinner than the wire-mesh and thus rusts away first.

Fig. 85   The thin binding wire has rusted through, releasing the wire-mesh from the supports, thus enabling predators, such as martens, to enter the aviary (cf fig. 81).

Fig. 86 This picture, dated about 1840, shows the Bruchthor in Lucerne which no longer exists. Note the deer pit and the wooden palisades under the bridge.

Fig. 87 For almost a hundred years this type of house for ungulates was predominant in the zoos of Europe. The stalls were dark and musty, the animals were out of sight of the visitors when feeding, the paddocks were designed with sharp angles. Such wooden structures were usually also inhabited by numerous rats and mice.

Fig. 88 Typical cage for Polar Bears, still in use in 1964, and which should be placed in a zoo museum.

Fig. 89 For many decades it was the fashion in European zoos to keep exotic animals in mosque-like houses.

Fig. 90 Keeping Polar Bears in stylized African huts looks out of place and is in poor taste.

Fig. 91   Not only rodents can gnaw through plants, transport boxes and so on; small carnivores will also do so. The hole shown here was bitten in the roof of a box by a Beech Marten (*Martes foina*).

Fig. 92   Marks made by the teeth of a marten are different from those left by a rodent.

Fig. 93 An ugly jumble of different fencing materials; several kinds of mesh and sharply-angled corners of paddocks.

Fig. 94 The fence should never project into the inner side of the enclosure; this presents a serious hazard to an animal which takes flight along the fence when scared.

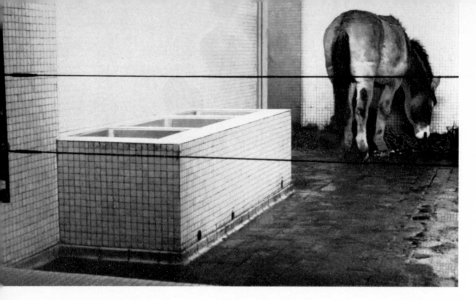

Fig. 95   The elegant barrier, reduced here to a couple of wire cables, and the attractive feeding trough with its sharp corners could both prove to be dangerous in the event of the animal becoming excited. The hay is being eaten from the floor.

Fig. 96   A stand for the water trough, dangerously near to the fence (ungulate paddock).

place after Dr Hans Wackernagel had spent $1\frac{1}{2}$ years as a keeper in Philadelphia, learning about all the departments in this zoo. His experiences will be referred to later but let us take first a statement by H. Wackernagel and Dr E. M. Lang, the present Director of the Basel Zoo, quoted from Ratcliffe: both reported that the keepers showed more reluctance to accept the new diets than the animals.

It is not possible to discuss here the individual recipes of the reformed diets; only one or two general comments will be made, as for example, on the Diet A-2 prescribed for "cage birds", a term which is highly questionable from the zoo biologist's point of view. All small animal dealers make a distinction between seed-eating birds and soft-billed birds but even this banal distinction is not made in Diet A-2. No seed is given in the diet "cake" of the Philadelphia Zoo. Finches, hawfinches and others which are naturally equipped with strong bills for splitting seeds in the wild are forced to peck at soft "cake" in a manner similar to the delicate-billed flycatchers, nightingales and their relatives. A simple footnote states that seed must be mixed with the ration for many finches, parrots etc. and so on, otherwise they do not recognize the ration as food!

The large carnivores such as lions and tigers are given no bones but instead, the necessary minerals are supplied in the form of oystershell flour. They therefore have no occasion to use their powerful jaws and can only "lap up" the "cake" which is offered day after day; unlike the traditionalists, no arrangements are made for a fast day. At the Zurich Zoo we were astonished to find that a six-year old tiger, which we took over from the Philadelphia Zoo in 1957, had to learn painstakingly how to deal with its ration of meat on the bone. To me a tiger which does not begin to know how to tear up meat is no longer a tiger but a creature far removed from nature that is already on the way to becoming a dairy cow or a pig for fattening. This represents a total misconception and a total neglect of the main aims of zoo biology. In America, due possibly to the commercial outlook of the animal trade, this misconception of animals has an even more grotesque manifestation: for example one can buy castrated ocelots which have had their canines and claws removed. An attempt has even been made to operate on quite young tigers to retard their growth and to put them on the market as an article of fashion.

K

Diet A, for omnivorous mammals and birds, consists of the following ingredients:

ground yellow corn (maize)	15%
ground whole wheat	15%
ground whole barley	10%
ground rolled oats	10%
peanut meal	10%
soybean meal	10%
Alfalfa leaf meal	5%
brewer's yeast	10%
dried skim milk	10%
oystershell flour	2%
iodized salt	1%
Vitamin A-D oils	2%

This basic ration can only be stored for two weeks. It is mixed in the proportion of 9 parts of the mixture to 1 part of ground boiled meat, left to harden in a refrigerator for 24 to 48 hours and is finally served in the form of "cake". One gram contains 4 calories. One to ten grams per kilogram of body weight is given every day. According to Ratcliffe this ration has been found completely adequate for such dissimilar animals as, for example, gorilla, doves, Capuchin monkey, ostrich, peccary, sloth, cranes, porcupines and pheasants.

To equate the teeth of the gorilla that lives in tropical forest with the bill and gizzard of the ostrich that lives in dry savannah is an astonishing over-simplification. What has happened to the idea that each species has individual characteristics of its own which should be taken into account? The new system has become a question of simply filling the animal up with sufficient food from automatic hoppers to maintain life, a life that involves existing under conditions of maximum monotony. Further "advantages" over traditional methods are claimed: it is economical, requires little kitchen space and relieves the keeper of a lot of work. The contact between man and animal which is regarded as so important from the standpoint of zoo biology is thus reduced to a minimum. The diet simply runs out of hoppers on its own.

Ratcliffe mentions with pride (1956, p. 8) that daily food costs can be considerably reduced. He says, for example, that the apes and monkeys in the zoo which at one time were fed six times each day are now only fed twice a day and should the need arise, as it sometimes does, a complete day's ration can be given at one time. The logical outcome of this would be an ideal state of affairs with a conveyor belt supplying complete ration "cake" and an automatic system for cage-cleaning, remote-controlled by a central switch. Soon we shall have a push-button zoo in which there is no room for any kind of man-animal relationship. This is in direct contrast to the view of the zoo biologist and, in my opinion, it raises points of fundamental significance.

A chemical firm has already recommended a complete diet for monkeys which they have tested in laboratories and in various experimental stations; tests include those made on space monkeys at the Holloman Air Force Base (U.S.A.). These "complete-diet pellets" as they are expressly termed, should now be used in zoological gardens according to their opinion. An assurance is given that these pellets contain all the protein, fat, carbohydrates and vitamins necessary for monkeys, weighed out to qualify as a complete ration. The manufacturers claim that it is a highly concentrated diet which does not cause any "unphysiological" burden on the digestive tract.

What does the term unphysiological mean as used by these manufacturers? In this context it is synonymous with biological. The natural food of monkeys in the wild, however, contains quantities of roughage. The laboratory-retort approach has reversed a perfectly clear concept and we are asked to believe that the biological conditions of the laboratory are superior to those in the wild which are now regarded as unbiological. This is the attitude adopted by these commercial organizations which are also responsible for supplying drugs to humans as well as to animals. It represents a complete distortion of the facts. It cannot be deprecated too strongly and radical corrective measures should be taken in zoological gardens.

To reasonable people, however, it must be clear that conditions of laboratory research and journeys into space, in which the monkey is fastened in a space capsule, present situations that are completely unnatural (unbiological). Results obtained under these conditions should certainly not be taken as a basis for the feeding and care of monkeys in our zoos. On the contrary their social bonds must be maintained by giving them the most natural food possible in conditions as near to the wild as possible. To adopt any other principle would be to betray the proper purpose of a zoological garden. I would like to emphasize here the term "garden" which is often wrongly suppressed and forgotten. A garden is a small bit of nature, fundamentally different from a laboratory or a space capsule, and it must remain so.

Zoo biology must ensure that action is taken immediately against this pronounced a-biological trend because it is based on a fundamental error which I have repeatedly emphasized—namely, the confusion of the aims of nutritional management of domesticated animals (in particular farm animals) with that of zoo animals. Many animals for which man has assumed direct responsibility have become artificial neo-biotypes but wild animals should be maintained, as far as possible, in their pure and natural form.

I explained in detail, in 1942 and 1950, how a wild animal thrives in a zoo, not only in a new environment but in a totally new world in which man no longer has any significance as an enemy but becomes a friendly fellow-creature—a kind of superior being of the same species. Zoos are oases in the big cities, secondary places of nature, and as such, they must be kept free of any suggestion of mechanical robots, and every device must be used to achieve a high degree of naturalness for animals and man.

To meet the requirements of zoo biology there should be an intensification of the animal-man relationship and not an elimination of this relationship as is so often necessary in the laboratory. Anthropoid apes in particular need intensive contact with man; outside Philadelphia there is hardly a single zoo specialist who has wanted to reduce the link which is established between man and animal by the act of supplying them with food.

The fact that Ratcliffe regards minimum contact as the ideal state of affairs, that is, the loosening of contact with animals in a zoo, arises from the fact that his specialized work kept him in the autopsy room. He was neither a medical man nor a veterinary surgeon but a "doctor of science" when he succeeded Herbert Fox, the well known pathologist at the Philadelphia Zoo. From the start Ratcliffe worked predominantly or exclusively on dead animals. At the same time, other zoo people (including myself) had been dealing with live animals, often since our childhood days.

The different points from which we started account for the opposing opinions we hold on biological training exercises that were originated by me (1942, 1950). These were designed to break up the monotony of zoo life and to offer the animals some kind of substitute for their normal activity in the wild by means of physical exercises. Ratcliffe (1950, pp. 10–11) considers this to be impractical and that the scheme would entail the employment of additional staff. He believes that the same effect could be achieved at less cost and more simply by measuring out food more carefully. He writes: "The animal that is just adequately fed becomes active several hours before feeding time." What a simple solution! And what a profound misunderstanding of the situation.

On this subject and others, I made the following statement (1942, p. 162): an animal living freely in the wild is dominated by the necessity to avoid enemies and to seek food. When an animal is taken into captivity, these two vital driving forces are suddenly suppressed. When one realizes that the captive arrival has lost its most important occupations, one appreciates the critical nature of this change. An enormous amount of energy is released and this must somehow be re-directed. It is obvious that lack of activity in captive animals is one of the most urgent problems facing zoo biology. This lack of occupation results in various tendencies which are disadvantageous, such as stereotyped movements which are almost pathological in form.

The loss of occupation in captive animals is naturally expressed more vigorously the higher the social organization of the animal concerned. It is not surprising therefore that one should start training exercises first with the anthropoid apes. Many progressive zoos have already gone so far as to go into the possibility of keeping the larger carnivores and even elephants occupied by giving them training. It is not yet known, however, whether certain ungulates (e.g. zebra, antelope, horned cattle, deer, camels, rhinoceros and even birds such as marabou, pelican, birds of prey, crane etc. might not benefit physically and mentally from undergoing suitably adapted training exercises.

I must refer here to two interesting experiments conducted by E. Inhelder (1955 a and b) on the play of ungulates with objects and on the play of animals in zoos. In this field, too, we clearly need a detailed biological investigation of animal behaviour. One of the main objections to applying training widely is inevitably the question of cost; training on a large scale requires staff. As with dietary matters, however, the zoo biologist can only state that it is not his business to keep animals under minimal conditions; he should aim much higher and provide his animals with optimal conditions.

It is legitimate to point out here that an increase in expenditure in this field, as in diet, is compensated to a large extent by better health, longer life and increased breeding success. An active animal is of much greater value as an exhibit than a miserable, comatose creature. It is often the case that certain training routines can be used when it is necessary to catch the animal for therapeutic or diagnostic purposes, such as the measurement of body temperatures and body weight or the administration of drugs and injections. Above all, however, it is important to banish the boredom of having no occupation, to break the monotony of life under the artificial conditions of captivity, by providing the animal with a new and adequate way of life. In this sense simple and beneficial training exercises which take into account the inherent characteristics of the species—not highly artistic performances of the circus but disciplined play—assume the importance of occupational therapy.

All this, according to Ratcliffe (1950, p. 11) could be achieved much more cheaply and simply through carefully calculated diet rations. Could one not equally well abolish the expensive sport indulged in by man and in return reduce his calorie intake?

To summarize: the Ratcliffe doctrine on diet, based on the retort theory, is in many ways directly contrary to the principles of zoo biology; the arguments on which its advantages are based are highly questionable or definitely mistaken, especially in the single instance where it is alleged that the decline in mortality is attributable solely to the dietary reforms. The efforts made to demonstrate the superiority of the diet reforms over the methods of the "traditionalists" are indeed considerable.

One of the first and keenest supporters of the diet reforms was Dr Hans Wackernagel. In his capacity as scientific assistant at the Basel Zoological Gardens, he published a brochure in 1960 entitled *Modern methods of feeding wild animals in zoological gardens*. In the introduction he states that the feeding programme at Basel is based on that of Ratcliffe. He explains that "the recipes given here present only a few of many possibilities" and thereby refutes the pretentious and provocative assertion of his teacher that every other kind of diet for zoo animals must be a failure or must result in malnutrition, as was shown to have occurred in Philadelphia prior to 1935.

It is not my intention to give the impression here that the traditionalists resisted every change from the old-fashioned methods of feeding; they only objected strongly to the Philadelphia Zoo's claim that its dietary dogma was the only one which was right for zoo animals, and they particularly resisted the dubious and invalid arguments that were advanced in support of it. Reports indicate that other zoos beside Philadelphia have made progress since 1935, not only with regard to nutrition but also to accommodation and on the whole subject of caring for animals in zoos. The Philadelphia Zoo is by no means alone in this.

H. Wackernagel (1960, p. 15) mentions that the Basel Zoo uses for example two different diets for the animals described as omnivores: "on the one hand a so-called 'cake', prepared from a modified Philadelphia formula, and on the other, a pellet based on a dog food formula." We cannot enter into a detailed discussion here of these formulae; we can only make a critical review of the way in which they are presented which is tendentious.

Wackernagel's brochure includes attractive photographs which illustrate clearly the breeding successes in the Basel Zoo e.g. tiger quadruplets, Grant's zebras with foals, giraffes with young, a female spectacled bear with her cubs, the baby gorilla "Goma", king penguin, stork and flamingo with young. In his concluding remarks (p. 33) he writes: "On the whole the health of our animals is very satisfactory and notable breeding successes have been achieved. We were able to obtain offspring, followed by the healthy development of the young animal, from gorilla, okapi, Indian rhinoceros, all large and small cats, brown hyena, hunting-dog and spectacled bear. Among the birds, ostrich, king penguin, flamingo and eclectus parrot may be cited. We may also mention the Malayan bear—but in this case, unfortunately there was no progeny to rear . . . " One photograph is captioned: "The Basel Zoo was the first to breed and rear the Indian rhinoceros successfully."

This presentation could—or perhaps is intended to—give the

impression that diet was a decisive factor in these gratifying breeding successes. If this were really the case, the breeding successes could not have occurred in zoos other than Philadelphia and Basel; in fact, many were achieved in other places and moreover they took place much earlier and without reformed diets. Improvement in feeding is certainly an important factor but it is not the only one in the progressive development of zoological gardens. Organization, animal sociology, accommodation factors and many others can also be of decisive importance; the animal-man relationships are also frequently involved.

There is no doubt that every zoo should take pride in its work; public relations, propaganda and advertisement all have an important place in the management of a zoo but the work done by these departments should not become mixed up with that of zoo biology if the advantages of scientific feeding methods are to be assessed seriously.

In this context, let us consider the case already mentioned of the successful breeding of the gorilla at Basel Zoo in 1959. Prior to this, in 1956, the first breeding success of this nature took place surprisingly enough at a zoo which was not very well known—in Columbus (Ohio). The parents of the young Columbus gorilla, "Baron" and "Christina", were caught in the Cameroons in 1950 and at this time were considered to be about 4 years and $1\frac{1}{2}$ years old respectively. They therefore spent a substantial part of their youth in Columbus. They certainly made remarkable progress on a diet which was avowedly traditional. According to W. D. Thomas (1958) this diet consisted mainly of cereals, grapes, lettuce, carrots, apples, bananas, grapefruit, raw eggs in milk, bread, some meat, celery, oranges, sweet potatoes and cooked beans. The necessary vitamins were naturally added to this diet. The parents of the first gorilla to be born in captivity flourished extremely well on this diet. Note the abundance of the diet. The reasons why the gorilla was not bred earlier and more frequently in zoos are various and to some extent they have nothing to do with diet. In contrast to chimpanzees, gorillas have always been more difficult to capture and to export from Africa. They were—and still are—much more costly than chimpanzees on account of their rarity.

For this reason many zoos have had to be satisfied with keeping only one gorilla. Many people do not hold with the principle of zoo biology that it is unbiological and unjustifiable to keep only one individual of a species. But if one is kept on its own, breeding is obviously not possible.

Another problem is that sex identification in gorillas, in marked contrast to chimpanzees, is somewhat uncertain particularly in young animals. It requires a detailed examination which could not always be arranged formerly. It has often happened therefore that when there were only two gorillas in a zoo, they frequently turned out to be of the same sex. The two gorillas Massa and Bamboo, which were so popular during their long life at the Philadelphia Zoo were a classic example of this.

The second case of breeding successes correlated with modern feeding methods, mentioned by Wackernagel in his concluding remarks, was that of the okapi; here again, it is worth mentioning that years before the birth of the Basel okapi, one was born in 1957 at the Vincennes Zoo in Paris as reported by J. Nouvel (1958). Since that date, several have been born in European and North American zoos and J. de Medina has had repeated successes in the Congo.

The third case quoted by Wackernagel was the Indian rhinoceros. Viewed impartially, is it possible to link this with special feeding methods? I do not think so; it is much more likely to be just a matter of organization, in that the Basel Zoo were the first to possess a compatible pair of this impressive species. (The animals were supplied by the well-known animal collector and dealer Peter Rhyiner in 1951 and 1952, and he also supplied the first Sumatran rhinoceros.) It should be mentioned in passing that at the time that this importation took place, I was Director of the Basel Zoo (1944–1953); also the house in which they eventually achieved the first breeding success was built under my direction (Hediger, 1953 a, b). The pair of Indian rhinoceros at the London Zoo were significantly different in age and the two in Brookfield, Chicago were so incompatible that they had to be kept apart.

Basel therefore had an excellent chance to be first in the field. In E. M. Lang's paper in the Basel Zoological Gardens' Annual Report (1956) on *The birth of a rhinoceros*, no mention is made of any special feeding given to the parents; Lang's scientific assistant, Wackernagel, similarly omits any reference in his forty-page work *Observations on*

Indian rhinoceros (Rhinoceros unicornis) (1961). One is forced to the conclusion that diet was not of significance in this remarkable breeding success. A much more obvious point is that this birth could not have taken place in any other zoo because at that time no other zoo possessed a compatible pair. Breeding of these valuable animals has subsequently been achieved elsewhere (e.g. Whipsnade in 1957).

L. S. Crandall gives many details concerning the first importation and rearing of rhinoceroses—and of many other mammals. (1964, p. 504 *et seq.*)

Let us take the next example of breeding success in the Basel Zoo, linked with feeding methods, which is quoted by Wackernagel, namely: "all the big and small cats." The critical reader is at once startled because there is a range of small cats which are moderately rare and difficult to breed—for instance, jaguarundi, margay, serval, pampas cat, ocelot, Geoffroy's cat, Indian leopard cat, rusty-spotted cat, fishing cat and many others.

It is only when one thinks the matter over carefully that one realizes that "all the big and small cats" must mean only the few species which had hitherto been kept at the Basel Zoo, and therefore, plainly not *all cats.*

The next example was the successful breeding of the South African brown hyena *(Hyaena brunnea)*. Hyena species are not known to be fastidious feeders. The striped and spotted hyenas are substantially carrion eaters and they also eat all kinds of herbivorous fare; according to J. Stevenson-Hamilton (1947, p. 209), the eminent authority on big game in South Africa, this also applies to the brown hyena. They also eat dead fish, crabs and other marine animals in coastal areas.

The brown hyena has become scarce in its native habitat and is therefore not often seen in zoos, consequently breeding successes are rare. I managed to obtain a pair for the Basel Zoo in 1950. E. M. Lang (1958) gave a detailed account of the subsequent breeding of this pair which was achieved with the aid of a bitch foster-parent and artificial rearing, but he made no reference to special feeding of the parents in his publication. Careful checks were made and after a prolonged interval, the sheds in the hyena enclosure were examined with the following result: "We were hit by a beastly stench of acrid ammonia fumes. The adults had repeatedly dragged their meat inside and had not eaten it up."

It was obviously not special food that was critical in this case but the spatial requirements of the hyenas. Both the male and the female, particularly the female were exceptionally nervous all the time. This was the subject of detailed research by my colleague E. Inhelder (1955a) and he made the following remarks (p. 123 *et seq.*): "When people approached the enclosure the adult female would either stand hesitantly at the bars or draw back, ready either to take flight or to defend, her mouth open and the hair on her back erect, making squeaking or snarling sounds. She snapped now and again at a visitor who provoked the 'wicked, crazy' animal still further . . . The animal was in a state of conflict, i.e. she was subject to an urge to flee or defend, and she reacted by running backwards and forwards along half the length of her cage; as she turned she reared up on her hindlegs against the bars, often scraping her foam-covered mouth against the cage and drawing blood . . . This behaviour appeared to be largely a question of the biological requirements for space . . . When I increased the distance of the gap between the animals and the public, by enlarging the size of the enclosure from 9 feet to 18 feet, the hyenas became noticeably calmer; the stereotyped flight and defence behaviour disappeared."

E. M. Lang (1958) also emphasized the outstanding nervousness of this pair of hyenas, with the same frantic grazing of the skin and the same dependence on space. In 1955 these animals were moved into more suitable quarters in the new carnivore house where it was not possible for them to come into contact with the public (p. 83): "The brown hyenas were visible through a display window constructed along the back wall of the house, which opens directly into the enclosure. A glass panel, 8 mm. thick proved to be a complete barrier. The animals could neither hear nor smell the public from their side and consequently were not disturbed. They were relaxed and moved freely about their enclosure." As mentioned previously, it was obviously a question not of the effects of feeding but of a critical reaction to space; so this example quoted by Wackernagel (1960, p. 33) was also nothing to do with methods of feeding.

The next examples mentioned by him were the hunting-dog and the spectacled bear. The hunting dog (*Lycaon pictus*) has often been bred in the Pretoria Zoo as reported by its Director, B. R. Bigalke (1954, p. 60). Hunting-dogs are prolific, with up to 12 in a litter, but he added that females with young were sensitive to disturbance and recommended keeping them in pairs for successful breeding. The hunting-dog has also been bred many times in Europe; in the Cologne Zoo alone, 63 were born and reared in four years, as quoted in 1960 in the *Guide book to the Zoological Gardens at Cologne* by W. Windecker and F. Zeller (p. 17).

H. Wackernagel indicates in his brochure on modern feeding methods that the rearing of spectacled bears is a speciality of the Basel Zoo. I had previously ventured to set down the principles involved in rearing this species in my booklet *New exotic friends in the Zoo* (1953). Here I would only reiterate the most important points in order that his breeding success should not be attributed to the magic worked by a reformed diet.

The first breeding success with the spectacled bear (*Tremarctos ornatus*) was definitely established when twins were born in the Buenos Aires Zoo in 1947, as reported in detail by E. J. Saporiti (1949). These two youngsters arrived at the Basel Zoo on 6 April 1949. On 25 November 1952, a second female, still young, which probably originated from the Buenos Aires stock, was obtained from a Dutch animal dealer. About two months after its purchase, this female was put with the previous pair for the first time and on 17 February 1953, much to the general astonishment, this young animal which was approximately 2 years old, gave birth to two healthy cubs. This female was undoubtedly pregnant on acquisition and this was the start of the breeding of spectacled bears at Basel Zoo. It was the first birth of this species in Europe—but it had nothing to do with a special diet.

H. Wackernagel concluded his list of noteworthy breeding successes, associated with modern feeding methods, with birds such as ostrich, king penguin, flamingo. It is well known that Carl Hagenbeck (1909) had already established a complete ostrich farm in his zoological park at Stellingen in 1909 and bred these birds on a large scale. Numerous other zoos succeeded in rearing them long before the so-called reformed diets.

The beginning of ostrich farming in Africa goes back as far as the middle of the 19th century (W. Bassermann 1911). Ostriches were hatched there in their thousands, also in the absence of Philadelphia's Diet A.

King penguins were first bred in the Edinburgh Zoo in 1919, as reported by T. H. Gillespie (1964) and they have subsequently been bred in numerous zoos. This distinguished authority on penguin rearing summed up his experiences with king penguins in his well-known *Book of king penguins* (1932). A special diet—apart from fish— is not mentioned in this book. The following statements from the most experienced authority on penguin rearing are of special interest from the standpoint of zoo biology. It is well known that the way in which food is presented to the king penguin is vital; each fish must be placed by hand in the bill of each king penguin. If a fish falls to the ground, the keeper has to retrieve it as the bird will not bend down to pick it up for itself. In theory, the king penguin is capable of starving on a mound of fish.

During T. H. Gillespie's long life (he was born in 1876), penguins played a role for 36 years. Nevertheless he only once saw a king penguin pick up a fish on its own; this occurred while a film was being made to show that king penguins seldom, if ever, take fish from the ground. To demonstrate this, he took a fish from the bucket and threw it on to a rock near the penguin. The penguin advanced immediately, bent down, seized the fish and swallowed it! This was the only time that this occurred in 36 years (T. H. Gillespie, 1964, p. 71).

A story about the distinguished Director of the Frankfurt Zoo, Kurt Priemel, who died in 1959, may be of interest to para-psychologists. When conducting a party round the zoo, he described the astonishing climbing ability of raccoons and mentioned that there was no known case of a raccoon falling from a tree. At this precise moment, one of the raccoons fell out of a tree right in front of his audience. I myself can contribute a third case of a similar strange coincidence—or whatever one likes to call it. During a students' tour of the Basel Zoo when we came to the shoebills (*Balaeniceps rex*), I explained that this bird never stood on one leg like a stork but always stood on both legs. At this moment, one of the shoebills lifted up its right leg and stood there just like a stork. I have never seen this happen again in the zoo or in the wild, nor have I seen a photograph of a shoebill in this position.

Let us now return to a critical review of Wackernagel's list of breeding successes in the Basel Zoo, in which he includes the flamingo. Nowadays these beautiful birds breed in several European and American zoos. It is not well known that the breeding of flamingoes in artificial colonies started as long ago as 1937. On 6 July of that year the first flamingo chicks were running about the artificial colony of flamingoes at Hialeah near Miami, Florida. Since then, approximately 50 to 100 flamingoes have been reared there every year.

The flamingoes live in a small artificial lake enclosed by an oval racecourse, $1\frac{1}{4}$ miles long. There are many islands in the lake, known as Infield Lake. The flamingoes nest there regularly under decorative palms; muddy clay is available for nest-building. The basic stock of this unique colony was laid down in 1932; when I visited it in 1951, the colony was estimated at 550.

The food consisted of cooked rice, dried shrimps, dog biscuits and some cod-liver oil. The cooking of the ingredients was done very simply out of doors, in large cooking vessels over open fires. The daily rations, consisting of 150 lbs rice, 40 lbs shrimps and 75 lbs dog biscuits, were drawn from huge stocks held in conveniently situated huts; after the mixture had been cooked, ten vessels were filled up and loaded on to a special red van with which the flamingoes appeared to be familiar. As an exception, I was allowed to ride on the van for the eleven o'clock feed. In this way, I was able to witness the whole operation in all its stages, from the preparation up to the actual feeding. This vast amount of food had in addition to suffice for a considerable number of black and black-necked swans and some geese.

In the same year, 1951, I also visited the San Antonio Zoo in Texas which bred flamingoes for the first time in 1956. At the time that I was there, I saw normal nests, from 9–18 inches high. According to a verbal statement from Fred Stark the flamingoes had to be kept in a covered aviary in order to provide them with shelter from hailstorms which were expected every spring. At the same time, in the San Francisco Zoo, where conditions were favourable, it was necessary to shut the flamingoes into a room at night to keep them away from the raccoons which lived free in the zoo, a procedure which naturally did little to promote breeding behaviour. The

Zurich Zoo has also lost flamingoes over the years owing to foxes breaking in and killing them.

In his series of glittering breeding successes, allegedly influenced by diet, H. Wackernagel (1960, p. 33) was not able to include the Malayan bear: "Unfortunately in this case there was no progeny to rear. After an extremely violent 'heat' in July 1959, two females whelped in March 1960 but the cubs were devoured."

The Malayan bear, however, was successfully bred prior to 1947 in the San Diego Zoo (San Diego Zoo Official Guide Book 1947, p. 65) and more recently (1961) by H. Dathe in the East Berlin Zoo at Friedrichsfelde.

To summarize the position regarding diet: an attempt must be made to take into consideration not only diet but all those branches of zoo management (accommodation, handling, veterinary care, transport, social factors, and so on), which contribute towards the improvement of living conditions for zoo animals. A glance at the development of zoos shows that remarkable advances have been made, often of a decisive nature, in every zoo worthy of the name.

These improvements, however, are not correlated in any way with the Philadelphia Zoo's diet reforms which are based on the retort theory. It is misleading to attribute the decline in death rates (as shown by statistics) solely to the reformed diets which were started in 1935, because other improvements also took place in Philadelphia, as in every other zoo. The feeding of a uniform pulp, produced on a stereotyped basis that is purely physiological, is contrary to the fundamental principles of zoo biology; according to these principles every effort should be made to combat the monotony of life for zoo animals and to counteract the manifestations of domestication.

Wackernagel's statement should be opposed because it is unscientific, as practically none of the breeding successes claimed by him were directly correlated with diet. In any scientific experiment of this kind appropriate control experiments would have to be undertaken. In this case, other zoos provide the control experiments. Nothing supports the superiority of the reformed diet claimed by Ratcliffe and Wackernagel because the crucial breeding successes were also achieved in other zoos with traditional feeding methods that were often extremely natural.

In 1964 a symposium was held at the London Zoo on *Zoos and*

Conservation in which reference was made to the feeding of wild animals in zoos. Bearing in mind what has been said in this chapter, it seems strange to find the following statement in the report on the symposium (p. 15): "As a rule the food which is sold commercially for domestic animals, worked out by dietitians, can be made use of for animals." Furthermore, in I.U.C.N. Publications, New Series: Supplementary Paper No. 3, there is a statement which reads: "Zoos cannot afford fancy diets for the normal run of animals." In the report on the symposium we are also told that the study of natural food in the wild is only profitable in certain special circumstances; the diets recommended are those based on the principles of modern agricultural science, namely the foolproof rations invented by Ratcliffe and taken over by Wackernagel.

This represents a complete reversal of the facts and a total failure to recognize the only valid standard, namely the standard set by nature: the diet, which for hundreds of thousands of years has proved satisfactory to animals living in the wild, is now deemed not worthy of study and is referred to as a fancy diet. The Philadelphia recipes are put forward as the only correct form of nutrition, that is diets based on experience gained with domestic animals.

It is ironic that this should have taken place in a symposium devoted to conservation and that domestication, as distinct from the preservation of wild life in its most natural forms, should have been given pride of place—the very opposite of the alleged aim.

This chapter on feeding should not be concluded without inviting the reader to think over the following: there is scarcely any other name which has been more closely linked with the development of zoos for half a century, or which has such a worldwide reputation, as that of Hagenbeck. Many generations of this family have provided not only animals but also ideas, advice and designs for zoos all over the world. The imaginative idea of enclosures without bars, generally accepted today, is but one example.

It would be difficult to find a zoo which has not learnt something, directly or indirectly, from Hagenbeck. The feeding methods which are definitely "traditional", whose success cannot be denied, are far removed from the uniform "cake" of Philadelphia. In his well-known work *On animals and men* which appeared in 1908 Carl Hagenbeck, the great zoo man, stated: "furthermore the active use

Fig. 97   This type of drinking trough, placed sufficiently far from the fence, has proved suitable for ungulates. The semi-circular trough equipped with an overflow and an outlet, is supplied from a water main.

Fig. 98   Young animals may have difficulty in reaching the trough but when they are present a stepping stone can be placed at the foot of the trough to make things easier for them.

Fig. 99   In the original Monkey Jungle in Miami, Florida, the visitors move along a tunnel of netting, virtually enclosed in a cage . . .

Fig. 100   . . . whereas the monkeys are free to move around in a small woodland complex which they do not leave. This amusing principle is unfortunately not in general use.

of the jaws is beneficial for every animal, but especially for the predators. In this way the teeth remain healthy, the natural exercise of the masticatory apparatus promotes digestion and as a result of this the animal becomes more lively." He also gives us a glimpse of the well-stocked larder in his zoo at Stellingen, which was famous in those days as well as today. He lists over forty different kinds of food, including turnips, carrots, eggs, milk, dates, potatoes, lettuce, millet, rice, hemp etc.

In 1949 the zoologist, physician and former zoo director I. Krumbiegel published an original kind of cookery book under the title *How do I feed captive animals?* It contains recipes for pretty well every animal from protozoans to gorillas. Lorenz Hagenbeck, one of the sons of Carl Hagenbeck, wrote the foreword to the second edition and in this he stressed the necessity for keeping individual diet sheets for the many inmates of the zoo. This does not mean that one ignores the results of nutritional research; on the contrary, one applies them sensibly, in the biological sense, to wild animals. Both Hagenbeck and Krumbiegel have, of course, heard of calories, vitamins, mineral salts, trace elements and so on; but as experienced animal men they are opposed to the stereotyped dispensing—automatic where possible—of a uniform food pulp to animals that are so different by nature.

Reference is often made in this book to *The Zoological Garden* (*Der zoologische Garten*), the international professional journal which has appeared since 1859 and is edited today by the distinguished zoo director Professor H. Dathe; almost every issue gives new and valuable information on the best method of feeding one animal or another. Anyone who takes the trouble to compare old and new issues will confirm that, even outside Philadelphia, important progress has been made in all fields of keeping wild animals in the zoo; the progress in feeding is by no means the least of these, although not by the use of the retort or conveyor belt method, but by making careful calculations based on the biological point of view.

8

Foreign Bodies

There is only a narrow dividing line in a certain sense between food, the subject of the last chapter, and foreign bodies. Food in a concentrated form that is particularly nutritious and easily digested is not always the best kind of food for wild animals. It is wrong to assume that a diet which is particularly beneficial to humans and to highly bred domesticated animals will be equally successful when applied to wild animals.

In fact many wild animals are adapted for dealing with roughage that is difficult to digest or even indigestible; concentrated, easily digested food of the consistency of dough can be fatal to them. This applies, for example, to the European roe deer (*Capreolus capreolus*). The digestive system of this ruminant has recently been investigated in detail by P. Juon (1963) who claims that the roe deer requires coarse-fibred woody substances to browse on at all seasons of the year. These organic substances are not easily digested. Juon (p. 19) states further: "the coarse structure of the food obtained by browsing on bushes and trees is indispensable to the functioning of the digestive tract, to the movement and utilization of the food in the stomach and intestine; under some circumstances this roughage may be just as important in the Cervidae as the true nutritional content of the food. Digestive disturbances may arise when coarse fibres are lacking. The daily rhythm of the animals (browsing and chewing the cud) is upset when they are offered soft food that is intended for domesticated animals and that is poor in fibre (e.g. compressed pellets and hay). The need to find something to chew as compensation merely

156

encourages them to search all the more intensely for tough shoots and branches, and in woodlands that lack an under-storey the risk of damage to stands of timber is increased."

This point is splendidly illustrated in the frequently cited pamphlet of H. Wackernagel (1960, p. 12), in which amongst other things he states: "our vegetarian pellets are so constituted as to satisfy the demands of the most delicate feeders." The relevant picture shows a family of roe deer with the buck actually eating the ideal food from the dish which is at the foot of a conifer; the trunk and branches of the tree have been chewed in characteristic fashion as high up as the roe could reach!

The indigestible roughage, which certain animals need to take in with their food, may in extreme cases include stones. These stones can really be described as foreign bodies but instead of being harmful they are useful and necessary. It is well known that in birds they serve for the mechanical trituration of the food (A. Reichenow 1913, p. 9; O. Heinroth 1955, p. 97 *et al.*). The ostrich is particularly notorious in this respect as it often takes really dangerous objects as well as stones that are suitable. More will be said about this later.

Stones are found in the stomach, as an aid to breaking up the food, not only in birds but also in many other animals. In his book on the biological anatomy of feeding H. Böker (1937, Vol. 2) contrasts mastication in the stomach with mastication in the mouth and crop. He mentions only the hard outer lining of muscular stomachs which are often equipped with horny processes and denticles; curiously enough, however, he makes no mention of the important part played by stones, except in the case of birds. It is therefore appropriate to point out that these occur widely in the animal kingdom and their importance should be stressed from the viewpoint of zoo biology because it is necessary to provide the animals concerned with adequate supplies.

This applies, for example, to some fishes and fish-eating turtles such as *Caretta* and others. It should be borne in mind when choosing the substrate of a tank in the aquarium. It has been known for a long time that stones and other hard objects are regularly found in the stomach of crocodilians. Their significance however does not appear to be the same as in most fish-eaters (herons, otters, seals and others); in the crocodilians the stones have the significance of ballast in the original sense of the word, simply as a load or dead weight.

In his comprehensive study of the Nile crocodile, H. B. Cott (1961, p. 236 *et seq.*) has devoted a section to the details of the stomach stones of these reptiles. Cott believes that in this case the stones found in the stomach have nothing to do with digestion, but have a hydrostatic function, corresponding to the ballast in the hull of a ship. The load of stones makes it possible for the crocodile to reach the necessary depth and to achieve stabilization in the water.

I cannot refrain from repeating here an animal legend which natives of Melanesia told me as a zoological fact when I was collecting reptiles for my herpetological thesis in 1930. The natives of New Britain drew my attention to the similarity in the external appearance of geckos and crocodiles. They maintained that all crocodiles first lived as small geckos in the bush and having reached a certain size, they then went down to the coast where they swallowed some stones to enable them to sink in the water, and thereafter they lived as crocodiles in the sea.

I have always held the opinion that there is a grain of biological truth in the majority of animal legends from the South Seas, Africa and other remote areas (Hediger 1958, p. 102). Nevertheless I had some difficulty in working out the legend of geckos and crocodiles until I became aware of Cott's work on crocodiles. This ancient legend from the South Seas had anticipated by hundreds of years Cott's work in which he first described the hydrostatic function of the stones in the crocodile stomach.

In his *Biologie der Säugetiere* (*Biology of mammals*) (1954, Vol 1, p. 123) I. Krumbiegel, a former zoo director, mentions that foreign bodies such as stones, sand, bits of wood and so on are additional components of food which many animals take in with their food quite freely. He adds: "Seals will swallow stones while playing but this has no connection with their digestion in view of the powerful chemical breakdown of their food. Sperm whales swallow fruits which are carried into the sea by rivers, young sea-lions swallow eel-grass and seaweeds. Elephants pick up stones which become polished flat in the process of digestion; sand, small stones, pieces of wood and grass are taken in by echidnas. Ant-eaters pick up dust and earth as well as termite excrement and saliva together with the termites. As substitute material for these animals in captivity I have introduced at least a certain amount of loam and sand."

In the case of stones in the stomachs of crocodiles, seed- and fish-eating birds and mammals, we are virtually dealing with normal foreign bodies that are physiologically appropriate or necessary; there are also foreign bodies that are pathogenic and which are possibly of even greater importance in zoo biology because they can cause sickness and death in many zoo animals. There is no doubt that every zoo has experienced fatalities due to foreign bodies. If one were to add up all the zoo animals which have died from foreign bodies, it would amount to a colossal and macabre total. It should not be forgotten that in such cases we are dealing with causes of death that in principle are avoidable.

The duty of the veterinarian is quite distinct from that of the zoo biologist in relation to foreign bodies. The former is responsible for the pathological report and in cases where death has been caused by a foreign body it is the job of the zoo biologist to do everything to prevent the occurrence of such unnecessary fatalities. Preventive measures depend on constructional technique, on the proper instruction of the craftsmen working in the zoo and on the training of the whole staff of the zoo. The asphalting of the paths in many zoos is an important matter because loose stones encourage some members of the public to throw them into the animal enclosures, where they may constitute dangerous foreign bodies. In Zurich Zoo, for example, we lost a perfectly healthy woolly monkey (*Lagothrix*) because a visitor offered it a piece of gravel the size of a hazel-nut which it swallowed, resulting in a blockage in the gut.

The expression foreign bodies has a number of meanings and in this context it requires closer definition. H. Krieg (1929, p. 773; 1948, p. 118) in referring to the viscacheras—the colonies of viscachas (*Viscacia viscacia*) in the Gran Chaco—speaks for example of the foreign bodies which these large rodents sometimes collect in front of their burrows. By this he means all kinds of bits of wood, stones, pieces of material, leather articles, bones, bottles, jam jars and so on. Reference was made earlier by Charles Darwin to the story of the hunter who lost his gold watch and chain while riding through the plains in S. America and on the following morning he went to the nearest viscachera where he found, as expected, his watch together with other "foreign bodies".

It seems that these foreign bodies are curious objects which are found in the natural habitat and which evidently attract a certain amount of attention from man and animal; however they are not dangerous or pathogenic. To the zoo biologist the criterion of the foreign body is that it is dangerous or pathogenic. A zoo is full of potentially dangerous objects which constitute a hazard that must be combated at the source as far as possible. We are not allowed to search the pockets of visitors but we can completely forbid the use of particularly dangerous materials in the zoo, such as staples and upholsterers' tacks as well as controlling certain activities such as the snipping of wire, metal and so on; we can also make sure that the ends are not left lying about.

There are two ways in which foreign bodies may be particularly dangerous from the point of view of zoo biology, namely as external objects which penetrate the animal's body through the skin and internal ones which reach the digestive tract through the mouth. In some circumstances the internal ones may cause fatal injury in the digestive tract itself (e.g. by blockage), or by the perforation of other organs. Virulent infections usually follow on the mechanical injury.

Before dealing in greater detail with objects which can truly be described as foreign bodies, consisting usually of metal or other hard substances, I would like to mention a type of foreign body of quite a different sort, which can also be exceptionally dangerous and pathogenic: I refer to poisonous plants in the zoo, particularly to the yew (*Taxus baccata*). I have already dealt with this (1956, p. 18) as follows:

In every zoo which I have taken over so far (Bern, Basel, Zurich) strange as it may sound I have come across fairly extensive plantings of yew; I am also aware that serious incidents have already taken place as a result, one for example being the death of cart-horses bringing supplies to the zoo. In species that are sensitive to yew the consumption of only a few needles of this dangerous plant is sufficient to kill even a large animal. It is not always easy to diagnose yew poisoning in a post-mortem examination, and I would assume that such poisonings are in fact more numerous than is generally thought.

In any case I cannot find one good reason for the planting of yew in zoological gardens, where it can only constitute a danger. It should therefore be in the ABC of zoo biology that yew is strictly excluded. Yew trees can be dangerous not only to perissodactyls, particularly horses, pony, hinny and probably also zebra, but also, according to A. Stählin (1944), to cattle, sheep, goats, pigs, dogs, rabbits, ducks, fowl and particularly pheasants. It is very likely that the list of animals endangered by yew is much longer than we suspect.

Although directives are often given that yew should definitely not be planted inside the paddocks, this is not an adequate precaution in itself because some animals are not confined to their enclosures; ponies, for example, may be required to pull small traps with children in them. There is also the behaviour of members of the public to consider, particularly as some people are only too ready to pick anything green so that they can offer it to the animal.

On 31 January 1964, Hans Psenner, Director of the Alpine Zoo in Innsbruck, informed me in a letter that he had just lost two bearded vultures (*Gypaetus barbatus*) from yew poisoning: "the two birds had begun to collect branches and in the process they completely dismembered a small yew tree. Who would have thought that bearded vultures would tear apart a yew?" The fact that nobody would have expected this to happen is an excellent example of the unanticipated ways in which yew may be fatal in the zoo.

This poisonous plant should justifiably be placed in the category of a foreign body in the zoo and determined efforts ought to be made to remove it on prophylactic grounds.

Let us turn now to the real foreign bodies, those of metal, stone, or some particularly tough material. In my paper on zoo biology and comparative behaviour research (1956), which has already been mentioned, I dealt amongst other things with dangerous objects that are already known to have caused avoidable fatalities in all zoos.

In the practice of surgery it is not necessary to stress the importance of seeing that forceps, scissors or similar instruments are not left behind in the body cavity of the patient—but in the zoo one still has to insist that manual work in a cage or paddock has not been completed until the last nail, piece of wire, metal splinter etc. has been scrupulously removed. Even today this rule is still not observed rigidly everywhere. Staples are still used, nails and wire-netting are allowed to rust and disintegrate, and serious losses due to foreign bodies continue to take place in every zoo.

In Basel Zoo, at the time of my arrival in 1944, there were so many losses due to foreign bodies, particularly among fish-eating birds and ruminants, that I had a special poster for internal use hung up in all the staff rooms, as a reminder to the keepers and zoo craftsmen. Members of the public, however, are an ever-present source of foreign bodies which include such objects as paper clips, safety pins, pins from flag-days and so on. A gorilla swallowed a ballpoint pen five inches long which had to be removed by an operation (Hediger 1953). The animal concerned later became famous as Achilla, the mother of Goma, the first gorilla to be bred in Europe.

During my first year at Zurich Zoo (1954) I lost a bison cow from a piece of wire $2\frac{1}{2}$ inches long, from the fence which had rusted. This foreign body had penetrated through the stomach wall and into the pericardium, This unpleasant experience was unfortunately repeated in 1964 with a one year-old bison, in a paddock where some building work was being undertaken. The animal became incurably sick and had to be shot on 10 September. In this case the post-mortem was carried out by Dr Gross of the Zurich City Meat Inspectorate who reported as follows: "there was a piece of wire about two inches long, which was already very corroded sticking into the stomach; the sharp point was protruding and had penetrated the diaphragm and pericardium. At the points of penetration the diaphragm and pericardium showed a deposition of fibrous tissue. The heart was covered all over with a thick, purulent, stinking deposit. The whole of the body was very emaciated." A caiman died from swallowing a rubber bung which the public had thrown into its pool. The symptoms caused by swallowing foreign bodies may be very varied and obscure. In long-legged birds sometimes an abnormal gait is a sign that something is wrong. A marabou stork examined for this reason was found to have a piece of wire sticking through the stomach and body-wall into the leg! In August 1962 in Zurich Zoo an X-ray of a rhea chick that was limping showed a piece of broken glass, an iron shoe stud and a remarkable semicircular object which later turned out to be a gold wedding ring bearing the initials M. P. Another rhea died from swallowing a haircomb. On 30 December 1955 a lammergeyer had a bone about seven inches long stuck in the oesophagus which pressed on the trachea and led to death by suffocation.

The danger from foreign bodies is particularly great in all the ratite birds (ostriches and relatives), because these have a natural tendency to pick up stones, and when suitable ones are lacking they will swallow pieces of metal, sharp-edged fragments and so on as a substitute. This makes the public think that ostriches can digest nails, horseshoes and similar objects, and in view of this they offer them the most outrageous objects.

L. Heck (1929) reports on a Masai ostrich which died in the Berlin Zoo, in whose stomach a coffee spoon and half a horseshoe were found. "Death was caused by the latter because its sharp jagged edge continuously scratched and irritated the stomach and intestine, causing continual loss of blood, finally resulting in the complete exhaustion of the animal." In the Zoo at Halle a Somali ostrich died from severe stomach lesions caused by swallowing a modelling tool made of nickel-steel (F. Schmidt-Hoesndorf 1930).

In his *Story of the Edinburgh Zoo*, published in 1964, T. H. Gillespie (p. 54) reports on four ostriches sent from Africa as a gift which all died shortly after their arrival. These valuable birds had been fed with cabbage in their transport cages; the heads of cabbage had been fastened to a corner of the box with a soft kind of string. The ostriches picked the cord loose and swallowed it; however, they were unable to digest this fibrous material and it eventually caused intestinal blockage. About 50 yards of this fatal twine were found in each ostrich at the post-mortem.

Gillespie mentions various other cases of death caused by foreign bodies in his zoo, such as that of an elephant seal, through someone having thrown a pointed stick into its pool. The seal swallowed the piece of wood and suffered a fatal perforation of the stomach (p. 62). Also the loss of a rhinoceros was due to a foreign body which perforated the stomach (p. 52); a very popular sea-lion died from swallowing a handkerchief (p. 65) and a gentoo penguin from an India rubber (p. 88). There is no doubt that every zoo director could supply a similar catalogue.

The elephant seals (*Macrorhinus*) are obviously among the animals which are particularly vulnerable to foreign bodies. One of these giant seals died for instance in the Vincennes Zoo in Paris from swallowing a tennis ball (J. Nouvel, P. Bullier, and J. Rinjard 1958, p. 243). In 1930 the historic bull elephant seal "Goliath", which weighed over two tons, was the victim of a foreign body in

Hagenbeck's Zoo at Stellingen. A visitor had thrown the neck of a broken beer bottle into its jaws, which caused severe lacerations and led to a very painful death.

A sea-lion died from a foreign body in Vincennes Zoo in 1956 (J. Nouvel, P. Bullier and J. Rinjard 1957, p. 300). In Leipzig Zoo 728 stones with a total weight of over 60 lbs were found in the stomach of a dead sea-lion (K. M. Schneider 1937, p. 70). In Copenhagen Zoo in 1930 two sea-lions died, one with 25 lbs of stones and sand in the stomach, the other with about 8 lbs of stones, leaves, horse-chestnuts and so on (Th. Alving 1932, p. 36). A sea-lion in London had its stomach full of fallen leaves and died from an excess of this indigestible material (L. R. Brightwell 1949, p. 23). A few stones in these seals would be normal; but excesses occur in captivity as the result of the animals being kept within narrow confines, leading to a "hypertrophy of values" (Hediger 1950, p. 31). We know that this also applies to many other animals. According to a report by A. C. V. van Bemmel, P. Zwart & J. C. Peters (1962, p. 823) an echidna (*Tachyglossus aculeatus*), had an excessive quantity of sand in its stomach, and R. E. Rewell (1948, p. 506) mentions a tamandua (*Tamandua tetradactyla*), whose rectum was completely filled and blocked with earth.

There is no doubt that certain animal groups, such as seals and ruminants, appear to be particularly vulnerable to internal foreign bodies, but there is scarcely a single species which can be said to be immune. Cases have also been recorded amongst the carnivores, such as cats and bears. A. Urbain and his co-workers (1949, p. 182) mention a polar bear with a fistula of the oesophagus caused by foreign bodies. In the stomach of a female camel in Leipzig Zoo, H. Tillmann (1944) found fifteen foreign bodies some of which were very sharp and had partially penetrated the stomach wall and diaphragm, causing inflammation of the pericardium, and led to the animal's subsequent death. Some of these foreign bodies showed a distinct deposition of calcium, which the author interpreted as a defence mechanism of the organism.

Prevention is better than cure when dealing with this problem as with so many others. The danger from foreign bodies must be fought at the source. There are three main sources: the craftsmen, the public and the wire-netting, particularly when this is used not only as a fence surrounding a paddock but also as a protection for trees inside the enclosure. Wire-netting should never be used to protect trees because it is well known that the trunks of trees increase their girth as they grow; this creates a pressure which eventually results in the wire netting breaking and the staples used to keep it in place are forced out of the wood. Bits of broken wire-netting are amongst the most dangerous foreign bodies.

Ungulates with antlers or horns have a tendency to make use of trees when cleaning the antlers for example, in marking (wisent), or because they regard the tree as a substitute partner in rival fights. The wire intended as protection is often torn during these activities and subsequently presents a hazard. The netting tends to be forgotten and comes away from its support, becomes rusty and disintegrates. Later the remaining bits of wire are often eaten with leaves, for example, or they penetrate the hooves.

A harmless fixture, in the biological sense, for protecting trees is a circular or semi-circular ring of solid poles, attached to stout iron hoops, placed at some distance from the trunk of the tree and fixed firmly in the ground, possibly set in concrete. These poles can safely be belaboured by the animals and if necessary they can be replaced. Any danger from foreign bodies is thereby excluded.

Pieces of wire, nails, metal splinters and so on not only cause injuries as external foreign bodies by penetrating the skin and entering the body but also give rise to infections which can lead to a very painful death, e.g. from tetanus. The animals do not always show immediate signs of lameness. Injuries may also be caused by lying on foreign bodies. In autumn 1963 a camel in Zurich Zoo lay on a nail which was protruding from a plank that had been left lying in the enclosure by a careless workman. The nail entered its fore limb and the camel was evidently unable to free itself from the foreign body for some time. When the keeper noticed it and removed the nail a severe swelling that was already infected developed.

I have repeatedly seen elephants with stones wedged in the trunk; these could not be blown out and the stones had to be gently massaged out towards the orifice, a procedure which is by no means simple with certain individuals.

9

Causes of Death in the Zoo

A hundred years ago it was common practice to bury animals which died in the zoo in the zoo grounds themselves without a proper investigation into the causes of death; this practice continued in various zoos until recently and amongst other things it was of benefit to the population of free-living rats. L. R. Brightwell (1952) tells the splendid story of Frank Buckland who was determined to eat a bit of every animal that died in the London Zoo where from 1861 onwards he acted not only as the first zoo journalist but also as zoo vet. Buckland was an army surgeon who was also a pioneer in the keeping of dolphins. On one occasion when he was away for some time a leopard died in the zoo; when he returned several weeks later he made the staff dig up the corpse, which had been buried in a flowerbed, so that he could taste a leopard cutlet.

At that time the London Zoo was under the immediate supervision of Abraham D. Bartlett, another great character of whom it was said that he was equally skilled with scalpel and broom; originally a taxidermist he occasionally undertook post-mortems. From these small beginnings however it was a big step to the establishment of comparative pathological examinations of all the corpses occurring in a zoo on a regular basis and even today this is still not done everywhere. The publication of detailed findings on the causes of death of zoo animals should follow but today this is carried out by only a few large zoos, which have sufficient specialists available. Regrettably, however, a large amount of material remains inaccessible and this is yet another example of the influence exerted by

166

financial considerations mentioned in Chapter 1. The evaluation of this material is also of great value to human pathology, as has been emphasized for example by B. J. Dobberstein (1951) in his work *Wesen und Aufgabe einer vergleichenden Pathologie* (Nature and tasks of comparative pathology). A short survey on the development of comparative pathology in its relation to the zoological garden was given by C. Krause (1939).

In the important work by Herbert Fox (1923) there are a number of references to comparative pathology in his chapter on feeding. In 1955 Patricia O'Connor Halloran, the veterinarian and vice-director of the Staten Island Zoo published a comprehensive bibliography of the diseases of wild mammals and birds, which included over 900 different publications over a period of 120 years, namely from 1830–1950.

In many respects this is a remarkable work which deals with those wild animals that have been wrongly neglected. Three species of animal are noticeable by their absence: rabbit, golden hamster and rat. This is because in a work of this kind it would not have been possible to include references to the vast amount of literature that already exists on these three animals which are particularly favoured as laboratory animals. The treatment of these three species as laboratory animals, an attitude of mind which is applied virtually to all wild animals, deserves to be thoroughly exposed. Unless this is done there is a serious risk that our combined biological, pathological and medical knowledge will rest on a few laboratory animals; to neglect the rich abundance of phenomena typical of wild animals is to present a picture that is alarmingly one-sided.

The challenge of including the whole wealth of wild animals that live in zoos should also be included as well as those that live in their natural surroundings, whilst remnants of these are still preserved. Many have already become extinct and are irretrievably lost to science today.

Patricia Halloran's work is of importance to zoo biology in other respects, in particular with regard to the health of wild animals. Now and again people who do not realize what a modern zoo is really like conjure up a picture of the so-called "glorious freedom" of life in the wild; in their naïvete they imagine the animals enjoying healthy, unrestricted lives in a kind of natural paradise.

I have dealt elsewhere (1950, 1961) in detail with how matters stand in this so-called state of freedom. Since then studies of territory and social relationships have confirmed my earlier statements. In the sense of spatial, temporal and individual relations the so-called free-living animal is by no means free to live without any restricting factors. Nowadays we also know that the life expectation of wild animals in captivity is much greater on average than it is in the wild. The frequency of disease among free-living animals to which Halloran refers, based on her comprehensive study of the literature and her practical experience, virtually shatters the last illusion of a glorious life of freedom.

The introduction to her work begins in the following way: "For many years, popular opinion entertained the mistaken conception that wilderness areas produced a healthy lot of animals. As a matter of fact, there is no other group of animals in which disease appears so consistently and so disastrously as it does among wildlife. Every animal in nature, from the smallest and least important minnow to the largest mammal, may be affected. While it is now realized that widespread disease occurs among all wild species, the occurrence of individual deaths usually passes unnoticed. Diseased wild animals have a tendency to hide, and they rarely recover from serious ailments. It is only when a disease assumes epizootological proportions and extensive destruction occurs that the incident is recorded."

This state of affairs must be constantly borne in mind as we consider the causes of death in zoo animals. We can learn a lot about the expectation of life in animals that live in the wild by marking individuals, using techniques that correspond with the ringing or banding of birds; the more we learn as a result of these studies, the more certain we become of the correctness of the hypothesis that the expectation of life is significantly greater in the zoo than it is outside (Hediger 1950, p. 36 *et seq.*).

We cannot concern ourselves here with the investigation of individual diseases and the hypothetical cases of death due to them in the zoo, as in general these can only be explained in veterinary terms, a sector of zoo biology which is of great importance. But we can discuss individual categories of causes of death in the zoo and consider these from various angles.

We have already dealt with one important category of possible causes of death: namely foreign bodies. Cases of this kind can be avoided in principle, providing the greatest possible care is taken to remove the source of danger. Strict control and inspection of the zoo premises can ensure prevention.

Since I first analysed the causes of death in zoo animals in No. 54 of the Ciba-Zeitschrift (1938), certain changes have taken place. Infectious diseases, particularly tuberculosis, digestive complaints and parasites claimed the highest proportion of fatalities at that time. B. Murer (1939, p. 65) also stated in his thesis on pathological and anatomical investigations on captive wild animals in the Basel Zoo: "the greatest number of animals die from epidemic diseases." At that time tuberculosis played an important part, particularly among the monkeys and apes. H. Fox (1923, p. 486) found tuberculosis in 38·5 per cent of 498 primates dissected in Philadelphia Zoo. J. Dobberstein (1936) regarded tuberculosis as a disease that occurred fairly regularly among the mammals and birds in zoos. The same author goes on to say: "Parasitic ailments—chiefly among young animals—as well as infectious diseases frequently give rise to fatalities."

Over the years improvements in quarantining, more hygienic accommodation, stricter methods of examination, more effective drugs and more appropriate feeding methods have resulted in a decline in the importance of infectious diseases, parasitic ailments and dietary disorders; in the meantime other categories have come more to the fore. One which is rapidly assuming significance is what I first (1956, p. 12) tried to characterize as "death due to behaviour". In view of its increasing importance it is essential that new and adequate prophylactic measures should be worked out and put into practice. The measures involved are of a very varied type, covering a range of different subjects such as tranquillizers and zoo architecture. (This will be dealt with in the next chapter).

"Death due to behaviour" is much commoner than is generally thought; its incidence is also widespread, affecting a great variety of animals from fish to mammals. There is no doubt that many cases never reach the pathologist because the cause of death is obvious, as for example in the case of a broken neck or fractured skull, due perhaps to the animal dashing against the fence when frightened. In other cases the diagnosis may be simply a ruptured liver or fractured ribs and the underlying cause of the injury left undetermined, even though the primary cause may have been social factors or some form of aggression. In order to show what is meant by "death due to behaviour" a few examples will be mentioned here, extracted from the reports published by large zoos that regularly give details of fatalities in their establishments. These examples also indicate that such deaths are astonishingly frequent.

In this context the publications of H. Ratcliffe from the Philadelphia Zoo are of special value, particularly those from 1950 onwards. In the annual report for that year Ratcliffe (p. 8) remarks that injuries form the largest single cause of death among both mammals and birds. This was also the case in a number of the preceding years as well as in the years 1951 and 1952.

In 1954, 1955 and 1956 injuries and accidents accounted for half of all the causes of death in mammals and birds. In 1962 they were responsible for about a third of all losses, namely 14 mammals and 72 birds, whereas in the same year tuberculosis accounted for only two deaths among the birds and none among the mammals. In 1961 nineteen mammals were killed through injuries and accidents, attributable therefore to the category designated as "death due to behaviour", but there was only one case in which a mammal died from tuberculosis.

In the annual report for 1961 (p. 6) Ratcliffe also mentioned one very important circumstance, namely that primary disease in the heart or kidneys was frequently found in those animals which were killed by their companions. It is a generally known fact that any kind of disease or sign of weakness is a direct provocation to aggression in other members of the same species. The animal that is sick or feeble represents a challenge and is killed by others, a form of behaviour that is not unknown among certain races and individuals of *Homo sapiens*.

It appears from the reports by R. N. T.-W. Fiennes that the experience of London has been similar to that of Philadelphia. The report for the year 1959 is a convenient one to cite because the causes of death for mammals, birds and reptiles are expressed in percentages. Cases of death from injuries, or in our sense "deaths due to behaviour", make up 14 per cent. Out of a total of 19 categories of cause of death in this organization, only two show higher percentages,

Fig. 101   Today such bare and restricted conditions for exhibiting crocodiles are scarcely acceptable any longer.

Fig. 102   Modern habitat presentation of crocodilians in an environment of living tropical plants.

Fig. 103   The zoos in San Diego and Frankfurt-am-Main were among the first to conduct visitors through a series of aviaries, so that the birds could be observed without any optical hindrance, as in 'open aviaries'.

Fig. 104   The ambition to collect as many species as possible is out of place in a zoo. The exhibition of a number of solitary animals is not in accordance with biological principles and suggests a museum. A zoo should exhibit a limited selection of species in natural breeding groups.

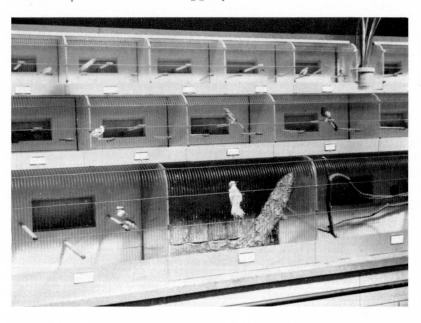

namely 16 per cent for diseases of the respiratory system and 27 per cent for diseases of the digestive organs (p. 491).

Figures for 1958 show deaths due to injury among the mammals in second place, with 34 cases, the list being headed by 46 cases of death due to diseases of the digestive system. One case of "death due to behaviour", is worth noting in which a short-tailed wallaby is cited as dying from fright (pp. 303, 307). A general fight had broken out in a group of these wallabies containing several animals. Only one individual was not involved, keeping itself apart in a corner; after the end of the fight this one was dead. Although the facts of the case were presented as though they had been observed with strict accuracy, nevertheless it is conceivable that certain factors were overlooked. Thus, for example, it might be reasonable to suggest that the animal had not taken part in the fight because it was not fit.

In the report for 1957 Fiennes (p. 134 *et seq.*) reports some unusual cases of "death due to behaviour": a young female Saiga antelope had to be destroyed because of extensive crush fractures probably caused by the heavy male attempting to mount her. A Canada goose died about two weeks after the death of its mate, since when it had ceased to take any kind of food. This could be a case of death through pining, which is by no means improbable in geese which are strictly monogamous.

Konrad Lorenz, (1963, p. 178 *et seq.*), the well-known expert on geese, describes the behaviour of a grey goose deprived of its partner, as follows: "The first response to the disappearance of the partner consists in the anxious attempt to find him or her again. The goose moves about restlessly by day and night, flying great distances and visiting all places where the partner might be found, uttering all the time the penetrating trisyllabic long-distance call. The searching expeditions are extended farther and farther and quite often the searcher itself gets lost, or succumbs to an accident. From the moment a goose realizes that the partner is missing it loses all courage and flees even from the youngest and weakest geese. As its condition quickly becomes known to all the members of the colony the lonely goose rapidly sinks to the lowest step in the ranking order."

Lorenz explicitly emphasizes that to a considerable extent the symptoms just described in a goose that loses its mate are roughly the same as those accompanying human grief, and that this applies particularly to the phenomena that can be observed in the sympathetic nervous system. He even believes that in both man and goose the expression of grief can be observed in the area of the eyes; this is brought about by the eye sinking back in its socket due to a lowering of tonus in the sympathicus.

Up until now little research has been done on grief behaviour, which is also of apparent importance in zoo biology. M. Meyer-Holzapfel (1964, p. 284 *et seq*,) has devoted an interesting section to it, which contains several striking examples from zoos.

There is one other case of "death due to behaviour" from Fiennes' report for 1957, to which I would like to draw attention. He mentions a puff adder (*Bitis arietans*) which swallowed a member of its own species which was $\frac{3}{4}$ inch longer. As a result it suffered a fatal perforation of the gut. Cannibalism is rather unusual in puff adders; it is possible that this was a case of both snakes seizing the same prey, e.g. a mouse, and then being unable to let go.

A similar incident involving pythons was described by Carl Hagenbeck as long ago as 1909 (p. 252 *et seq*.): "about ten years ago it so happened that a python nine feet long swallowed another one seven feet long together with a rabbit, which had been put into the cage with the two snakes the evening before. According to subsequent observations one must infer that both of the snakes had seized and killed the rabbit at the same time. The two snakes, one at the head and the other at the hind end, tried to constrict the rabbit and in the process the larger snake had caught hold of the smaller one and swallowed it."

Not all snakes have such a pronounced appetite. It frequently happens that these reptiles in the zoo refuse all food and finally die from inanition and anaemia. It is doubtful whether all these cases can be regarded in the category of "death due to behaviour" in view of a statement by Fiennes in the report cited (1957, p. 136 *et seq*.); this indicated that all the snakes which refused food and eventually died of anaemia and inanition were heavily infected with haemogregarines, (parasites which live inside the blood corpuscles). By so-called forced feeding (more accurately described as assisted feeding) it often happens that snakes refusing food can become accustomed after a time to a normal or even ample amount of food. In Zurich

Zoo assisted feeding of an anaconda had to be continued for almost two years before it would take food normally of its own accord.

The pathological report of the London Zoo for the year 1953 was written by Osman Hill. In it (p. 305) he gives some interesting details on the theme "trauma and accidental deaths" which we have referred to as "death due to behaviour". Under this heading fights between cage companions play an important role; in birds this applies particularly during the breeding season. In other cases fatal injuries were caused during panic flight reactions which were due to cats roaming at night. The introduction of a new individual into an existing group of animals often proves to be extraordinarily difficult or even fatal.

People who make a gift of an animal to the zoo and who express a desire to be present when the newcomer is introduced to its future companions should be warned about the reception it is likely to receive from members of its own species. Animal lovers usually imagine a touching scene of welcome being given to a monkey, for instance, as it joins the others. When zoo officials warn them that in the majority of cases fights occur that are a matter of life and death, they are unwilling to believe that this happens. These animal lovers know nothing about animal sociology; they are unaware of the fact that every animal group in the zoo has a sociological structure. This social order is sensitive to disturbance and the relationships of individual members are affected by every change in the composition of the group, whether this is due to the death for example of the leading animal, the so-called alpha animal, or to the arrival of an unknown and usually unwanted stranger. In man also, it is well known that a stranger who is compulsorily billeted on a household is not necessarily received with open arms.

Osman Hill reports on a Malay bear (*Helarctos malayanus*), which was introduced into a group and immediately killed by the companions of its own species. Every zoo has witnessed scenes of this kind on more than one occasion. In fact, the incorporation of a new member into an existing society is an extraordinarily difficult task, about which more will be said later. Many animals die in the process if the necessary precautions are not observed; this procedure is one which does not fit in with the expectations and demands of donors and journalists who do not understand the situation.

173

In the same report by Osman Hill mention is also made of the loss of a family of chinchillas (*Chinchilla laniger*)—an exhibit that was very costly at that time—which was killed by rats. In the zoo one must of necessity be on guard against rats, mice and cats. (This subject will be dealt with in a later chapter).

Osman Hill, a leading primatologist, also mentions in his report a shattering example of "death due to behaviour" in which some macaques (*Macaca irus*) held a rival under water so long that it drowned. Some swimming birds, particularly swans, also adopt these tactics to drown members of smaller species gripping them by the bill and holding them under water until they are dead. On the other hand there are numerous examples of animals being saved by members of their own species; there are cases known from Zurich Zoo and from the wild of monkeys, e.g. hamadryad baboons (*Papio hamadryas*), falling into the water and being actively grasped by the members of its troop or of having tails held out to help in the rescue, behaviour which in this context is equivalent to throwing a life-belt into the water.

Finally Osman Hill mentions a leopard that bled to death as a result of a wound inflicted on itself. This too could be regarded as an apparent case of "death due to behaviour". Meanwhile it should be noted that the leopard had suffered a sarcoma of the tendon sheath of the front paw, which stimulated it to self-mutilation. Such cases of auto-mutilation are primarily the result of a pathological condition.

These examples from a few of the annual pathological reports of the London Zoo show quite clearly the heterogeneous nature of the background of what is meant here by the term "death due to behaviour". The introduction of this term serves the purpose of drawing attention to the need for considering all the possible aspects of behaviour which could have contributed to the causes of death, because some behaviour patterns can be influenced or prevented, although unfortunately this does not apply in every case.

It is not always as easy to differentiate "death due to behaviour" from other categories as it is in cases such as infections, carcinomas, visible signs of senility and so on, where some particular factor dominates the picture. Fractures are less easy to classify, if we disregard those that are purely accidental, in many cases for instance they can be traced back to fighting and flight, in other words they can be attributed clearly to behaviour patterns.

The underlying purpose here is not to establish a "new" category of causes of death for its own sake, but to create a greater awareness of the behavioural components in many causes of death and thus devote greater efforts to establishing effective preventive measures.

H. D. Schmidt (1958, p. 104) was among the first to take up the idea of "death due to behaviour". He reports on a case of jealousy concerning food in puppies. Four eight-week old puppies were kept in a spacious run during the day and in the evening they were released for a time into a big garden at the Institute of Psychology, where they had even more space in which to move. On the evening in question they had been released as usual into the garden; they were not due to receive their evening meal until later and having eaten nothing since midday they immediately went in search of any bones or scraps of meat that they could find. In one corner of the garden they found the bowl full of lots of meat and scraps intended for the bitch. The puppies immediately rushed at the food and— with reciprocal threats and growls—began to gulp the pieces down without chewing them, swallowing the meat with the utmost haste. One puppy suddenly withdrew, made choking and retching movements, stretched itself out, then fell down and after a few convulsions was dead. The post-mortem showed that a rather hard piece of cooked food (horse-flesh, 24 grams, $5 \times 3 \times 3$ cm) had torn the oesophagus in two places, so that it pressed on the trachea and caused death by suffocation.

The swallowing of excessively large pieces of food in prey animals also occurs not infrequently in the wild. Karl von Frisch (1959) has described a number of such cases under the title of "greed punished". Animals in the wild are by no means spared from fatal accidents, bodily injuries and many other causes of death "due to behaviour".

Other annual reports of large zoos also throw light on the importance of "death due to behaviour" from the viewpoint of zoo biology. For example the report for 1954 of the Vincennes Zoo in Paris by A. Urbain and his colleagues attributes (p. 123) the highest figures of death to traumatic influences and various accidents in the mammals, namely 19 out of 140; this grand total however includes 59 animals that were newly born or less than 10 days old and if we exclude these, then the "deaths due to behaviour" account for almost a quarter of the mammals lost.

In addition this report gives the following details: three young baboons were bitten to death by older members of their own species; a mouflon succumbed to the infection of a traumatic wound; a duiker received a fatal abdominal injury while fighting; two young wapitis were killed by an old stag; three foxes confined in a space that was too restricted died from wounds suffered in fighting. A Californian sea-lion born in the zoo was still having to be forcibly fed at the age of 10 months as it was not feeding itself; this meant it had to be caught up every day, a procedure in which it suffered a torn diaphragm with a fatal pleuro-peritoneal haemorrhage. Two Chinese water-deer broke out of their paddock; the male suffered a fractured foot in the process and the pregnant female died from exhaustion shortly after recapture. A nilgai taking flight likewise suffered a fracture; a Barbary wild sheep made a fatal leap; two blackbuck suffered multiple fractures, while a giraffe $1\frac{1}{2}$ months old died from a fractured skull.

Among the birds also a higher percentage was attributed in the same year "death due to behaviour", namely 37 out of a total of 153 deaths; of these 52 were newly hatched and if we subtract these from the total, the "deaths due to behaviour" amounted to a third. The total number of accidents included 9 from exposure, which cannot be regarded as "death due to behaviour"; 11 birds were the victims of a fox that had broken in, namely 2 peafowl, 3 snow geese, 1 Egyptian goose, 3 silver pheasants and 2 demoiselle cranes. The ravages of foxes in Europe can be devastating as we well know from our experiences in Zurich Zoo. This point will be referred to again when discussing buildings (Chapter 10).

Various birds were listed as fatalities due to behaviour in other ways e.g. two emus. A five month old black-footed penguin drowned beneath the thin sheet of ice in its pool. Two herons suffered fractures. A stork came to grief when it had to be caught up in a large aviary. An adult swan was fatally injured by another; on the other hand a young swan was killed by a chimpanzee, when it went too near the chimpanzees' island. A Cereopsis goose received fatal injuries from a hog deer. A barnacle goose died from a ruptured liver, another from a skull injury. A young tree duck was killed during an attempt to catch it up. A buzzard was killed by its companions, and so on. The reports from the Vincennes Zoo for 1956 and subsequent years published by J. Nouvel and his colleagues are full of information and in quoting a few more cases from them I must emphasize that corresponding material would undoubtedly be available from virtually every zoo if only such informative reports were to be published; this is unforunately not possible for the majority of zoos because many of them do not have sufficient scientific specialists available for such work.

In the report for 1957, for example, a Californian sea-lion died from swallowing a foreign body, as already mentioned in Chapter 8. In a certain sense, this type of death should also be included in the category of "death due to behaviour". Another fatality was that of a gibbon (*Hylobates concolor leucogenis*) which drowned in the moat surrounding the gibbon island.

The exhibition on islands or in open enclosures with water-filled barriers of anthropoid apes—in which we reckon to include the gorilla, chimpanzee, orang utan and gibbons—doubtless provides the spectator with plenty of interest but from the professional point of view it presents dangers, because all these anthropoids—like man—are not born with a natural ability to swim. Deep water barriers are therefore dangerous to them and shallow ones are inadequate. The famous gorilla Makoko of the Bronx Zoo, the first male of its species ever to reach sexual maturity in captivity, was tragically drowned in a water-filled barrier in 1951 (L. Crandall 1964, p. 158).

In Chester Zoo a shallow water barrier that could be waded proved to be fatal, in that a chimpanzee left the enclosure in 1962, climbed a high tension pylon and was electrocuted on the live wires. It is only the non-anthropoid primates—like most other mammals, including even the sloths—that can swim.

According to the same report from Vincennes (p. 299) a fennec fox also died "due to behaviour" when being caught up. A serval died from a fractured spine; the extraordinary disposition of this attractive African cat to fractures of the limbs has already been mentioned. Others which should be included are: the accidental death of a Himalayan black bear, of a mouflon caused by jumping and of an Indian blackbuck through a fractured skull.

"Death due to behaviour" stands top of the list for the birds

(p. 306). An adult ostrich died from a fracture of the tibia, four young ostriches died from fractures and dislocations of the limbs. In Zurich Zoo we have also lost several ratite birds through limb fractures, for example three half-grown ostriches in 1961. The fracture of a leg in these giant birds with their highly specialized fast growth palpably means certain death.

The Vincennes report also mentions a heron with a fractured spine, a flamingo with a tibial fracture, two mallards with injuries resulting from fights between rivals and a peafowl which was killed by a wild turkey cock. A common pheasant suffered an accident; two male golden pheasants were partially eaten, presumably by a cat. Of two wild turkeys one died from an open fracture of the tibia; the other was killed by a marabou stork. A crowned crane died of a fracture of the humerus; two herring gulls were killed by a skua; two black-headed gulls died from accidents. An Abyssinian ground hornbill was killed by a member of its own species.

As I have already emphasized we are concerned here not with details or statistics, but with the principle of extending preventative measures in new directions. From the examples cited it is quite clear that this prophylaxis must take into consideration items of architecture, the composition of social groups and the exclusion of enemies of other species; improvements in the methods of catching up, feeding and so on are also involved. The proper use of tranquillizers acquires a particular significance in dealing with animals that are in an excited state, due to some temporary circumstance; the overall effect in such situations should be advantageous in that it reduces excitability and prevents such reaction for instance as sudden flight.

According to H. S. Raethel (1958) accidents and injuries make up 50 per cent of the total losses of mammals and birds in individual zoos and as we have already seen from the examples cited here these come first in the causes of death in zoos. This does not mean that the category of "death due to behaviour" has increased significantly in recent times, but rather that other categories such as tuberculosis, other infectious diseases, dietary complaints etc. have decreased thanks to improvements in drugs, nutrition and management.

Today there is a pressing need in zoo biology to analyse "death due to behaviour" in more detail and on the basis of this analysis to achieve an effective prophylaxis. Attention should be focused on

Fig. 105 A drinking-trough installation with two unsuitable features: too close to the fence and too close to the ground, enabling the water to become infected with ascarid eggs which adhere to the hooves.

Fig. 106 Shallow-water ditches as a barrier for anthropoid apes in Chester Zoo. Subsequently an electric wire has had to be installed along the centre of the ditch close above the surface of the water. The water barrier alone does not provide complete security.

Fig. 107   Spider Monkeys in an open enclosure.

Fig. 108   A bad edge to a pond: the overhanging stones make it difficult or impossible to climb out of the pond. A sloping edge of obliquely placed stone would have made it satisfactory.

Fig. 109 In the zoo as in the wild, the scratching tree forms an important fixed point which is used by the big cats for bodily maintenance.

Fig. 110 At the foot of the scratching tree one often finds large pieces ($1-1\frac{1}{2}$ inches) of abraded horny sheath. If no scratching tree is available the claws may grow too long and curve round into the ball of the foot.

Fig. 111 Modern type of barrier in the Giraffe House at the London Zoo. This raises the question of whether a few, broad, black transverse bars are less disturbing to the viewer than a wire fence of the correct mesh.

Fig. 112 Curiously enough the Himalayan Black Bear, the Malay Bear and the Sloth Bear in Zurich Zoo spare the small fig trees which grow every year between the stone flags of their pit. Other animals have been known to behave in a similar way.

Fig. 113 Improved bear pit: here one can see the animals from ground level through bars as well as by looking down on them from above.

various forms of incompatability and in 1942 (p. 111 *et. seq*) I listed eleven of these. In 1959 I expanded this survey at the Zoo Directors' Conference in Copenhagen and here I would like to indicate the background to "death due to behaviour" using the following key terms, which doubtless require considerable amplification.

A. Interspecific incompatability
   a) Predator-prey situation (e.g. fox—pheasant)
   b) "Sworn enemy" situation (e.g. dog—cat)
   c) Mobbing, i.e. song-bird—bird of prey
   d) Biological hierarchy (e.g. lion—leopard)
   e) Different reactions to contact and distance
   f) Different behaviour relative to stance (e.g. deer—kangaroo)
   g) Differences in activity rhythms (at the extreme, nocturnal and diurnal animals)
B. Intraspecific incompatibility
   a) Social hierarchy
   b) Territorial disputes
   c) Individual antipathy
   d) Sexual hyperactivity (rut)
   e) Misinterpretation of expressive behaviour
C. Disturbance reactions
   a) Refusal to feed (inanition)
   b) Automutilation
   c) Killing of the young (abandoning, eating)
D. Reactions to man
   a) direct: extreme flight, e.g. when being caught up
   b) indirect: spatial effects (unfamiliarity, fright reactions), injury in transit or transfers
E. Nutritional defects
   a) Quantitative (over-feeding)
   b) Qualitative (toxic effects)
   c) Picking up of foreign bodies

Further details can be found in my *Wild animals in captivity* (1950) and reference should also be made to the investigations by E. Inhelder (1962) on reactions to disturbance. A word may be said here on the subject or the abandonment or even killing (possibly also eating) of the young which is so often observed in the zoo.

I have shown elsewhere (1956, p. 15) that from 1930 to 1954 in Zurich Zoo the following animals, among others, were killed and/or eaten by the mother:

leopard	7 cases
lion	8 cases
tiger	5 cases
puma	3 cases
brown bear	4 cases
dingo	3 cases
agouti	4 cases

There has also been a number of similar cases since then, e.g. in tiger, lion, jaguar, leopard, jaguarondi, coati etc. According to the report of van Bemmel and Zwart (1962 p. 831) 48 per cent of the newly born mammals in Rotterdam in 1959 and 1960 did not survive. Similar numbers have undoubtedly been observed in most other zoos.

The underlying features of what may appear to be a high rate of mortality are extraordinarily diverse. In many cases hormonal immaturity or disturbances were responsible. Reference should be made in this connection to the excellent survey of D. S. Lehrman (1961) of the hormonal regulation of parental behaviour in birds and sub-human mammals. In many other cases, however, external factors affecting the behaviour doubtless have an effect, e.g. abnormal noise such as is produced by machines, slamming doors or by excited shouts from the public. For many animal mothers or parents, optimal seclusion is indispensable for normal rearing behaviour. Spatial conditions are extremely important in this respect. Allowing the animals to be on view can have fatal results. In Zurich Zoo on 28 November 1963, a female leopard killed her three-month old cubs, apparently because she had got into a state of extreme agitation owing to the attentions of an unauthorized photographer. Many of the cases in which the young are killed or abandoned are "due to behaviour" and should therefore be included in this particular category.

In view of what we now know regarding conditions of life in the wild it is not feasible to picture the animals there dying naturally of old age; the so-called freedom of the wild holds too many dangers.

Animals that are aged, weak and suffering from serious diseases are ruthlessly eliminated by predators or external factors. On the other hand there are many animals behind bars, living under the protection of humans, that generally speaking have the opportunity to live out their lives literally to the last possible moment. At this age, which in fact is unnatural, they develop various complaints including those that were previously regarded as incurable; the question then arises of whether man, who has been responsible for lengthening the life of these animals, should not also bear the responsibility, under certain circumstances, of ending the animal's life by putting it painlessly to death. I might add that such "mercy killings" should be accepted without a public outcry but these problems do not apply only to zoo biology.

It can also happen in the zoo that, for various reasons, such as limitations of available space, living quarters can no longer be found for animals that are still healthy and not unnaturally old. Animals in captivity may reproduce at such a rate that over-production takes place. In these very rare cases, mainly lions, brown bears, and males of certain species of antelope, deer and cattle—the publicity given to the problem is sometimes based on sentiment and lack of knowledge of the facts. The naïve suggestion that such supernumerary animals should be released would inflict indefensible cruelty on most of them. This is yet another example of the fact that one cannot have animal protection without a knowledge of animals.

Anyone who is simple enough to believe that surplus zoo lions should be taken to Africa and released there should be forced to read and re-read Joy Adamson's unique book (1960) on a lion reared by man being returned to the wild in Africa. The reader will realize that in practice this remarkable experiment would scarcely bear repeating; if the newcomer does not die of starvation, it is badly harassed by the wild lions. The release of tame foxes and roe deer in Europe has already proved undesirable since it usually means a painful death for the animals involved, contributed to largely by the members of their own species as well as by hunger. It is likely that intruders in occupied territories are unwelcome and thus forced to keep on the run, often to the point of exhaustion.

This problem is a serious one in zoo biology. Although I have repeatedly faced inquiries on acute cases I see no grounds for trying

181

to avoid dealing with this thorny problem; nevertheless I would be glad to find better ways of solving it. In my opinion there are two kinds of criteria, namely subjective and objective, on which a decision to kill zoo animals should be based.

Subjective criteria: when an animal is subject to pain arising from incurable disease, injury or the complaints of old age, the level of suffering may reach the stage at which it clearly outweighs the animal's enjoyment of life; when this happens it should be killed painlessly and dispassionately. To prolong life at this stage, in my opinion, is to impose an unbearable burden on the animal which is non-biological, and life should therefore be terminated by man. This decision is naturally not an easy one, but it should be taken in regard to all the circumstances, including the corresponding conditions in the wild. This duty falls on the zoologist in collaboration with a competent veterinarian or *vice versa*. If necessary an expert representative from an animal organization can be brought in.

Objective criteria: in zoos there may be a situation in which for example there is a total lack of accommodation which makes it no longer possible to keep alive an animal that is otherwise quite healthy. This involves a question of space, a problem that is by no means confined to the zoo but which exists in principle everywhere on our planet. It is also the determining factor in hunting regulations. In order to protect the space taken into cultivation to serve man's need for food, in central Europe it is necessary for example to shoot a certain number of roe and other deer, hares etc. Game is not always immediately killed painlessly in hunting but by contrast the killing of an animal in the zoo is characterized by the fact that it can be performed absolutely painlessly.

The killing of a zoo animal for reasons of lack of space is the last resort; before this is done scrupulous inquiries must be made to ensure that there is no other zoo that could take the animal. Even when the chances are known to be slim, every effort should still be made because there may be a zoo which, through some unexpected circumstance, is in a position to accept the animal that was due to be killed.

10

Building for Animals

Discussions on the building of new zoos as a rule are primarily concerned with the choice of the locality but decisions on this are not always based on considerations of zoo biology, e.g. sheltered position, sunny site, water supply, possibilities for extensions and so on; quite different factors such as land prices, property speculation, technical considerations of traffic etc. often play a decisive part. In the course of their development there have been several occasions when zoological gardens have been transferred from one place to another or rebuilt on a completely different site. This applies for example to the West Berlin Zoo, to Schönbrunn Zoo in Vienna, to the Animal Park at Dählhölzli in Bern and to many others.

Up until the end of the First World War the ideal site was considered to be one that was as central as possible; thus for example the zoos of Antwerp and West Berlin are immediately beside the railway stations, that of Basel is very close to the station and is even intersected by a railway line. Circumstances changed with the arrival of the motor-car and the rapid growth of mechanical transport immediately after the Second World War. When pedestrians and horse carriages were in the majority the central site was ideal but it became more and more unsuitable as motor traffic developed and extensive parking areas became necessary. In addition the zoos themselves required more space, not only because of the expansion in the number of animals and variety of species which were exhibited, but also because the narrow cages with bars increasingly gave place to enclosures that were more spacious and appropriate. Finally the

183

successful development of the use of the ditch as a barrier for the animals instead of the old-fashioned type of bar also demanded much more space.

Thus, from the point of view of town-planning, the ideal site of the zoo has shifted over a period of barely four decades from the centre to the periphery of the city or even beyond. Nowadays adequate parking facilities are particularly important. It is no wonder that more and more zoological gardens are giving up their out-moded central site and are rebuilding outside the city at a sufficient distance. Thus for example Rotterdam abandoned its zoo in the city and set up a completely new one at Blijdorp in 1940. Antwerp Zoo is completely surrounded by houses. In Paris in addition to the historic and centrally situated Jardin des Plantes, a spacious new zoo was built in 1934 in the Bois du Vincennes, after which it is named. London supplemented the zoo at Regent's Park as long ago as 1927 with the large area of Whipsnade Park near Dunstable; Milwaukee retains the zoo founded in 1892 in the city centre but also has the extensive Milwaukee County Zoological Park. These few examples may be sufficient to demonstrate a tendency to decentralize which is becoming increasingly apparent.

Although rapid progress in the field of zoo architecture is certainly very necessary and desirable from the point of view of zoo biology, on the other hand, the lack of respect shown to old buildings, and the summary way in which out-moded structures are dealt with is greatly to be deplored. When a decision is made to build a new animal house to replace an unsuitable one which was built in the old-fashioned style of our grandparents, and has possibly been gnawed by rats, the zoo director is so delighted that he arranges for the demolition to go ahead without taking the trouble to record, even in pictorial form, what the old building with all its ancient equipment looks like.

This attitude is understandable but it leads to the irretrievable loss of historical material as, unfortunately, there is still not a single zoo museum anywhere in the world today. Every zoo which was founded in the last century, which still possesses a building of this period has the opportunity to preserve it as a zoo museum. Such a museum would be unique and for this reason it is easy to predict that in the immediate future it would constitute an attraction to those interested in zoos and offer valuable opportunities for study.

Material which was hitherto destroyed or thrown away without heed should be presented by all old zoos to such a museum. Even the visitors to modern zoos today can no longer predict the conditions under which wild animals will be kept in a few decades from now. In certain cases the changed methods of building have contributed as great a share to some recent breeding successes as the dispensing of vitamins and new-fangled food compounds; some of the earlier breeding successes are no longer achieved today and it is possible that we can learn more about the reasons for this by studying the external conditions under which the animals were kept. In this connection it is important to have information not only about the dimensions of the earlier cages in use, but also detailed facts about the flooring, the wiring and the dishes used for dispensing food and water; security precautions of all kinds, including locks and chains, may also be important. Fresh light is thrown on some pathological data, such as can be seen in the skeletons of animals from old menageries, when the conditions in which these animals were kept and cared for at that time are known. It is sufficient here to mention only one case which is known as the menagerie disease of bears.

This disease was already known from fossil animals, namely from the cave bear (*Ursus spelaeus*), and has been worked on by palaeontologists such as O. Abel. In the skeletons of this long extinct bear various disease symptoms have been confirmed; these show deformity of several vertebrae with severe osteophytic spondylitis giving limitation of spinal movement. H. Virchow has shown that symptoms of this kind are also found in recent brown bears which have been kept for many years in cages that are too small for them. In the opinion of the experts the pathological skeletal changes in the cave bear can probably be attributed to the fact that these animals spent about two-thirds of their life in winter sleep in damp cages, and then, like brown bears kept in too confined surroundings, became ill on account of the excessive restrictions on their movements (Hediger 1938).

At some stage bears that were originally kept in pits were given trees to climb which allowed them more exercise and a chance of getting into the sun. When did man start this and how were these climbing trees fixed? Is the disappearance of the menagerie disease from zoos today due to different constructional methods and the use of new materials?

In 1956 (p. 21 *et seq.*) I indicated briefly how stimulating it would be, for example, to write a *History of Bars* or to follow the development in detail *From barred cage to territory*. A zoo museum would be exceptionally valuable for the study of this subject and many similar ones which could be of considerable interest from the cultural point of view as well as being of significance to zoo biology. It is to be hoped that some zoo will eventually decide to establish such a place. Potential material is being lost at an increasing rate. The value of antiquities is usually only recognized long afterwards. In this case we still have a chance.

The oldest form of cage in which large animals were kept by man is the pit, such as can occasionally be seen in the form of the so-called bear pit. The standard type of bear pit is generally speaking the original form of a wild animal trap, that is a pit in the sense of a depression in the ground with walls that are as smooth as possible. This primitive form of trapping an animal by letting it fall into a pit is the actual method for example by which all the wild okapis or Indian rhinoceroses in our zoos were caught in the wild.

The ditch, which was often part of a city moat once used for defence, is a much later development and is the second oldest method of keeping animals in an enclosure. In the typical ditch the two long sides are usually banks of earth or stonework; a new element in fencing, the palisade, is already in evidence along the short sides of the area. The palisade, made of stout posts of timber often pointed at the top, is the original form of fencing. In various Swiss cities (e.g. Bern, Lucerne, Zurich) street names such as "Deer moat" are a reminder of this ancient method of keeping large mammals captive.

The next decisive step was taken when the animal was metaphorically and literally raised from a depression in the ground and kept in an area which was at the same level as the humans. This meant a much more extensive use of palisades, which now had to surround the animal on all sides. Such palisade enclosures are still found in use today in the acclimatization of large animals (e.g. okapis) in catching camps or in the large stockades used in elephant catching in India. Nowadays wooden palisades have almost completely disappeared from zoos; in 1945 they were still much in evidence, e.g. in the Lange Erlen Animal Park in Klein-Basel.

When animals were kept in a pit or a ditch it was possible to have

Fig. 114   An Oryx made this gap in the paddock gate of welded steel rods. It rushed through the opening without damaging itself (Zurich Zoo).

Fig. 115   In this case, too weak a wire-mesh was used for the big Ankole cattle. The strength and endurance of the animals are often underestimated in the choice of materials.

Fig. 116   An example of the present-day use of primitive wooden palisades in the capture of Okapi in the Congo rain-forest (Photo H. Goldstein).

an uninterrupted view of them from above but by raising them to
the level of the humans this was no longer possible; the observer then
became restricted to peering through the narrow gaps of the palisades. With the replacement of the relatively soft wood which
obstructed the view by strong iron bars quite new prospects opened
out; on account of the far greater strength of the new bars they could
be correspondingly thin and this considerably facilitated the visual
observation of the animals.

New fencing material was subsequently developed in the form of
wire-netting which was far less optically disturbing then the rigid
iron bars and this was improved further in the form of extremely fine
steel wires fixed in firm frames under tension; for small birds the
wires could be almost a hair's breadth. As the fencing material
became more transparent and elegant, the risk of injury to newly
arrived animals increased; there was a danger that a newly caught
animal or one which had recently been moved from other accommodation, would not be aware of the fine fencing material in the
initial excitement and in certain circumstances it would rush into it
at full speed. For this reason transparent fencing material, including
glass, of course, has to be made obvious at first, with laths or strips of
paper, in order that restless animals can avoid the danger of colliding
with the fencing.

The more "elegant" a fence is, that is, the finer it appears to *us*,
the more unnatural it seems to the animal; many unnecessary broken
necks and other injuries have arisen because this fact has been forgotten. To a large animal—whether bear, hyena, deer or antelope—
a fence of bars or wire pencil-thick may even simulate an obstacle
that can be easily broken through as the excited animal rushes
headlong at it. Zoo animals must first learn that a fence represents
an impenetrable barrier. Animals which have grown up in the zoo
learn this automatically so to speak, and we tend to take their reaction to fences for granted. A young tiger, for example, that has been
moved from a zoo with fenceless open paddocks into a zoo with
barred cages may rush at the iron bars or steel netting as though it
were insane; it is only then that we appreciate that such an animal—
still less one that has been newly caught in the wild—has had no
opportunity to learn an adequate behaviour pattern when faced with
a fence. But even when an animal is familiar with the fencing there

are times when it no longer recognizes the fence as an obstruction; for example during the transfer of an animal or on some other unforeseen occasion, the animal may become frightened and due to its state of excitement make a fatal rush at the fence. On 10 October 1964 Zurich Zoo lost a young female kudu because it was frightened by a falling branch during a storm; it immediately rushed straight at a fencing post, with the result that its neck vertebrae were broken. Where risks are involved in the transfer of an animal, failure to use an efficient tranquillizer today must be counted as an error in working technique.

Even during the heyday of the iron bar method of fencing a development along completely different lines was introduced at the beginning of the century; this was the so-called barless *open enclosure*, based on an idea conceived by Hagenbeck. It was laughed at and ridiculed to start with. The Zurich sculptor and animal lover Urs Eggenschwyler (1849–1923) played an important part in the first realization of this concept. A bronze tablet in Carl Hagenbeck's world-renowned animal park at Stellingen-Hamburg commemorates him with a portrait and the legend "To Urs Eggenschwyler the builder of the rock terraces". He was originally a Zurich man who ran a small animal park of his own for a time in his native city.

Carl Hagenbeck created a ditch or moat that was completely different in origin and function from the old type of sunken ground, namely a ditch to serve as a barrier in contrast to a ditch or pit as living quarters. The ditch, which does away completely with bars or netting, provides two kinds of barrier: it is either a dry ditch or one holding water. In neither case is it designed for the animal to live in; this new type usually serves to separate the animal from man, more rarely also to separate one animal from another. The animal lives on a platform, blocked at the rear by a wall or a steep cliff, which is sometimes somewhat raised up in relation to the visitor, in order to make the animal seem even more powerful and imposing. With very efficient jumpers however, e.g. lions and tigers, the platform is kept somewhat lower on safety grounds in order to make it more difficult for the animals to jump over the ditch.

As was already appreciated by Hagenbeck, this ditch system naturally allows for a highly pleasing stage-like presentation of several paddocks arranged in various ways in echelon formation;

this system however was not always efficient. All kinds of misconceptions have arisen from the ditch system because in contrast to the erection of a fence based on careful calculations, a ditch is only relatively efficient as a barrier; it does not provide complete security. Fundamentally it is possible for every animal to fall into a boundary ditch at any time or—where several animals are living together—for one to be pushed in.

Practical experience has also shown that indeed in every zoo where ditches are used animals have already fallen in by their own actions or involuntarily. With water-filled ditches cases of death by drowning have occurred, some of which have involved very valuable animals (e.g. gorillas); on the other hand deaths from fractures have repeatedly resulted from cases where animals have fallen into dry ditches. A great many examples could be cited; it is not necessary to go into detail here but the fact that this state of affairs exists should serve to indicate once again the close relation between causes of death and constructional methods in zoos, and how necessary it is for the architect to cooperate very closely with the zoo biologist.

Several points arise from this. Apart from the fact that water ditches quickly become fouled when the water in them does not circulate properly, if they hold sufficient water they constitute a hidden danger for many animals as they may drown in it; the danger is especially acute for the anthropoid apes which do not know how to swim. But if the water is sufficiently shallow to prevent drowning then the animals can wade across the ditch which consequently loses its value as a barrier. Furthermore in regions with cold winters the formation of ice on water ditches may completely destroy their effectiveness as barriers because apes for example, simply walk across the frozen ditch. For ungulates however the smooth ice surface constitutes an additional hazard, particularly when—as for example in the new camel paddocks in the London Zoo—the water or ice is so to speak flush with the floor of the enclosure. In the summer, marsh antelopes, water buffalo and other amphibious mammals and birds like to spend time in the water-filled ditches, thus the separation of one animal from another as also the animal from man, is largely illusory. The water ditch therefore has various disadvantages and it is only to be recommended in special cases.

The fact that the dry ditch is also not completely without danger has already been mentioned. Since there is no certainty that animals can be prevented from falling into the dry ditches some form of emergency exit must be envisaged from the beginning. Improvised steps of bales of straw or other material may or may not be used by an animal when it is startled and nervous; in some circumstances they may even provide the animal with an opportunity to climb up the wrong side, namely towards the public. Ticklish situations may arise when physically powerful and excitable animals are involved, such as large carnivores or rhinoceroses.

Dry ditches are increasingly being used inside houses to avoid the use of bars. Faced with the fact that in the long run one cannot be sure that the animals will not fall into them, the bottom of dry ditches ought never to be of a hard substance. Cement floors to ditches must therefore be designated as serious constructional faults, unless they are covered with a sufficiently deep layer of soft material, such as loose gravel, humus, peat etc.

Taking into consideration quite different factors R. Bigalke (1961, p. 62) comes to the conclusion that dry ditches have the advantage over water barriers. In the same volume of the *International Zoo Yearbook*, following Bigalke's contribution, an anonymous writer from the Detroit Zoo gives profiles of 30 examples of dry ditch barriers. Some of these give ground for comment from the angle of zoo biology, e.g. the fact that for such different animals as sloths, tapirs, peccaries and porcupines (*Hystrix*) the same figure is quoted for the height of the outer wall of the ditch nearest the public, namely 6 feet (1·8 metres) of vertical concrete. For sloths and African porcupines 1·2 metres is certainly enough. For cranes and Dorcas gazelles the figure is 8 feet (2·4 metres). Here it needs to be said that this should only apply to pinioned cranes and that this height would be insufficient if animals such as the Indian blackbuck and particularly impala, should become excited for any reason, e.g. during attempts at catching them up or at the appearance of a dog. In Zurich Zoo we have had repeated opportunities of observing that blackbuck could have jumped over the 2·2 metre high fence with ease, had they leapt at right angles or obliquely across the fence instead of making their leaps as they ran parallel to the fence.

With large animals such as elephants or rhinoceroses it should be remembered that these certainly cannot leap, but the males at least are capable of lifting themselves up on the back of the female for mating. The figures of 1·5 metres or 1·8 metres for elephants quoted in various publications are therefore rather low in height particularly if there is any possibility of the elephants getting a firm hold with the very extensible trunk. For elephants I therefore consider that a height of 1·5 metres for the walls of the barrier ditch is insufficient.

It was more than 20 years ago (1945, p. 59) when I drew attention to the fact that the subjective height of a barrier may be significantly reduced by the so-called mood factor, that is, in conditions of excitement. As a rule we are liable to underestimate the physical capabilities of wild animals in respect of surmounting obstacles. Were it not so, escapes of zoo animals from their enclosures would not still be taking place.

On the basis of checking on numerous cases in which brown bears (*Ursus arctos*) climbed out of their enclosure, I recommended that the height of the external wall of the ditch should be 5 metres, a height which is regarded as excessive by various colleagues. Nevertheless T. H. Gillespie (1964, p. 116) refers to a bear pit in the Edinburgh Zoo of about 5·4 metres. H. M. Wegeworth and N. Morgan (1953, p. 79) in fact report the escape of a brown bear from its companions over a wall 4·8 metres high. In principle it is naturally difficult to determine maximum potential records attainable by wild animals under certain circumstances. The unexpected tends to occur not when the animal is in a quiet mood but when it is affected by a situation that is out of the ordinary and such circumstances cannot be provoked experimentally but only estimated on the basis of numerous incidents.

In a discussion of unusual methods of locomotion among mammals, H. and K. Hediger-Zurbuchen (1964) have pointed out for example that in certain conditions polar bears can develop a surprising swimming technique: when they are in the water—without pushing off from the bottom of the pool—they can shoot up out of the water against a smooth wall to a height of 2·6 metres, a feat which no one had previously thought to be possible. The maximum was taken to be 1·5 metres.

Sloth bears (*Melursus ursinus*), which were once held to be giant sloths, can not only climb vertical bars, but they are also able to move extremely efficiently along the roof bars by hanging in the manner of a sloth.

In the thirty types of ditch mentioned from the Detroit Zoo, it is noteworthy that the external wall of the ditch is always vertical, but the inner one is sometimes at such an oblique angle that the animals can move from the platform into the ditch without effort. While they are being fed by the public there is a great danger that they will mostly remain at the bottom of the ditch, instead of exhibiting themselves on the platform. In my opinion the barrier ditch, as already emphasized, should never serve as a living space for the animal, that is, it should not form a part of the animal's territory but should be exclusively for the purpose of providing a boundary to the territory. Normally therefore the animal should not climb down into it and should not be enticed to do so by having the inner wall sloping. The wall that is strictly vertical is therefore the correct one. In the Detroit ditches it is worthy of note that the wall on the side of the animal is only vertical for rhinoceros, elephant and lion; for bears, monkeys, ungulates etc. the walls are oblique to a very shallow slope, thus enabling the animals to get down easily into the ditch, indeed they are virtually invited to do so. In this case the barrier principle is not clear cut, and this is something I disagree with; it is a kind of regression to the ditch as a place to live in.

The basic tendency in zoo architecture however is to use materials for barriers as discreetly as possible; the increasing reduction in thickness of the metal fencing serves this purpose and finally, with the barrier ditch, even the finest wire-netting can be dispensed with. The ditch however represents progress only if it is minimal, preferably not in evidence, thus helping to promote the illusion among the visitors that the animals are not fenced in. This is a concession to the public and it is in no way a deception of the animal; the method by which its territory is made secure is all the same to the animal, the only important thing from its point of view is that the security is guaranteed.

It is odd that in the San Diego Zoo which is undoubtedly one of the greatest in the world, the true significance of the ditch should have been misunderstood. For instance the elephant enclosure which was brought into use in 1962 is surrounded by a ditch made of concrete and therefore dangerous; also the tigers are able to get down comfortably into their broad ditch (H. Pournelle 1963). This ditch is therefore no longer merely a barrier, but is part of the living space of the animals' territory—and therefore part of the exhibition area—into which the public can look and indeed must look if the tigers happen to remain in the ditch in search of shade. This however is indicative of a partial retrogression to the practices of a century ago when the ditch was used as living-quarters and it also implies a misunderstanding of the use of a ditch as a barrier.

Falls into ditches are particularly dangerous for elephants, especially when the bottom is hard. This may lead to severe tusk injuries and to fatalities. With the intention of removing this danger, in many zoos the elephants have been kept away from the edge of the ditch, by providing it with sharp iron spikes that are often arranged in several rows. This precaution however only constitutes a new danger; the heavy animals injure themselves on the iron spikes when trying to get as near as possible to the public when they offer them food or because their companions push them on to the spikes. Injuries to the soles of the feet caused in this way will naturally become infected and therefore tend to heal slowly. Almost everywhere that spikes of this kind have been introduced, they have been removed later on account of unfortunate incidents. In Zurich Zoo, for example, they have also been removed as both elephant and rhinoceros have fallen from the platform, fortunately without suffering injury.

Quite apart from their proven danger spikes of any kind that look conspicuous against the animals are out of place nowadays in the zoo. They suggest something of the forcible restraint of the earlier bear pits. Animals used to be restrained by force in certain circumstances for specific purposes; above all they were restrained by being kept in a restricted area, in a real prison. The pit is basically a medieval installation. No zoo should have anything in common with this, nor with iron spikes in any form which formerly forced the animal to remain in its allotted prison-like space. The spikes like barbed wire were designed to injure any animal that tried to break out. A zoo where this situation still remains is no zoo in the modern sense. Zoos today must make serious efforts first to protect the animals against injury in any form and secondly to offer them living conditions which correspond as far as possible with those in the natural habitat. At the same time however the animals must be provided with greater security than they have in the wild, namely an absolute freedom from thirst and hunger, and complete security from dangerous rivals of their own species and enemies of other species.

To the animal no proper zoo should represent forcible restraint in the style of an old-fashioned human prison; in principle the animal should regard the zoo as an area that corresponds in all significant points to its territory. It is for this reason that the study of territory occupies such a vitally important place in zoo biology. It has taught us that the so-called free-living animal does not live in complete freedom in practice but in fact, as has been mentioned several times, it is restricted by spatial, temporal and personal relations. So far as we know today, it is fixed in an inexorable space-time system (Hediger 1942, 1950), together with a strict social system.

The zoo cannot interfere with the social system by making changes because like other specific characters the latter is largely tied to the chromosomes. The zoo can only regulate, subdue and avoid excesses caused by confinement. We know for instance that spatial restriction increases aggression; by paying sufficient attention to the social structure of the species this aggression can be tempered. Thus by taking steps appropriate to the circumstances it is possible to establish an equivalent or even greater social harmony than normally exists in the wild. With sufficient knowledge and care injuries and deaths from social behaviour can largely be avoided. This is one of the tasks of zoo biology which is by no means unimportant.

As a cause of death in the so-called "golden freedom" of the wild, the threat from enemies belonging to other species plays a dominant role; as far as animals in the zoo are concerned this danger can be completely excluded—above all by suitable buildings and methods of management. Types of fencing in the zoo serve this purpose primarily and not the prevention of a chance escape as the uninitiated sometimes think.

In every good zoo the animal does not feel itself in any way a prisoner, but—as in the wild—it feels more like the tenant or owner of a piece of land; it should feel like the occupier of a territory, the possessor, that is, of that unit of space to which the animal instinctively lays claim. The size of its natural territory, as we know for certain today, is not determined by its desire to go for a walk

Fig. 117 A newly caught Okapi moving along the corridor made of wooden stakes, which leads from the pit, in which the animal is trapped live, to the transport lorry.

Figs. 118 and 119 Old-fashioned fencing made out of heavy timber, which seriously impedes a view of the animals. This old-fashioned material should no longer be used in exhibition paddocks.

Fig. 120   Wooden palisades used in conjunction with a wide-mesh wire-netting in an African zoo. Former Belgian Congo, 1960.

Fig. 121 Grills should be avoided as far as possible, particularly those with heavy iron bars. Double fencing should only be in a zoo museum.

Fig. 122 The palisade type of fencing is thick but relatively weak compared with the much thinner but stronger fencing of steel bars. The latter constitutes an improvement although horns and antlers are often damaged on this unnatural material.

(because wild animals do not go for walks), but exclusively by its food requirements and the supply of food in the surrounding neighbourhood. In the zoo it is not necessary for a pair of lions to have antelopes, zebras or other prey animals present in their artificial territory because the necessary food is brought to them by the keeper six times a week. For this reason the artificial territory can perhaps be a thousand times smaller than a natural territory in the wild.

Animals are subject to the influence of a temporal system and man is less able to make adjustments in this field. Many animals by their very nature are tied to certain rhythms which may be largely or completely independent of external factors, as for example cycles of activity, breeding, moulting and so on. In the zoo, man can of course interfere with these cycles by the process of increasing or reducing external stimuli; this can be done by means of changes in lighting, periodic separation and bringing together of the sexes, alterations in the diet, etc. These changes may cause modifications in the timing of the cycles but man cannot make far-reaching changes that will release the animal from its deep-rooted temporal ties, such as a state of readiness for flight from enemies of other species.

Likewise we cannot and should not free the animal from its tie to the spatial system. Just as the web spider carries in itself its specific web pattern as a character of its species, so also the deer, the peccary, the raccoon dog, the armadillo, the gorilla etc. carry around with them the ground plan of their territory. It is the responsibility of the zoo biologist to get to know the territorial plan of each species, as well as the scientific names of all the animals, and to explain the relevant points to the architect.

It is known that the average territory of an animal consists of a system of fixed points which are interconnected in a characteristic way—by paths in land animals (Hediger 1942, 1950, 1961 etc.). As a rule the most important of these fixed points is the home, the place of optimal security, which so to speak represents the point of origin of the system of coordinates; at first the animal investigates the surrounding area slowly and cautiously until eventually it becomes the master of the territory.

In the most obvious cases the place which becomes of primary importance to the animal is an earth burrow or hole in a tree, a thicket, a crevice, a branch or something similar. This extremely simple characterization of the home as the most important fixed point of the whole spatial system inevitably shows up the absurdity of the spatial form of the cube which for centuries past has been the traditional offering which an animal can expect as its home in the zoo.

Anyone who sets out to build homes for animals should be quite clear that in the zoo the cube is the most unbiological and therefore the most inappropriate of all spatial forms. Unfortunately it is also the cheapest, the simplest and the most familiar to man, and therefore an obvious choice. Owing to the fact that for technical reasons human accommodation has been built on these lines, the same format was carried over without further thought and applied to accommodation for animals (aquaria, vivaria, bird cages, monkey cages, antelope paddocks, rhino dens etc.). In the process a monstrous humanization is involved, an unparalleled example of anthropomorphism, particularly when one bears in mind that completely flat surfaces at right angles to each other occur just as rarely in the wild as the straight line (with the notable exception of the spider's web).

The most inadequate home of all that can be offered to the animal is the corner of a cubical space in which three planes are joined together. Even this absolute minimum of a home is denied to the animal which is kept in an exposed cube that is open on all sides and constructed for instance out of fencing or bars. Where the cube only has bars at the front, then the two back corners furthest away from the public are favoured by animals that are not completely tame.

The bareness of the interior is often toned down by means of all kinds of internal fittings, such as straw, benches, climbing branches etc.; nevertheless one cannot deny that the cube represents the basic form of the cage for zoo and laboratory animals; frequently cages still look bare and comparatively unadulterated in form. Zoo biology's requirement of "away from the cube" (Hediger 1956, p. 17) therefore cannot be sufficiently stressed. The cube is a false starting point for zoo architecture.

Even humans do not feel comfortable in bare cubical rooms; they find them insufficiently cosy and then try to make them more "homely" by means of suitable fittings, subdivisions etc. During recent times the close relationship between man and his living space has been the subject of increasingly detailed study by architects (R. Neutra), anthropologists (E. T. Hall 1963) and psychiatrists (R. Sommer 1959). Newly acquired characteristics are not in any way involved in this but attention is focused on the original theoretical principles which have temporarily been displayed and buried by the overriding influences of technology. In more primitive animals these elementary requirements and spatial relationships are of much greater significance. In some cases indeed one can even identify the animal from the form of its home (e.g. hermit-crabs). The biologist recognizes the importance of these requirements and for this reason the zoo biologist pays serious attention to them when building. It is high time that building for animals freed itself from being guided along lines that are old-fashioned and anthropomorphic; it should be done according to the principles of zoo biology and the concept of the cube excluded.

In nature the territories are not homogenous but differentiated. Within each animal enclosure in the zoo the available space should be similarly arranged to allow for certain fixed points. Places for resting, feeding, bathing, grooming and defaecation can be of far greater importance to the well-being of the animals than a tenfold increase in the size of the ground area. Within certain limits the quality of the space is much more important than the overall size as I have repeatedly stressed (1950). A piece of timber to gnaw, a branch to mark, a couple of shovels of sand, a bath, suitable cover, adequate illumination etc. can make the difference between sterility and reproduction, indeed even between life and death.

In the zoo there should be room for all important fixed points. Cages and paddocks should no longer be cramped cells or abstract cubes, but ought to represent artificial territories with all the necessary fixed points characteristic of the species. The following principle of zoo biology is valid: the zoo animal behaves in its artificial territory as a free-living animal behaves in its natural territory. In order that the zoo animal can behave like this, everything that is important to it as a species must be at its disposal within the enclosure.

To illustrate the biological importance of fixed points let us take a place for bathing as an example. The question of whether a given enclosure ought to contain a bath cannot and should not be decided by the architect or landscape architect but the final decision should

197

be made by the biologist. If shoebills (*Balaeniceps rex*), capybaras (*Hydrochoerus capybara*) or hippopotamuses (*Hippopotamus amphibius*) are kept without water troughs—and I have seen this done even since 1950—it is not only wrong but inexcusable because a bath is one of the indispensable fixed points in the territory of these animals.

To deny beavers (*Castor*) the opportunity to bathe means, in some circumstances, certain death, because these animals can only defaecate in the water. If this opportunity is lacking, severe constipation may result leading to death. Here again methods of construction and causes of death are very closely linked.

Let us examine the territories of two closely related species of deer, such as the red deer (*Cervus elaphus*) and the roe deer (*Capreolus capreolus*), which in Switzerland for example occur in overlapping areas and habitats. In the territory of the red deer the mud bath or wallow plays a very important role, particularly during the breeding season. The deer take over a naturally boggy place and make a wallow by churning up the mud with the fore feet; in some places the wallow is used for generations. At definite times and after a certain ritual both sexes wallow in these strongly smelling pools of mud. The wallow should not be confused with an ordinary bath and there ought to be a suitable place for it in any paddock occupied by red deer. With the roe deer on the other hand a fixed point of this kind is completely unnecessary. In the natural territory of the roe deer there are no wallows as this species belongs among those that do not wallow. Fixed points in the territory can be just as constant as a specific character like, for example, the number of toes or the dental formula. Whether a deer should or should not have a wallow therefore does not lie within the choice of an individual or even of the architect, for it is compulsorily prescribed by the nature of the species.

Ignorance of such facts has been responsible for much of the bungling and errors committed in the past when buildings have been designed for animals in the zoo; unfortunately this is still the case today. Thus for example, some people regard a bathing place for elephants as a luxury—as though there could be such a thing as a luxury with animals! Luxury is a concept that is of itself anthropomorphic. Nowadays we know that elephants—both Indian and African—normally bathe every day, usually in the late afternoon. This is in fact a necessity for keeping their skin in good condition. It was for this reason that a bathe in the river before the evening feed was part of the daily programme of the Station de Domestication des Elephants, formerly in the Belgian Congo.

Elephants were kept for decades in some zoological gardens, as for example in Basel, without any chance of having a bathe, usually because it saved costs. In Zurich the elephants were only able to bathe in an unheated pool and therefore bathing was confined to the summer months. This state of affairs is unfortunately still in existence. Anyone who builds elephant enclosures today without facilities for daily bathing independent of the season is making a serious constructional error. In elephants which are unable to bathe regularly the skin soon loses the suppleness which is reminiscent of a good soft india-rubber; it becomes hard and scaly. Elephants have a delicate skin; the old-fashioned term Pachydermata (meaning thick-skins) is completely erroneous in this sense as well as in the psychological sense and it has not been used in zoology for a long time. The tail of an elephant in which the long tuft of bristles forms a special adornment in healthy specimens is also a fine indicator. The hairs on the tail are as thick as a pencil lead or a toothpick and in zoo elephants that are unable to bathe these beautiful hairs soon fall out; the tuftless, cracked and scabby tail then takes on the appearance of an old weatherbeaten ship's rope.

Other animals do not require to bathe regularly but they need fixed points for grooming the body. In rhinoceroses the grooming behaviour includes rubbing the horn—or the two horns—against a tree, for example, in order to sharpen them. All rhinoceroses in zoos have an unfortunate and typical habit of rubbing their horns in stereotyped movements against structures such as doors or cement walls; they often rub the horns completely away when their enclosure is not properly equipped, that is, where there are no tree stumps on which these massive animals can groom their horns properly. In Zurich Zoo we give the African black rhinos (*Diceros bicornis*) pine trunks for this purpose; these are periodically cemented into the paddock. Thanks to this cosmetic equipment their horns are then kept in very good condition, that is, they are long and pointed.

On the other hand animals with large pre-orbital glands such as antelopes for example need suitable twigs or branches, in order to be able to apply their marking secretion. It is a distressing sight for zoo biologists when antelopes in zoos are driven to using the iron bars of their enclosure for this purpose for want of anything more suitable, because to zoo biologists metal is a totally unbiological material. Anyone who builds for animals should bear this in mind.

Metal noises of all kinds, including mechanical sounds, have the effect of exciting and unsettling the animals, thus stimulating them to flight. Where there is any danger of this occurring, for example by the clanging of metal doors, care must be taken to service them regularly; particular attention should be paid to trap-doors, locks etc.

There are a great many details which could be discussed here but let us concentrate on the subject of bathing as one example of the problems which may arise. There are two ways of going astray on this subject: there can be either too little or too much bathing.

The provision of water as part of the enclosure for the European otter and its relatives has been allowed to get out of hand because of the special fascination to the human spectators of watching the movements of these animals in the water. For a long time it was the practice in European zoos at least to exhibit otters in the equivalent of a cement bath-tub with little or no area of dry land in the enclosure. This was bad management because it overlooked the well-known biological fact that otters spend the greater part of their lives under dry conditions on land; they only swim and dive in the water to catch fish, which make up a part of their diet. There is no doubt that this is the reason why the European otter (*Lutra lutra*) has never yet been bred in zoos, with the single exception of the London Zoo in 1864.

The stereotyped keeping of otters in more or less large cement baths, still in evidence today, is however an example of a far too conservative approach in the matter of building for animals in the zoo. In 1944 I pointed out that antelope houses were an example of the incredible way in which people hold on to a design—and a bad one at that—and that once launched a design is copied again and again. Other examples are the "castles" for owls which have been copied for at least a hundred years, the bear pit which is still being imitated as I have already mentioned several times, and the grotto style.

It would be worthy of an architectural dissertation to go into the subject of how the remarkable fashion arose in Europe of keeping certain animals in various showy looking imitations of antique temples and mosques. In the last century this peculiar style of zoo building, devoid of any biological or even religious attributes, amounted to a disease; a typical example was the elephant house built in 1891 in Basel, now fortunately demolished. At that time the two famous Basel biologists, Fritz and Paul Sarasin, personally donated the golden half-moon as the crowning glory of this mosque-like building constructed in the Moorish style.

During my period of office there (1944–1952) I received a protest that was perfectly understandable from an Indian Muslim against animals being kept in a mosque-like building. He could have found other buildings of this kind in many European Zoos at that time. His argument was that European Christians would probably not have appreciated it if animals in the Orient were kept in church buildings.

The remarkable idea of using imitation temples and mosques as animal houses in Europe is probably connected with the fact that exotic animals have a much greater exhibition value than endemic ones. Their exhibition value could evidently be further enhanced by keeping them in exotic buildings. If I am not mistaken this exotic style of building has not spread to the New World. Nowadays in general the objective style of functional building prevails in the New World; this is more in accordance with the requirements of zoo biology. In North America however the fairy-tale and Walt Disney approach can be seen now and again in the zoos there; this is a tendency which is scarcely conducive to the promotion of the biological approach in zoo architecture.

This book is concerned with basic principles rather than with recommending specifications for buildings or individual formulae for diets. In America it so happens that there are firms such as McFad-zean, Everly and Associates, Park and Recreation Planning, Winnetka, Illinois, from whom one can order ready-made zoos together with animals and director. In many cases this may meet the requirements of the situation completely because today zoos, parks and recreation centres are necessary and, as constituent parts of every city with a certain population, their requirements are to some extent standardized.

A zoo however should be much more than the required norm; its contribution to the city should reflect something that is of significance to the locality. Its site, historical connections and its function in the community should have the stamp of the individuality of the particular city. In my opinion therefore there can be no single blue-print for zoos. Each zoo must reflect the peculiarities of its city architecturally; its organization and the animals it keeps should all be considered in relation to the local situation, quite apart from the fact that climatic conditions must be taken into consideration. A zoo in central Europe must differ in several respects from one in Texas, Israel, South Africa, Pakistan or Australia. In principle even zoos that are close neighbours such as Rotterdam and Amsterdam, Basel and Zurich, or Frankfurt and Cologne, ought to show distinct differences from each other; this is because for one thing every visitor to the zoo from another city should be offered something new, some-thing different from the zoo of his own city. Every zoo like every city should have its individual image; in practice this is not always easy to achieve. In any case instead of trying to compete and outdo each other zoos ought to give more weight to the desirability of providing complementary institutions.

For example when a city such as Athens is ready to build another zoo—and in the long run it will not be able to desist from doing so—the whole conception should take into consideration the unique grandeur of the city. The site, the layout of its buildings and the organization of its animal stock should be prepared by a team of architects, zoologists, archaeologists and tourist experts etc. working in close collaboration. The aim should be to achieve a zoo that is unique in taste and style, appropriate to the history and landscape of the city.

In principle this should apply to every city, but for one with such important classical associations these considerations are overriding. An industrial city needs a zoo planned and organized in a different way; again, a city on the sea coast requires something different from a town in the hills. One should not aim at the average or standard but at uniqueness.

The erection of a new zoo by routine technical experts has the disadvantage that the peculiar significance of the zoo's relationship to the city concerned may be overlooked; nevertheless it has the advantage that the technical details such as perimeter fencing, drain-age, water supply, facilities for visitors (including lavatories, kiosks, parking places and restaurants) will be worked out properly and the

Fig. 123 An unprotected tree in the zebra paddock, completely barked with the result that it died.

Fig. 124 A completely barked tree, gnawed by zebras. For protecting trees one should use a solid ring of rounded poles, but no wire-netting.

Fig. 125 Wire fencing that is too loose and insufficiently secured may lead to all sorts of accidents. Wire fencing must be stretched taut in all directions.

Fig. 126 The Black Rhinoceroses (*Diceros bicornis*) in Zurich Zoo have relatively long and pointed horns.

Fig. 127 A fir-tree is mounted periodically in the paddock, from which they eat strips as thick as a man's finger and on which they can keep their horns in good shape.

Fig. 128 In some zoological gardens, where attention is not given to the layout of the enclosure from the biological viewpoint, the rhinos rub off their horns by stereotyped movements.

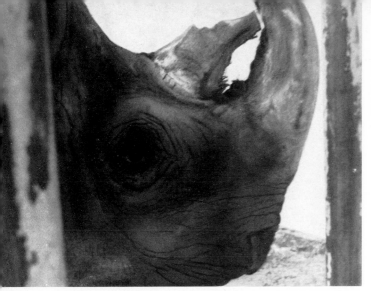

Fig. 129 Great Indian Rhonoceros (*Rhinoceros unicornis*) with horns completely worn down as the result of cramped living conditions.

Fig. 130 Black Rhinoceros (*Diceros bicornis*) with deformed horns, partly rubbed away and partly shortened artificially.

Fig. 131 Reclamation of natural grassland that is too soft and damp by spreading a layer of concrete rubble as a basis for a top layer of dry, hard marl.

Fig. 132 In zoos all protruding structures of horn and dentine—from zebra hooves and antelope horns to elephant and even walrus tusks—tend to become abnormally abraded or deformed when the necessary spatial or structural measures are not taken.

Fig. 133 Iron spikes in this form are reminiscent of the old-fashioned cages. They look ugly and are dangerous. In this case too an elephant suffered serious injuries on them.

Fig. 134 For Indian as for African Elephants an artificial termite mound offers a welcome opportunity to scratch (fixed point for grooming).

layout will be efficient. It so happens that some zoological gardens even today are founded on the initiative of idealists who have had no previous experience and to whom the basic principles of running a zoo are alien, such as representatives of the local building industry, of commerce and tourism, of schools and sport, of the press and finance houses.

It is understandable that people who have shown the necessary initiative and enthusiasm to work hard at collecting subscriptions, for the most part paltry sums, should find it rather painful to see their hard-won money spent on work which is invisible to the public— that is in "digging holes in the ground" for general drainage and water mains, foundations of paths, drainage of paddocks etc. There is a great temptation to use the money for cheap buildings and for the purchase of animals, from which the visitor "gets something". Savings are often made in the wrong place by amateurs. Cheap makeshifts frequently prove to be very costly in the long run.

After the Zurich Zoo had been in existence for about forty years we had to spend considerable sums of money on drainage that had been left out at the start, and also on electric and water mains. Until 1958 water supplies for several ungulate paddocks had to be taken by a hand-propelled water-cart. It is clear that this method took so much time that it did not allow for cleaning the water troughs. The perimeter fence was inadequate from the start and numerous holes soon developed; owing to the rusting of the material, repairs could eventually no longer be made effective. This led to numerous raids by foxes into the zoo which lies between the city boundary and the forest. In the 24 years from 1931 to 1954 the list of livestock which disappeared in this way included the following:

> 15 turkeys, mostly while incubating
> 21 peafowl, mostly while incubating
> 9 cranes of various species
> 8 flamingoes
> 2 screamers
> 21 geese of various species
> 3 black swans
> 1 black-necked swan
> 1 marabou stork

As a constructional item the type of perimeter fence is closely connected with the causes of death. In Zurich losses caused by foxes did not stop until the whole area was surrounded by a $7\frac{1}{2}$ feet high diagonal-mesh netting with an 18 inch wide overhang angled acutely towards the outside, set in a cement base 24 inches deep.

A fox which got into the Vincennes Zoo in 1955 caused considerable damage, as mentioned earlier.

Other zoos suffer losses from other kinds of animals. Thus in America coyotes and raccoons are often troublesome. In Miami Zoo the ponds for waterfowl are surrounded by a fence 3 feet high, surmounted by an electric cable which is switched on at night. Dogs and cats may also be dangerous to zoo animals. H. M. Wegeworth and N. Morgan (1953, p. 152 *et seq.*) report that dogs which ran along the ungulate paddock in San Diego Zoo, caused panic among the deer, which rushed against the fence and the trees and broke their necks. Some Airedales even climbed over the 7 foot fence and attacked the kangaroos. Feral cats are also a serious menace in San Diego—as in many other zoos.

Finally mention must be made of stereotyped building faults which could easily be avoided and that can be seen in almost every zoo.

We have already mentioned that the mixing of animal species which are susceptible to foot-and-mouth disease with those that are not is generally questionable in places where this devastating disease is a repeated threat. It would be more appropriate to accommodate susceptible species in such a way that they could be easily and unobtrusively isolated in the event of an outbreak. In any case this separation of species is recommended in Europe where practically every zoo may be threatened each year by foot-and-mouth disease. Naturally the proposed separation cannot be put into effect everywhere immediately. All new schemes however should bear this in mind from the start, because it helps to prevent disease and thus avoids shutting the zoo with a consequent total loss of gate money.

Sharp angles in the ground plan of cages and paddocks are among the stereotyped constructional faults that recur. Angles of less than a right angle are not permissible; obtuse angles (greater than 90 degrees) should be used everywhere if at all possible. In Chapter 9 (*Causes of death*) it was shown that a relatively large number of animals are killed in fights with members of other species or of their own. The more difficult it is for the animal to get away the easier it is for such fights to take place; in fact the chances of fleeing from aggressive animals are less in the relatively restricted space of a zoo than in the wild. Flight becomes that much more difficult the easier and quicker the pursued animal can be driven into a corner or blind alley. The more acute the angles of a paddock the more pronounced is the fatal blind alley situation. This applies from the lizards to the monkeys and also for those animals such as fish and birds which live in three dimensions. As the statistics show the pursuer can easily injure or kill the pursued when the latter runs headlong into a corner from which there is no chance of further flight. The greater the number of obtuse angles the greater is the chance of the pursued to escape from its pursuer.

It is natural for the flight from a dominant pursuer to extend to the boundaries of the cage or paddock, that is it follows along the length of the barrier. Often the pursuer standing in or near the centre can chase the victim along the periphery with a minimum expenditure of movement, so that the pursued animal is soon in a physiologically dangerous state of exhaustion, in addition to suffering from psychological stress. In many cases the headlong dash into a blind alley or into a sharp angle means certain death. Situations of this kind should be avoided by taking careful account of the social relationships of the inhabitants of the cage or paddock concerned, and also by making the enclosure as safe as possible from the constructional aspect.

The position of obstructions of all kinds is of the greatest importance in this context. Serious constructional faults include all supports which project inwards, e.g. paddock posts. Craftsmen and technicians have an understandable tendency to put the posts of a fence so that they face inwards, instead of fixing them on the outside. As we have already seen any form of inward projection can be dangerous and for this reason the zoo biologist ought never to tolerate an enclosure in which the supports face inwards; this also applies to the posts that support the wire-netting of the perimeter fence. From my own experience I know how extraordinarily difficult it can be to see that this requirement is observed in practice. On some points technical people and financiers think differently from zoo biologists. This does not mean that the former have no place in the zoo. They cannot be expected to know that frightful accidents sometimes take place when the experienced advice of the zoo biologists is disregarded or ridiculed. Where insight and goodwill are lacking, even the zoo biologist cannot always achieve his purpose if the official channels and the advice of real experts are not available to him.

To mention only one example: I will never forget the behaviour of a frightened nilgai which ran along so close to the fencing that it broke its jaw against the posts, which were wrongly positioned on the inside, and smashes its muzzle with the loss of several teeth. With the blood pouring from its face the antelope bumped against each post and in its panic-stricken state it was in fact no longer aware of these obstructions. From a rational point of view and in all decency anyone who is familiar with the many instances of this kind that occur must take all possible steps to ensure that the mounting of the enclosure supports is done on the outside of the fencing.

Nevertheless, the upright posts fixed inside an enclosure or even as oblique struts are not the only dangerous obstructions to frightened animals that run along the fencing; other fittings can be equally dangerous, such as hay-racks, food containers and drinking troughs. As already stressed in the chapter on *Food* all these items of equipment should be placed, not along the periphery, but well inside the enclosure; they should be far enough away from the fence at least to leave a sufficiently large gap between them and the fence so that when the animal is alarmed it can get by them quickly and easily.

The objection that food containers projecting inwards have been tried and tested for years without incident is not lasting proof of their safety. Untoward incidents can take an animal by surprise. One day some unforeseen circumstance may drive the animal into a panic, causing it to take fright and bump violently against the projecting food container, injuring itself badly and possibly suffering a fracture which in certain circumstances may be fatal.

Naturally it is sometimes easier and simpler to fill feeding troughs and water containers from the outside, directly through the perimeter fence; nevertheless such an arrangement is wrong from the viewpoint of zoo biology, even when the keeper is nervous of going into the paddock of the animal concerned. This leads us to another widespread failure to take zoo biology into account when planning enclosures: even in those climates in which the animals can be left out continuously in a single paddock, there should in every case be an inside den or even a small auxiliary paddock, into which the animal can be taken temporarily when the main paddock is out of commission for some reason or other (such as repairs, fallen trees etc). It is much simpler to isolate an animal in a small adjoining (and therefore familiar) den or paddock than to try to catch it up in a single large paddock that cannot be divided up. It also happens frequently that a certain animal has to be removed from a herd in order to give it more detailed investigation or medical treatment. With a den or a small side paddock that can be sealed off, the operation can be done much faster and with much less excitement, which is very important. Catching an animal in a large paddock entails driving it and incurring the risk of a broken neck, fractured skull or other serious injury. Even with the use of drugs accidents of this kind cannot be completely ruled out.

When the inner part cannot be completely sealed off from the outer area of the enclosure this always leads to tricky or even dangerous situations. There must be few zoos in which the original layout has not been subsequently altered by putting in ancillary dens or some kind of partitioning. It is much better to embody the appropriate partitions in the layout right from the start.

While writing the above (March 1964), three reports concerning the subdivision of enclosures came into my mind: in one case the security of a lying-in den for spectacled bear cubs proved to be inadequate. The father broke in and killed the three valuable young which were already well grown. Another case that occurred some years ago in Zurich Zoo concerned a male polar bear which got in to the female's den and killed the young. A simple bolt is often an inadequate form of fastening for a polar bear enclosure. There is no doubt that many zoos have had similar experiences.

The third report concerned a male giraffe which had not been properly separated from the calf and the latter was found dead in the morning.

When the anthropoid ape house was built at Zurich in 1959 experts tried to dissuade me from having separate sleeping dens on grounds of economy, arguing that these were not used in other zoos. Since this house has been in use, however, the sub-divisions built in the form of spacious sleeping dens have proved their value in various situations, e.g. in the removal of individual samples of urine and faeces, in the narcosis by injection of an unapproachable orang utan for X-ray examination, in separating young chimpanzees from their mothers. On one occasion a high-spirited youth jumped over the flower-bed towards the cage occupied by chimpanzees and shattered the pane of glass which he had not noticed, causing thousands of glass splinters to scatter into the cage. In this situation it was only necessary to draw back the slide of the sleeping den in order to bring the animals to safety. The young visitor suffered severe cuts and was taken to the first-aid station as quickly as possible.

Naturally it is important that these inner and auxiliary dens are familiar to the animals. They should therefore also be used as feeding or sleeping places, so that they attract the animals into them. Thus when there is any disturbance outside, the inner den is sought out by the animals as a place of security; the inner den in effect becomes the essence of the home. In designing paddocks architects are often inclined to allocate only one area for each animal species, particularly when the relevant climate or the hardiness of the animal species does not appear to make a house absolutely necessary. With this all too simple arrangement sooner or later one runs into trouble. It has been found again and again that subdivisions are necessary for various operations in a zoo: these include separation of the young or the removal of animals that are sick, aggressive or constantly getting the worst of fights, and for releasing newly arrived animals or removing others for transfer. It is much better that such areas should be allowed for at the planning stage than that they should be added afterwards. Suitable auxiliary enclosures in the form of transfer cages are an absolute necessity for venomous snakes and for bull elephants. Every keeper of venomous snakes should be able to move these dangerous animals from an outer exhibition cage into a side cage by simple manipulations, so that the empty display area can be cleaned quietly and without risk. With reference to elephants, in the August 1963 number of the monthly magazine *Das Tier* I recorded numerous examples of bulls having become suddenly dangerous after reaching sexual maturity; this nearly always happens without any warning— in fact it is the general rule—and fatalities occur among the keeper staff if the animals cannot be transferred into suitable transfer dens.

Only a few days after the publication of this article, a bull elephant claimed a further human victim in a German zoo.

It is important that elephants should become accustomed to being chained at night in a definite place in the den and that this should be done while they are still non-dangerous and relatively simple to handle; the need for this is closely linked with the problem of making a subsequently dangerous elephant secure. When possible the chaining-up of them every evening should become such a habit that they are disturbed by its omission and actively look for it. In view of the massive disparity in size and strength between elephant and man which exists in nature, one should not delay in taking the opportunity offered in the zoo of fixing the animal to one place; fixed points of this kind, for feeding and sleeping should serve as a method of preserving the more direct contact between man and elephant. The daily chaining of elephants should be continued until the animals show that they are ready for a more direct relationship. It is only possible to keep elephants in a state where they can be handled for any length of time after reaching maturity by having established the process of chaining-up as part of the daily routine and not, as formerly, as a method of forcing the animal to be obedient. This simple act of chaining is capable of being carried out with human strength and of becoming a deeply rooted habit over the years; if it is omitted in the early stages then I see no chance of man being able to subdue an excitable elephant in an emergency. It would be impossible to get an excitable elephant to tolerate the restriction of a chain in time if being chained were an unfamiliar experience to it instead of being accepted as part of a routine. Serious situations that are potentially full of danger can arise in this way.

It should be repeated as an axiom that a single enclosure is not feasible for the maintenance of large animals that are particularly easily excited and potentially dangerous; it is essential that these animals can be made to go into familiar adjoining enclosures or dens, where they can be shut in.

Double security is a further basic essential: the principle is that when building for zoos any animal that escapes should not find itself completely free; care should be taken to see that if it manages to get through an open door or a defective barrier it is then contained by a further enclosure.

In an organized zoo the final boundary, beyond which no animal should ever get as the result of some untoward incident, is the periphery fence or wall. Nevertheless the principle of double security should be carried out in each animal house. In houses for the big cats, for example, in which all the cage doors can be opened from the service passages, the latter should be capable of being sealed off with *solid* doors; in various zoos I have seen light wooden doors used for this purpose, of similar construction to those in a human house, and these do not meet the safety requirements of a zoo. Experience shows that an animal escapes now and again from nearly every big cat house. When this happens the animal should then be contained for example in the service passage or in the exhibition enclosure; with the animal's escape route blocked by suitable doors it cannot go any further and the public is not endangered. An escaped animal can be brought back much more easily from this inner area than when it has got right outside its own house or even out of the zoo.

Corresponding structural arrangements for monkeys, bears, ungulates, snakes etc. should be envisaged from the beginning. Providing they are thought of at the right time these security doors and other built-in methods of shutting off escape routes can usually be constructed very discreetly. In several zoos where I have had to install additional safety precautions, often after some serious accident had occurred, these were in places where people had made up their minds that such measures were apparently superfluous.

There has been and still is a great deal that is wrong in regard to the arrangement of enclosures from the viewpoint of zoo biology. In climates with cold winters it is common practice to keep certain animals in summer and winter quarters. In so far as these two types of enclosure are not immediately next door to each other, with access between them, this represents a serious fault in design according to modern views: when the summer and winter quarters are in separate places it is necessary to catch up the animals twice a year in order to transfer them. In the process the animals often become over-excited and serious losses may be associated with the move. Zurich Zoo and many other zoological gardens have had most unfortunate experiences of this kind.

It is true that nowadays the trauma occasioned by the move can be reduced to a certain extent by the use of tranquillizers. Nevertheless these methods involve serious disadvantages, above all on ecological grounds: the abrupt change between being shut in for a considerable part of the year in the winter quarters and then suddenly being subjected to the exposure of the summer quarters is totally unbiological. Furthermore with this system there is no chance of letting the animals out on mild and sunny days while they are occupying their winter quarters; instead, they have to remain inside in winter dens that are usually rather gloomy until the spring, even when the conditions outside would be much more suitable and healthy. In Zurich there are several of these widely separated quarters left over from the early days of the zoo but we are making an effort to reduce them.

As well as the technical aspect of moving an animal from one enclosure to another there is also a psychological aspect, which is usually underestimated. As in many other apparently simple manipulations, it is possible to do something wrong, which may even be fundamentally harmful. On the other hand one can sometimes learn a lot from watching skilled keepers, who understand the "art of moving house", when they are transferring animals from one place to another. This will be referred to again in the next chapter.

One of the common errors in construction is based on the idea that natural substrates are the best. This may be true in individual geographical areas with particularly favourable substrate conditions; paradoxically, the natural substrate in other areas is the worst and the most unhealthy type that one can think of. This applies for example to a meadow (grassy substrate) in central Europe. Trodden by rather heavy animals it will not only be trampled into an unsightly morass after a short while but it will also become dangerous because it cannot be cleaned; in this state it soon provides an immense reservoir for parasites. Ungulates on a soft substrate of this nature also develop bad hooves. In spite of this one repeatedly finds new enclosures of grassland simply surrounded by wire-netting, because the people responsible believe that they will get cheap and beautiful paddocks in this way. This kind of enclosure with grassy substrate is typical for example of big private animal parks. The illusion does not usually last long and in dry weather only a little longer.

I also found this type of enclosure in Zurich Zoo; the morass was deep and the parasites were at a high level. Then by happy chance truckloads of broken cement became available due to building work in the main street of Zurich; these truckloads consisted of material that was ideal for my "foundationless" paddocks. Several trucks clattered up the Zurichberg and the result was a cheap form of substrate sanitation. The broken cement, topped with a thin layer of marl, produced a hard, dry surface that was easy to clean.

It is only possible to keep heavy animals on grass when very large areas, the size of a big field, are available. In zoos, however, animals have to live in much more restricted areas and in much greater densities, thus making grassy substrates totally unsuitable. Such substrates, although natural, are therefore not recommended for the zoo.

There are however other building materials which should also be banned. Some of these have already been mentioned in Chapter 8. Staples should be prohibited on principle, because sooner or later they seem fated to be pulled or to fall out of the timber; once they become detached there are endless ways in which they can end up in the stomachs or feet of many animals. Nails are considerably more dangerous than screws and the smaller they are the more dangerous they are. Therefore only screws should be used, but the greatest care should also be taken with them and they should be protected if possible by lock-nuts.

Where something needs strengthening temporarily in paddocks or cages, wire-mesh ought not to be used as it provides a constant source of foreign bodies; a strongly secured cable, or if necessary a chain should be used.

In every piece of wire and wire-netting that is not neatly installed and faultlessly maintained there is a potential danger which could also prove lethal. As already mentioned it is wrong to use wire-netting to protect trees. As the girth of the tree increases this kind of mesh will either break with the strain or it may rust before this and present a dangerous source of foreign bodies.

The bad habit of fastening relatively solid wire-netting to the frames with disproportionately thin wire is difficult to eradicate. I have seen evidence of it in zoos all over the world. The logical outcome which can easily be foreseen is that the thin binding wire rusts long before the netting, so that gaps appear and the animals can get out. Also the rusty pieces break off the defective binding wire and remain inside the enclosure, giving rise to injuries of one form or another.

It is important that the netting should be neatly and firmly attached to the framework but it is equally important that long lengths of wire-netting fences should be carefully anchored and stretched taut. Slackness in a fence leads to accidents.

Nowadays the principle applies in zoos that iron bars and wire-netting should be used as sparingly as possible. This unbiological material really belongs to the past, particularly where it can be seen by the public; it is still necessary in the service areas. In any case no visitor should be expected to look through more than one mesh. At all costs one should avoid having one mesh in front of another, bars within netting or one cage inside another. Nevertheless one still encounters these constructional faults here and there.

Steel brushes, steel wool etc. are regarded as extremely dangerous; they should be prohibited everywhere except for use in the workshops. In animal enclosures they are capable of producing every conceivable kind of foreign body.

Also glass wool, fibreglass and similar insulating materials ought not to be allowed in the zoo. The reassuring arguments of architects, contractors and workmen are all too familiar to me. They say, for example, that these insulating materials will positively only be used in new buildings before the animals are housed in them and will then be completely covered up, thereby totally excluding all contact with the stock. However one must keep a watchful eye on the way the material is brought into the zoo, its storage and its subsequent use. In spite of this, after minor gales, I have found scraps of fibreglass the size of a man's fist as well as larger pieces in enclosures at a considerable distance from the building site, carried there by the wind. It is possible for veterinary pathologists to identify this fine material in the skin, eyes, mucous membranes, respiratory tract and digestive organs of the animals and to make a correct diagnosis, even though cases of dermatitis amongst the workmen, due to the same cause, are not always easy to establish.

It should be obvious, or so one would think, that as strict precautions should be taken against the use of poisonous pigments, paints, varnishes, mastics, impregnating materials as against the presence of poisonous plants (yew, *Thuja* and others).

To some extent the rules which apply to the building of homes for animals are different from those that apply to human habitations. This needs clarifying. Some insulating materials that are suitable for human houses are totally unsuitable for animal houses. Nevertheless among the older zoos I have scarcely met one in which the hot-water pipes were not lagged with kapok, wadding or some other soft fibrous material. This is just what mice enjoy. These ubiquitous rodents suffer no shortage of food in a zoo but warm, soft fibrous material for their nests is just as important to them. The insulation materials mentioned are among the most effective in attracting mice. If the insulation is not properly protected with mouse-resistant material, which the experts do not usually like doing, the material is quickly stripped as a rule. Sometimes the mice organize a regular shuttle service, in order to carry the fine nest material to where it can be used in what appears to be the most suitable place to them. As a result the pipes soon become bare and they take on a supplementary function: they serve the mice as traffic routes. As the mice run along the pipes they spray urine on them and this corrodes them at an astonishingly fast rate. This is referred to again in Chapter 12.

On the special subject of work done by heating engineers in zoos it is worth mentioning one more example of the way in which these specialists operate, which is much the same in whatever country the zoo happens to be situated. They treat zoo buildings as though they were to be occupied by humans rather than animals and unwittingly demonstrate a sympathetic understanding of the biological needs of mice by installing central heating radiators so close to the walls that the mice are able to build wonderful nests in the intervening space with a few pieces of paper, straw (and insulating material). At the same time the radiators serve as ideal camouflage.

It is only after considerable trouble that I have sometimes been able to persuade a heating engineer to shift a radiator from the position in which it had been installed to a more suitable one, for example in bird cages it needs to be so far from the wall that there is no room for either the mice or their nests. Four inches may make all the difference and reduce the general plague of mice. A radiator that stands away from the wall is also much more inviting to a broom because sweeping is easier.

Cavities or awkward corners that are difficult or even impossible

214

to get at must in general be classed as faults in design. They serve as collecting places for vermin and hiding-places for small animals that have escaped, including snakes. There are only two ways of dealing with such cavities: they must either be easily and conveniently accessible by means of suitable openings for checking and cleaning or they must be so thoroughly bricked up that neither mice nor insects can get into them. I will spare the reader a description of what has faced me in various zoos on opening such cavities, in the way of stinking provisions, mummified animals and live vermin.

Just as with other sections in this book it is not possible to include all the typical constructional faults that one finds in zoos. Unfortunately the few hints and suggestions mentioned must serve as an indication of the size of the problem.

Buildings for animals are often constructed of a strength suitable for humans or a little stronger, with the result that they are still not sufficiently strong to contain wild animals. Descriptions by the zoologists on the weight and powerfulness of wild animals, the strength of their jaws and claws, their endurance and persistence in destroying fittings are inclined to be regarded as exaggerated by the building experts. When in fact the material first used has proved to be too weak, then something more solid is put in, but as a rule this is still of insufficient strength. This leads to yet more repairs. The damaged metal-plate is replaced by a somewhat thicker one, the bent angle-iron by a more resistant one and so on. The quality recommended by the zoologists however is seldom accepted with alacrity at the first attempt, because to the uninitiated it appears excessive. Thus the strength of the materials is gradually increased and often the rise in costs is rapid.

Another persistent fault in zoo building is the mixing or crossing of service and exhibition areas. Like machines that are necessary, other technical installations should generally be as discreetly installed as possible, that is out of sight of the visitor who should enjoy beautiful views of habitats and should not see cleaning apparatus, remains of food, dustbins, brooms, brushes, dung etc. Another reason why the division between service and exhibition areas should be as sharp as possible is on grounds of security.

Nevertheless there are exceptions. In certain circumstances a scrupulously clean, properly designed kitchen for the anthropoid apes, say, has great exhibition value for the public; equally a fault-lessly maintained engine-room, with pumps and filters, in a large aquarium can be of interest. There is no reason why the public should not be given views of appropriate service areas through proper windows. It is usually found that the visitors are interested in practically everything that goes on "behind the scenes".

Some zoo directors install such show windows not only for the benefit of the visitors, but also for what amount to educational purposes. They assume that the model kitchens and technical instal-lations exposed to the public view will be maintained by the staff with enthusiasm and kept in a state of model cleanliness.

There is indeed no doubt that certain forms of presentation encourage keepers to meet the public half-way as they enjoy the role of being the expert in charge. Generally speaking a proper pro-fessional pride is desirable and legitimate. In this context however it should be kept within reasonable bounds; it can encourage an exaggerated form of showmanship in which the keeper neglects the apparatus that is out of sight in his service area.

A final example of stereotyped constructional fault must be mentioned briefly here: most animal houses are not built from the outset to be rat- and mouse-proof, and this subsequently entails much trouble and expense. This subject however is dealt with in Chapter 12.

Finally I would like to make four points which summarize the position regarding building for animals: 1. animal buildings should be designed with greater reference to the characteristics of the various types of territory instead of as variations on the cube. 2. Iron bars and wire-netting should be avoided as far as possible; similarly the bad smells associated with the old types of animal house should be banished and a luxuriant supply of living vegetation is desirable. 3. The sterile imitation of existing structures should give way to new ideas and methods in zoo architecture; restrained by the principles of zoo biology, new ideas and bold fantasies of the greatest possible scope should be encouraged. 4. One should build elegantly and in good taste and in accordance with biological principles (cf. Jean Delacour 1961, p. 107).

I I
The Art of Transferring Animals

A whole book could be written on this subject because the transfer of an animal from one place to another involves far more than meets the eye. The moment when the animal makes its entrance into its new living quarters is as full of drama as a first night at the theatre and a new world can be opened up for both animal and the observer.

People with old-fashioned ideas, who regard an animal simply as an item of merchandise, have no conception of what is involved. Unfortunately the present procedure for dealing with new arrivals destined for the zoo is still somewhat rough and ready in a number of places. This is approximately what happens: the transport cage is treated like any other kind of box and lifted with or without care out of the aeroplane or railway wagon and loaded on to a lorry. It is then driven to the zoo where it is unloaded to the accompaniment of all kinds of noises. The transport cage is positioned in front of the new cage or paddock in such a way that the doors are approximately opposite each other; the rules are that in the case of a large and powerful animal the transport cage has to be firmly secured with rope to the new cage so that the newly arrived animal has no chance to escape through a crack. Even if people are aware of these instructions they are not always willing to observe them and I could recount many stories of accidents that have been due to inadequate care at this stage. After this the sliding door of the new cage is then raised, followed by the equivalent slide in the transport cage; finally, accompanied by vocal encouragement the newly arrived animal is ready to step into the new, unfamiliar surroundings; this should take place with as little delay as possible.

According to the species and the previous history of the individual animal one of two things may then take place. In some cases the animal bolts out of the transport cage without more ado and tears around the new enclosure, rushing excitedly from one corner to the other, possibly jumping up to the roof and down again, and even falling against feeding and drinking troughs positioned on the periphery. The animal may injure itself in the process or, if there is no disaster it gradually quietens down. It is a good sign and therefore a great relief when the animal starts to take food and water without undue delay.

Other animals however "cling" to the transport cage and refuse to leave it in spite of all efforts at calling it out; this severely tries the patience of the men, particularly if it should be time for a meal break or to knock off work. Sooner or later someone starts knocking on the back wall of the transport cage in order to make the animal "get a move on". If this noisy encouragement does not work someone tries to force the obstinate animal to come out with the aid of an iron bar or a broom handle. Shaking and tilting the cage are also favourite methods providing such manœuvres are practicable.

This is roughly what happened in the early days of my zoo career, and I had a lot of trouble getting this problem dealt with from the approach of zoo biology or animal protection, the two aims being largely identical. To unload the animal as though it were an inanimate object and thrust it into new surroundings is not only unseemly for the animal but above all it is wrong on the grounds of zoo biology. Unfamiliar places make animals thoroughly uneasy; this also applies to children and to quite a few adults. A situation of this kind therefore should arouse our sympathy.

It is fundamentally wrong to use any kind of force in such circumstances. By using force the result achieved is precisely the opposite of what one is striving for, namely a transfer that takes place as quietly and smoothly as possible. Two rules of animal psychology are involved in this which although commonplace are nevertheless insufficiently recognized. When an animal is pushed from behind, it endeavours to resist moving forwards and braces itself to resist the pressure from behind. When it is pulled from in front, however, it

Fig. 135 The Salk cage for chimpanzees, about the size of a wardrobe. It is obvious from the economy of space that one cannot expect normal behaviour to take place.

Fig. 136 A habitat enclosure as a contrast to the laboratory cage or pit type of den. This gives a living impression of tropical jungle to the visitor and provides a quasi-natural territory for the animals. (West Berlin Zoo.)

Fig. 137 The long rows of tethered parrots once seen in many zoos are now disappearing. The public no longer wishes to see chained animals.

Fig. 138 Giant aviaries of this type are more suitable for tropical and subtropical areas where there are no falls of snow in the winter and the birds can be left out all the time.

Fig. 139 Care must be taken in designing a Polar Bear pool. The animal shown here jumped up against the back wall to a height of 115 inches without pushing off from the bottom. The line of the normal water level is clearly visible half way up the back wall; the bottom of the grill in the background is at a height of 120 inches.

Fig. 140 Although regarded as typically plantigrade—walking on their soles—most species of bear like to climb.

Fig. 141   Re-building of a deep, water-filled barrier ditch in which a valuable Gorilla drowned. The anthropoid apes are not born with the ability to swim, any more than a human is.

Fig. 142   A cage door torn by bears and repeatedly repaired. This is one of the common constructional errors, of using material that is not strong enough, even when strengthening has to be done.

Fig. 143 A blackbuck (*Antilope cervicapra*) marking. A few twigs and branches can be of great importance to such animals (Photo Jurg Klages).

Fig. 144 Stump of wood in a Blackbuck paddock with the secretion from the pre-orbital gland and a few hairs.

also resists and throws its weight backwards. The classical example of this is the "obstinate mule", whose behaviour if the truth were but known was actually caused by the incompetence of uncomprehending man. The alleged proverbial stupidity of the mule does not correspond in any way with modern research in animal psychology; it is much more a matter of the obstinacy of man, who—in biological matters—in some respects is still tied to the mentality of the Middle Ages. A voluminous book could be written about this by people who work in zoos.

Let us stick to the facts or treat them from the biological angle—which often amounts to the same thing. I would recommend a simple, completely painless experiment with the classical laboratory animal, the white rat which is said to be the best investigated living creature after man on our planet. If a laboratory rat is placed on a board with a surface that is not too smooth and the board tilted slowly first to one side and then the other, the rat is seen to resist the tilting with astonishing regularity. If we tilt the board obliquely downwards, the rat shows a distinct backwards thrust; if we tilt it upwards, the rat likewise strives not to slide down and therefore climbs further upwards.

If we now place the rat on a horizontal table and then pull it by the tail, it will show a forward thrust. But if we push it gently forwards at the base of the tail then it will put on the brakes as much as it can.

I am probably the last person to claim that generalizations should automatically be made, based on the findings in one animal—as so often happens—and that the results of the rat experiments should be applied directly to all other mammals. The behaviour described however appears to be a reaction that has a wide application in the animal kingdom—and perhaps not only in the animal kingdom. At all events this conjecture has been confirmed in a striking manner in the course of a zoo career lasting decades, which has brought me into contact with a great variety of animals.

The trauma of a necessary change of locale should not be made worse by the addition of unnecessary disturbances as is often unfortunately the case in zoos, particularly when the new arrival happens to be a "star" attraction. There are newspaper men and regrettably also zoo people who set great store on getting a photograph of the animal actually setting foot in its new surroundings. At the precise moment that the animal is forced to leave the relative intimacy of the transport cage a flash is let off in its face; there could be no worse moment to do this to an animal as it steps over the threshold, not only into new living quarters, but often into what is virtually a new world. The tenseness of the situation may be dangerously heightened by such alarming incidents. There are many cases in which delicate animals have been injured immediately on arrival or as they have dashed against the walls or the roof in panic-stricken flight.

One of my colleagues who had to fly the Atlantic in charge of a young elephant was harassed by press photographers on landing. The young elephant was already suffering from severe diarrhoea as a result of the excitement of the journey but the journalists demanded that it should be taken out of the transport cage so that they could photograph it on the spot. The man responsible for the frightened animal finally decided that there was only one way of keeping the photographers at bay: before they realized what he was doing he quickly smeared a little of the liquid elephant faeces on to the lens of the most importunate photographer. It was only then that the animal was left in peace.

It is obvious that reporters, press photographers and film cameramen etc. are of the greatest importance to zoos and that every possible assistance should be given to them; I even flatter myself that I might receive a reasonably good testimonial in this respect. It is both pleasant and fruitful to cooperate with those members of the press who have become familiar with the problems of zoos due to repeated contacts; such people understand why photographs should not be taken in certain circumstances, e.g. in the case of a tricky transfer or a difficult birth. They know that decisions of this kind are based solely on consideration for the animal and they understand that in every proper zoo the following axiom applies: the living animal is a thousand times more valuable than the best picture of it.

In any case the animal emerging from the transport cage is certainly not of greater interest than say its initial exploration of the new quarters, the taking of food for the first time or the first contacts it makes with the new keeper.

In certain circumstances the actual transfer from the transport cage into the new accommodation requires great patience, as has already been mentioned. Animals are accustomed to having plenty of time and excitement is anathema to zoo animals. The only correct method therefore is to spare the animal as much excitement as possible and to give it plenty of time to step out of the cage; it should even be given the opportunity to go back again into the transport cage, as a temporary measure when the individual animal feels more secure there. It is less likely to do this if the home that we have prepared for it in the new quarters is sufficiently attractive. On taking an animal into a man-made territory our primary duty is to provide it with a suitable home—that is a place which represents the fixed points that are of the greatest importance.

Transfer is a very wide term. By it we always mean a deliberate and organized change from one set of quarters to another. Hitherto it was mainly a question of transfer from the transport accommodation into unfamiliar quarters. The transport of zoo animals is obviously a specialized subject on its own. Here too, as in other fields of zoo biology, there is a lot of bungling and unfortunately fraudulence also occurs. Zoos are frequently called in to deal with the security of wild animals in transit; the animals may be in the process of escaping from their transport containers, or they may already have vanished into the cargo holds of aircraft or behind freight in railway wagons. I could mention incidents of this kind involving bears, snakes, pumas, monkeys and many others.

There are only two other points which should be made on this subject. First, every zoo worthy of the designation devotes the greatest care not only to incoming animals but also to outgoing ones; care is taken to ensure that the animal in transit is looked after in the best possible way and that every precaution is taken to prevent any possibility of escape. Incidents involving the escape of animals while in transit are usually caused by inexperienced and irresponsible management; occasionally they are due to animal lovers and often to so-called animal dealers who have just made the discovery that trading in animals can be commercially profitable. It has been our experience that animals from such sources are extremely carelessly and inappropriately crated. Nobody is particularly pleased to be suddenly confronted with a leopard on the deck of a ship, a tiger walking through a railway compartment or giant snakes crawling about under the passengers' seats in an aeroplane. Even though such incidents are caused through negligence, they often lead to complicated regulations or a refusal to accept live animals for transport, creating difficulties for the more reputable undertakings.

The second point which needs clarifying is concerned with careless and irresponsible packaging, in which deliberate fraud is involved by the insurance of freight. This was practised for a time by unscrupulous dealers in some countries. These people packed an excessive number of animals into unsuitable boxes, insured the consignment and dispatched them, without any regard for whether the animals would survive the journey alive or not. Such a consideration was irrelevlant in that the business deal had already been assured with the comp etion of the insurance.

Some of the worst jobs we have ever had to undertake in Zurich Zoo have been concerned with sorting out consignments in transit, e.g. from South America. From layers of dead and dying monkeys we had to extract the few survivors and look after them before re-shipping them. To quote only one example: in September 1956 we had the job of opening up a macabre consignment of this kind in transit from Brazil. Out of 138 marmosets crammed into one box 110 were dead! It is at moments such as this that one wishes some of the "animal lovers" could be present, so that they could realize that by creating a demand for the purchase of these "charming little monkeys"—which are quite unsuitable for keeping in private houses—they are encouraging their importation and consequently contributing to the horror of mass destruction. The zoos naturally do everything they can to put an end to the practices of unscrupulous dealers.

Having discussed the behaviour of an animal on leaving the transport cage, let us now look at the other side of the picture and consider the behaviour of the animal as it leaves the familiar living quarters and enters the transport cage. Once again it should be stressed that enormous differences may occur according to the species and the former history of the individual animal. Only a few of the many possible reactions can be given here. For circus animals, which are continuously on the move, the entry into the transport truck eventually becomes a matter of everyday routine.

The large cats in the zoo, such as lions and tigers, can be accustomed to changing from one cage to another and this may amount to what is virtually an automatic procedure. These animals have to be shifted daily so that cleaning operations can be carried out; they are also used to being encouraged to move from one side of the cage to another, to being let out into another half of the compartment for feeding, and so on; they may be shifted around several times a day as a matter of routine from one cage into the neighbouring cage. To start with this is naturally a lengthy process with a big cat but the time soon comes when the animal gets up as soon as it notices the raising of the sliding door in its immediate neighbourhood and it will walk through the opening without waiting to be summoned.

This routine behaviour may become so automatic that it is sometimes possible to get an animal to enter a narrow transport box in the neatest possible manner. For this purpose the transport container must be placed at the right time, preferably some days beforehand, as discreetly as possible in the neighbouring cage with its door open in front of the connecting slide. If the normal daily routine is followed strictly according to every detail and the slide of the cage is raised at the critical moment, it can happen that the unsuspecting big cat will march straight through the hatch into the transport cage; the animal is preoccupied and is not aware of its mistake in time before the slide of the transport cage is lowered behind it. This may not sound quite fair to the animal but it is nevertheless justified because, although the animal finds itself inadvertently being transferred, the process is carried out with the absolute minimum of fuss. By adopting these methods a great deal of shouting is avoided and there is no need to use threats such as jets of water or any form of the other paraphernalia which still accompany such manœuvres in some places today. It is interesting to note that we have occasionally been able to use this element of surprise in carrying out the transfer of animals that are much more alert than the big cats, such as with some of the ungulates. Nowadays in such situations—as already stressed several times—the use of tranquillizers is indicated.

It is obvious that deceptions such as I have just described cannot be repeated or at least not very often; animals have an astonishingly good memory about experiences involving deception. This applies particularly to polar bears which do not like being locked up and are therefore especially cautious and indeed positively suspicious. I have already described their behaviour earlier (1961, p. 239) with text and illustrations.

In Zurich Zoo there was a long-established tradition of leaving the polar bears out for the whole week in their spacious open-air enclosure, where there is a large pool, and only shutting them up into the relatively restricted inner den for cleaning operations. I only became aware of this recently and it should have been stopped a long time ago. Initially the bears were enticed into the inner den with meat and the sliding door was then closed behind them as soon as they were inside. The restricted quarters of the inner den however did not suit them and it became increasingly difficult to entice them in with food. At first the keeper avoided showing himself by leaving the slide down and moving discreetly to one side; he then operated the slide from his hiding-place by means of a length of rope attached to the chain. The suspicious polar bears however soon became aware of what was invisible and preferred to renounce the alluring pieces of fat and meat rather than allow themselves to be cooped up. When I took over the Zurich Zoo in 1954, I found that the inner den of the polar bears had a highly sophisticated piece of apparatus welded on to the bars, which resembled a gigantic mousetrap: there was a strong hook attached to the outer side of the iron bars on which a large piece of meat could be suspended. After the polar bears had made sure that the keeper was not lurking in the hiding-place but had actually gone away, the hungry bears then went into the inner den and pulled the enticing piece of meat towards them; in doing so they released the catch of the slide which operated on the principle of a mousetrap, and this fell down behind them with a frightening clatter.

This ingenious gadget worked splendidly—but unfortunately on one occasion only. The shock of the descending slide frightened the polar bears to such an extent that until the pool was completely choked with mud, they preferred to go short of food rather than face the trap again. Although the gadget was designed as a trap, it turned out to be snare and delusion from the animal psychological angle and it was useless for the polar bears.

Familiarization plays a leading role in transfer techniques as it does in all other matters relating to living space. The change from one space to another can become a matter of routine, even automatic, but it can also lead to a fixation; for example a passage that is used only in one direction cannot be enforced in the reverse direction. This appears to occur particularly frequently in giraffes. While I was in Basel I knew a giraffe that for years left the main enclosure by a high door without any fuss, but there was no way of persuading it to come back the same way. It could only be brought back into the main enclosure by taking another route through a different door. Similar observations have been made on giraffes in other zoos.

As well as the positive familiarization of leaving one place for another as soon as the trap door is raised, and the unilateral fixation of only using a door in one direction, there is also the negative familiarization of never leaving an enclosure. In 1933 there was a black leopard in Zurich Zoo which could never be made to enter the outer cage. While cleaning operations were undertaken it could be moved with difficulty into an inner cage nearby. Later on it broke out of the inner cage and was finally killed several weeks later some miles from the Zoo (Hediger 1950, p. 64 *et seq.*). Gerald Iles (1960, p. 98) has written of his tigress Bella, which refused to leave its cage in Belle Vue Zoo, Manchester, at any time from the time of its arrival until its death seven years later.

If a newly arrived animal is allowed sufficient time and not disturbed in any way as it actually steps into its new living quarters— as is only right and proper—it is possible to observe a highly interesting phenomenon: the exploratory or investigatory behaviour. This has only recently been noted from the scientific aspect although it takes place almost daily in every zoo. Interest has been shown in this behaviour primarily because it is seen as an early form, simple but analogous to the way in which modern man carries out research. Expressed in very broad terms the rat snuffling about in a new cage is seen as following the same biological urge as the electron microscopist who wants to delve into the increasingly fine structure of matter; similarly the astronauts and other pioneers of the space age are beginning to find their way around in space.

Nowadays one can scarcely open a new book on behaviour research or animal psychology without coming across discussions of this exploratory behaviour of animals (e.g. J. P. Scott 1958; W. H. Thorpe 1956). In the meantime this type of behaviour, which many people have suddenly found so exciting, can be observed without the aid of white rats or laboratories; to see it at its best, with any number of variations, one has only to watch carefully while transfers are taking place in the zoo.

During exploratory behaviour it is primarily the sense of sight or smell, taste or hearing that is used, according to the species of animal; it is probable that other senses are also involved, about which we still know very little, such as ultrasonics, sensitivity to temperature or to magnetic forces, the use of electric organs to determine distances etc. It becomes clear to us that the animals live in a different sensory world and therefore in quite another environment in the sense of von Uexküll; in any event their world is different because large animals such as bison or leopard can pass by each other "blindly", without taking any notice of each other, primarily because it is not their visual appearance that is important but their smell or the traces of their smell. It is the living area which must be explored first; the possible inhabitants are only of secondary interest. In some animals it is obviously the sense of taste which is of the greatest importance, in others it is the sense of hearing and so on.

Nearly every species has its own methods of exploration. To quote just a few that do it in special ways: electric catfish, raven, python, Capuchin monkey, rhinoceros, etc. Bearing in mind the fact that every small zoo accommodates hundreds of species—Zurich Zoo for instance has 350—and that exploratory behaviour can vary as between the species, this is yet another huge specialized subject which is best left to be dealt with in a book on its own.

In concentrating on the moment when the animal enters its new surroundings we are still dealing only with the most elementary phase of the transfer. Attracted by being presented with a cage or paddock that has all the fixed points and in ideal circumstances corresponds with its natural territory, the newly arrived animal slowly steps out of the transport cage; watched patiently at a discreet distance by an understanding keeper whose presence may even have a quietening influence, the animal then starts to explore the enclosure in the manner typical of the species. It no longer returns to the transport cage, even though the latter has acquired a certain degree of familiarity, because the new accommodation offers certain attractions: the food is enticing, the substrate pleasant, the lighting adequate and the appropriate dimensions make it a much more attractive place in which to live and feel safe than the narrow

Fig. 145 In front of the Chimpanzee cage the children have the same kinds of climbing equipment available (Zurich Zoo).

Fig. 146 Tough chrome-steel mesh, notched, electrically welded and individually stretched, replaces a heavy steel grill and interrupts the view to a far less degree.

Fig. 147 Where a glass barrier is necessary on grounds of hygiene, as for example with anthropoid apes, care must be taken in arranging the sources of light in order to avoid disturbing reflections.

Fig. 148 An antelope with severely deformed hooves as a result of the ground being too soft and an insufficiently active way of life.

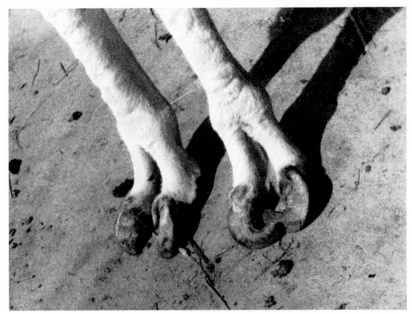

Fig. 149 Excessive growth of the hooves in a Llama kept on a substrate that was too soft.

Fig. 150 Mountain Zebra with extreme growth of hooves, which is painful to the animal. This is the result of keeping it on a substrate that is too soft, or of too little exercise. Both factors often affect each other.

Fig. 151   Some zoo visitors find it embarrassing to see themselves in a cage labelled for a species of monkey or ape, due to the failure to avoid the mirror effect of the glass when the cage was constructed.

Fig. 152   Open aviaries without glass or netting, as first built in St Louis (Missouri) and Philadelphia, and subsequently in Europe (1954), are very much in keeping with the requirements of the present-day zoo visitor and for this reason they will soon be found in every zoo.

transport cage. The doors of the latter are now shut and fastened as carefully and noiselessly as possible before being removed altogether; it is then thoroughly cleansed and stored away in a proper manner.

I will not go into all the possible deviations from the ideal situation here but a single example selected at random from the professional literature will serve to show that results can be less successful. In his annual report for 1961 R. N. T.-W. Fiennes (p. 33), then Pathologist at the London Zoo, mentions the death of two adult Bennett's wallabies, of which the first had lived there for almost two years, the second for over seven years. Both died of shock as a result of the fright experienced during the move into another enclosure. Post-mortem examination confirmed all the typical changes characteristic of death from shock, and the author adds that this cause of death is in no way unusual in wallabies.

For my own part I can add that cases of death of this kind are by no means restricted to wallabies, nor are they in any way confined to the London Zoo.

There are many other instances which could be cited, such as the following from the annual report of H. L. Ratcliffe (1950, p. 10) which is full of information. It records the death of three Canadian otters (*Lutra canadensis*), three minks (*Mustela vison*) and a raccoon (*Procyon lotor*) all of which died while being moved from one cage to another. None of these animals was in any way injured. Ratcliffe adds that within the previous two years four other animals dropped dead when repairs were being carried out in neighbouring cages in the big cat house. These were a lynx (*Felis lynx*), a caracal (*Felis caracal*), a serval (*Felis serval*) and a cheetah (*Acinonyx jubatus*). All these animals were excessively fat. In addition to the change in the immediate environment, it is implied that obesity caused by overfeeding may have been a contributory cause. The result of the post-mortem must have come as something of a shock, since Ratcliffe had introduced the highly praised reformed diet into his zoo about 15 years previously.

So far we have dealt only with the relatively simple case of transferring an animal into a new place that is unoccupied. To introduce an animal into an enclosure that is already occupied by other animals however, is a much more complex matter. The risks attached to this operation are significantly greater. H. L. Ratcliffe (1950, p. 8) has reduced some of the things which can happen under such circumstances to a refreshingly simple formula: "Introductions of new specimens into an established exhibit is always an invitation to disaster unless the space is unusually large. If the new specimen is larger than the others, all of them are terrified. If it be smaller, it is certain to be attacked. If, in the exhibit, there be others of the same species and sex, the newcomer is also certain to be attacked. It seems best to add to an exhibit only after all specimens have been removed from the space and kept separated for a time. Then new and old specimens may be introduced into the area with some expectation of success."

The prospects therefore are never hopeful. The truth of the matter is that transfers of this nature provide one of the main sources of "death due to behaviour", and it is imperative that progress should be made in zoo biology so that these fatalities no longer take place. Ratcliffe's concise statement contains the traditional rule-of-thumb procedure of the zoo man, which is to put a new group of animals with an old one, specially caught up for this purpose, into an enclosure that is unfamiliar to all of them. The basic biological idea behind this practice is to give every individual an equal chance when they take possession of the new enclosure. It is worth mentioning perhaps that this is not a simple matter and cannot always be carried out.

The basic principle is undoubtedly correct, nevertheless the idea originates from the time when the risky business of catching up animals was considerably over-simplified and social factors, theories of territory and so on were seriously underestimated. The link binding the animal to its familiar quarters is not severed by removing the animal for a short period. The correct formula therefore would be to put all the animals out together, into an area that is unfamiliar to each one of them, and to leave them there. Bearing in mind that one of the cardinal rules of the zoo is that no empty cages or enclosures are to be visible, it is a little difficult to find a zoo that has sufficient space to do this.

The professional literature mentions the attachment of the animal to its accustomed quarters but the strength of these ties and the remarkably good memory that an animal has for a particular locality was brought home to me vividly while I was at Bern Zoo. In the autumn the storks, cranes, herons, and flamingoes etc. were caught up and transferred to their winter quarters; after spending at least six months there, they were brought back again in the spring and released in the spacious paddock. They immediately took up their familiar positions again. By contrast, the birds which had been acquired during the winter season failed at first to show any kind of orientation after they were released. Admittedly this is not surprising when one thinks of the behaviour of migratory birds—nevertheless it was an impressive sight.

The inmates of a cage or enclosure develop ties of one kind or another, whether these are strictly territorial or simply individual preferences for certain areas, and it is not possible to break these ties by short-term evacuation of the enclosure. According to an elementary principle of zoo biology (Hediger 1942, 1950) familiarity with surroundings stimulates; unfamiliarity depresses. Thus not much is usually gained by catching up the resident individuals for the benefit of the newcomers and in certain circumstances the general level of excitement is only increased by this measure.

The social structure of the group may be as important as the subjective dividing up of the available space within a given area. The introduction of rivals (members of the same sex and the same species) in the majority of cases must be regarded as hopeless, and therefore to be avoided. There is no sense in endangering the harmony and the life of an existing population by adding a male monkey, for instance, just because someone has made a gift to the zoo. To accept the new arrival might in fact be irresponsible. It is not safe however to make generalizations. New World monkeys for example are much more tolerant than Old World monkeys and woolly monkeys behave in an exemplary manner in this respect.

An animal community in the zoo is by no means rigid in its social structure but often shows a considerable degree of flexibility. The human keeper as the top or Super-Alpha animal can often exercise an astonishing amount of control by interfering and taking positive action. This has already been demonstrated by the famous ornithologist O. Heinroth (1941, p. 8). He even managed to keep order among doves, wrongly regarded as symbols of peace, by administering suitable blows on the rump: "it is usually necessary for man to take a hand if the best use of the dovecote is to be achieved; he waits for the birds to start squabbling over nest-sites, then seizes the unauthorized intruder and gives it a good beating before thrusting it back on to its own ledge. If this is repeated a couple of times, one has established a regular pattern of behaviour, because the punished dove evidently senses that the insult would be inflicted on it by the doves at the strange nest-sites, and therefore no longer regards itself as stronger than the rest."

Opinions may differ as to whether the dove that suffered the beating actually attributed the action to the other members of its own species. I do not subscribe to this view. On the basis of numerous comparable examples in many other animals I maintain that it is much more likely that the rebellious pigeon let itself be imposed upon by the superior human in his Super-Alpha role. I could cite a large number of cases in support of this but I will confine myself to one. The monkey house in Zurich Zoo, which for good reasons is far removed from the anthropoid ape house accommodates about a dozen different species or families of primates. As might be expected, tensions sometimes build up and there are incidents. The statistics show a striking increase of these incidents on Tuesdays which is the keeper's day off. The keeper unquestionably plays the role of a Super-Alpha animal in this house. The monkeys use his absence for social assaults and other pieces of impudence.

It is generally accepted that in a group of lions, tigers or mixed group of performing animals the trainer is regarded as the socially top animal and as such he maintains law and order (Hediger 1961). Very often however the keeper in the zoo also has to do this, not only with big cats and monkeys, but also with ungulates, kangaroos, geese and rodents. In some circumstances this is done with a broom in his hand and it may be of decisive importance during the introduction of new individuals into existing groups. In my opinion there is no alternative but to allocate one or more keepers armed with brooms to the enclosure and leave them there for hours or even days, until the new social hierarchy has been established.

Discipline and control should be established not by any abnormal methods but by making threatening gestures with the broom which is treated as the equivalent of sharp claws, pointed canines, hard hooves and so on; the latter are the weapons used in the wild by the animals' own alpha individuals. To be able to interfere correctly and effectively in such situations one must naturally be pretty familiar with the social interplay of the species and with the social structure of the group concerned.

None of this is possible however without the necessary keeper staff at one's disposal and nowadays this is not always easily arranged. Not everyone can see the sense in allocating one man to do nothing except supervise the social behaviour of a group of animals. Nevertheless anyone who has had the constant experience of one animal after another being seriously injured or killed by the others shortly after being introduced into the group will not give in to unwarranted pressure but will insist on this initial supervision. The serious annual loss of many valuable animals to zoos all over the world through false economy in failing to meet this requirement of zoo biology should not be forgotten.

Social factors can definitely be significant even in the case of transfers involving fish. Konrad Lorenz (1966, p. 143) gives an excellent example of the effect of transferring cichlids while they are in the early stages of pair formation: "Transfer to another aquarium can at this stage completely upset pair formation. The closer the acquaintanceship becomes, the more the picture of the partner becomes independent of the background, a process well known to the Gestalt psychologist as also to the investigators of conditioned reflexes. Finally, the bond with the partner becomes so independent of accidental conditions that pairs are transferred, even transported away without severing their bond."

Social factors play a large part in moulding the animal's approach to such important matters as the acceptance of food, the attitude to man and the place in which it lives. In effecting a transfer the animal must be considered not just as an isolated individual but against its social background; our knowledge on this subject is still very modest but in so far as this is possible the previous, present and future relationships should be taken into consideration. In any case the irresponsible idea of transporting an animal as though it were just an item of merchandise is no longer acceptable.

Thus every arrival implies a departure even in the world of animals. In spite of the fact that thousands of animals are transferred every year in zoos all over the world, little or no knowledge is gained from them. How often for instance does one see any publication of observations or detailed investigations into even one case of transfer. How much money, for instance, has ever been devoted to providing a foundation for the basic comparative investigation of grief or of homesickness? In influential circles a zoo is still regarded mainly as a place where the children can go on a Sunday afternoon, to buy ice-creams and laugh at the alleged comic behaviour of the monkeys, and nothing more than this. The main aim seems to be to run the zoo at the lowest possible cost and to economize on staff, particularly on the scientific side.

Occasionally one hears stories about the unusual way in which a dog will behave when its master dies. In the chapter on causes of death in the zoo I mentioned a pair of geese in the London Zoo, of which the surviving partner pined to death. Occasionally evidence comes to light when separating families, involving perhaps the removal of the offspring from the parents or when one partner of a pair dies, which provides food for thought. I cannot give detailed examples here but I must emphasize that one should not proceed without giving some thought to this sector of zoo biology.

In animals, as well as in humans, there are pairs that get on well together and those that do not. Even among the latter the loss of a partner can release remarkable reactions. I recall a pair of pumas which did not get on at all well together and when the male died suddenly the female apparently tried to find her late partner; as she searched every possible corner she gave the impression not of being bitterly disappointed, but rather of becoming increasingly confident.

Naturally such a statement would be discounted by those research workers who only consider behaviour objectively. Let us therefore accept that the interpretation of the puma's behaviour cannot be explained in these terms, even though the person who gained the above impression of the puma's behaviour had virtually spent his life among animals, dealing with this kind of thing every day. I can only add that the female puma literally bloomed physically, filling out in figure and acquiring a glossy coat while showing more liveliness than it had ever done previously.

Aggressive behaviour due to social factors, may seriously handicap transfer into new accommodation; under some circumstances, however, it is also possible for social factors to ease the habituation. This happens when a social vacuum exists and there is a need for both parties to form a bond. Thus, for example it is easier to move a female blackbuck into a paddock already occupied by a herd than into an empty one. The newly arrived antelope will immediately try to join up with the others and be incorporated in the herd; this has the effect of reducing excitement to a marked extent and calming things down. No running along the fence takes place and there are none of the high jumps, typical of blackbuck and impala, in which there is an increased risk of injury.

Sometimes a pacifying influence is achieved by the presence of individuals of a different species the other side of a wire fence, provided the species are not too dissimilar. In Zurich Zoo for example we used a group of vicunas for this purpose during the introduction of blackbuck into the adjoining enclosure. The vicunas were interested in the new arrivals and moved over towards the fence. The antelopes, of approximately the same size and similar in colour, soon approached the vicunas on the other side of the fence although they had probably never seen these South American mammals before. Whatever the reason the result was that the animals quietened down.

When making a transfer one tends to forget to take into consideration the immediate effect that the newly arrived animals may have on the animals already established in the neighbouring accommodation. One takes for granted, for example, that in the big cat houses, lions, leopards and cheetahs live in full view of each other, and that in the ape house gorillas live alongside chimpanzees, etc. The presence of a superior competitor however always arouses great excitement at first and this only subsides gradually as acclimatization takes place.

I was once guilty of this kind of thoughtlessness when arranging the transfer of a very docile yak cow which is really a harmless domestic animal; I forgot to take into account the effect it would have on its neighbours, which were guanacos. The yak cow was led into its new den without any trouble but when it went out of the door into the paddock for the first time a neighbouring guanaco took fright; due possibly to the sudden appearance of this unfamiliar black apparition the guanaco leapt right over a fence seven feet high, a feat which it had never attempted in the previous year. The yak cow had to be taken back into its den and then introduced later on to the guanacos step by step with the necessary care.

We also gave a thorough fright, unintentionally, to our Persian gazelles in Zurich Zoo by moving a pair of Arabian camels into the neighbouring paddock without appropriate warning. Oversights of this kind earn a "poor mark" in zoo biology.

At one time we were mystified by the behaviour of our two Indian elephants which suddenly started to make a great fuss. They became so restless that they refused to allow themselves to be chained up any more. We eventually discovered the cause: a small group of collared peccaries had been put into accommodation which was close to the elephants; although they were actually out of sight the elephants were unaccustomed to them as neighbours.

The extent to which one can make mistakes in the field of moving animals is illustrated by the results of a decision taken by a very large European zoo to provide artists and sculptors of animals with a special studio for this purpose. This represented quite a serious step for the zoo as it involved providing a room, with views from all sides for the artist, into which particularly interesting and attractive animals could be put and used as live models. The idea in itself was praiseworthy but however well-intentioned, the result was quite disastrous. This should have been foreseen because the room was like a circular cage with no cover of any kind and the unfortunate animals never got over the trauma of the move and they made a sorry impression in their highly nervous state.

Animals that have recently been moved do not like to be stared at from all sides; when they are nervous and afraid they do not look happy. Furthermore it is a basic principle of zoo biology that every animal should be given a minimum of protection at the rear; the cage or enclosure must have one part that is solid, from which it cannot be threatened or even disturbed under any circumstances whatsoever. An animal's living quarters therefore should never be constructed so that the public can stand on all sides and stare in. A circus ring, designed for an all-round view does not constitute the animal's home, moreover the animals are only exposed to view in it for a few minutes at a time.

As a yardstick the proportion ought to be 1:1, that is, the part of the enclosure boundary which provides protection from the rear and is absolutely free of disturbance, must be about equal to the part open to the public. The formula 1:1 therefore means: the sheltered part

Fig. 153 Nowadays plants are as important in the zoo as the animals. A pleasing corner with tropical vegetation in Berlin Zoo.

Fig. 154 In natural territories the various fixed points or localities, at which the animal turns up at certain times for specific purposes, are connected by self-made paths, known as runs.

Fig. 155 In its natural habitat an animal's territory is not homogeneous, but consists of various features. These include certain fixed points. African Elephants, for example, will visit termite mounds from time to time where they scratch themselves, causing these massive insect structures gradually to assume a polished appearance.

Fig. 156　The New World camels defaecate and urinate at well-defined fixed points. The grass at the edges of these places receives more manure than elsewhere but although it thrives particularly luxuriantly it is not eaten.

Fig. 157　Built-in trap for catching up Polar Bears: a piece of meat is fixed to the hook. When the Polar Bear pulls on it the shutter falls behind it. But this is only successful once because the animal quickly learns from the alarming experience.

Fig. 158 Often the transport box is handled like any other packing case, loaded on to a truck, driven to the zoo and then, to the accompaniment of all kinds of noises it is placed before the definitive cage in such a way that the doors are roughly opposite each other.

Fig. 159 During the transfer of animals from one place to another it is particularly important not to shove the animal into a strange place and treat it like a load of bricks; this is not only unseemly but it is also contrary to the principles of zoo biology.

Fig. 160 In areas with a hard winter climate the summer and winter quarters should be in close proximity. Here it was necessary to catch up and transfer Rheas regularly twice a year.

Fig. 161 For a tall animal every transfer from one place to another is the equivalent of entering a new world. It is akin to an actor's first entrance on to the stage in a drama.

Fig. 162 During transfer from winter to summer quarters, the animals are in an excitable state and less likely to be aware of the danger of running into the fence. In order to avoid losses at the time of transfer the fencing was made conspicuous and less dangerous.

for the animal equals the part of the cage or enclosure exposed to humans. Generally speaking this is the proportion observed in zoos. In cages with solid back and side walls and only one side open to the public, we have proportions of 3:1, ignoring the keepers' door at the back. For breeding dens, where the mother must be given maximum protection from disturbance, there ought to be only a peep-hole, so that the ratio in this case is of the order of 1,000:1.

It is only in the case of domestic animals or extremely tame wild animals, or in places where broad water barriers offer the animal increased security, that one can risk increasing the public part to a ratio of 1:2 or more. The old-fashioned cages for a single parrot were circular and in these—like the totally unbiological animal studio— the cover from the rear was absolutely nil.

Even in a cage with the ratio 3:1 in certain circumstances some recover astonishingly slowly from the trauma caused by a transfer. I was able to demonstrate a case in point to my students in the summer term of 1963 with a young female black leopard that had been moved from another zoo into the big cat house at Zurich Zoo, a building which is by no means ideal. After its arrival in April 1963 the leopard lay continuously in a cramped corner at the back of the cage, far away from the public. It did not stir at all. Its meat was not touched for the first few days; later, it disappeared only at night, and it was only months after that it was taken from the keeper at feeding time. During the course of the summer term, from April to July, I had hoped to be able to show my students the gradual release of tension with the loss of inhibitions and finally the leopard moving freely; the position, however, remained virtually stationary through-out the summer. This was an unusually difficult animal and it was not until the autumn that the awaited signs of habituation set in; it was not until the latter half of the winter, that is after about nine months, that it could be put with a male leopard, and this was accompanied by a further marked improvement. It became increas-ingly familiar with its surroundings and after one year its behaviour was such that the acclimatization could be said to be complete.

The big cats normally react badly to being moved but a year is an exceptionally long period of time for acclimatization. In other cases settling in takes only about three months and in particularly favour-able conditions only a few weeks. From the viewpoint of zoo biology

R   235

naturally every effort must be made to shorten this difficult period, but limits are sometimes imposed by such matters as architectural features. In the case of the leopard we were handicapped because we could not provide better conditions or increase the distance of the cage from the barrier and we were also unable to improve the cover at the rear; there was also the delay in introducing it to members of its own species etc.

While it is very depressing to see animals in the zoo which have not yet overcome the trauma caused by being moved, on the other hand it is very encouraging to observe an animal that is moving completely in tune with its environment; its whole appearance and behaviour suggest that it is entirely at one with its surroundings. The full sense of achievement can only be enjoyed completely perhaps by someone who knows at what cost and by what methods it has been attained.

For instance there is nothing haphazard about the way a fish lies poised in the water: its location in the aquarium tank and the position of its body are the result of a delicate balance between all sorts of factors, such as distance from the bottom, from the water surface and from the four walls of the tank; its position is also relative to the current, to the illumination and to the growth of algae and water plants. The composition of the picture presented by the fish is completely faultless like the scales or other covering of the fish's skin. The very tiniest change would be equivalent to a tear or a disturbing blot in a valuable picture. Compositions of this nature however are not rigid. The movement starts, barely perceptibly or with extreme rapidity, the changes merging one with the other and retaining harmony with the surroundings as a whole.

There is nothing disunited or uncertain, nothing convulsive or frightened, but only simple elegance and beauty. This applies also to a bird on a branch. The position taken up is definitely one and no other, moreover it is appropriate for a time. If it leaves this chosen spot which is biologically significant it makes a short flight on a carefully prescribed course. The start, the turns and the finish are worked out as naturally as the set of each feather in its smooth plumage.

The same principle applies to reptiles in a planted vivarium and to ungulates in a paddock. The dimensions and special features of their surroundings are very familiar to each one of them; when resting they take up a position at what is biologically the focal point; and when they move about every step is in relation to this.

A fish, a bird and a mammal or a group of animals that are familiar with their surroundings make a wonderful picture, in which there is not a sign of the nervous anxiety of the initial period. They become attuned to their environment, both externally and internally, as is shown so well by the condition of the skin. The skin is by no means a mere covering or armour; it represents a unique frontier that is penetrated in several different ways by the external and internal media.

Much could be said here about the skin as the mediator between two worlds and of its character as a frontier dividing the external from the internal; this applies whether the skin is the mucus epithelium of a fish, the hide of an elephant or the carapace of a giant tortoise, which appears merely to serve a mechanical purpose. We will content ourselves however with the statement that the skin constitutes an important indicator from the viewpoint of zoo biology, and where inspections are still carried out the most careful attention should be paid to it on each occasion.

Dr Walter Fiedler, the Scientific Director of the Schönbrunn Zoo in Vienna, who has had comprehensive training in anatomy, zoology, primatology and animal behaviour, has devoted an investigation into the subject of "The skin of mammals as an organ of expression" (1964). This research is both fascinating and of basic importance to zoo biology.

Assuming that harmony has been established between the animal and its accommodation, we can now look more closely at the way in which different species react to the surroundings outside their cage or paddock. Two types can be distinguished: the introvert and the extrovert, these terms being used in the biological sense. The division into these two types does not appear to follow any particular rules within the zoological system as it does perhaps in the use of tools, the degree of general awareness or in reaction to distance and contact. One cannot tell to which type a species belongs without gradually building up the picture by means of extensive observations.

In general animals are liable to be underestimated in this respect as in others. Most zoo visitors, for example, think that the crocodile and its relatives lying around like "stuffed dummies" can neither see nor hear; this is by no means the case. These armoured reptiles which always appear to be lazy and sluggish are demonstrably extremely alert. On the basis of experiments it must be concluded that they take in every movement in the immediate and distant surroundings, but they do not react visibly without further stimulation. The psychiatrist and animal psychologist R. Sommer (1925, p. 218) was undoubtedly the first to demonstrate that the lack of movement in the crocodile was not a condition of sleep but was a state of awareness and readiness to move which he interpreted as a good example of catatonia (a form of schizophrenia). In any case these animals can react at lightning speed from their apparent "stuffed dummy" condition; I found it extremely difficult to approach them in Africa as well as in the South Seas because of their continual state of awareness. Even in Bern Zoo I noticed that when they were expecting the keeper to bring food they reacted to tiny movements of the trapdoors in the service passages.

With regard to reactions to distant stimuli, however, in my opinion the Capuchin monkeys are highly extrovert. There was a male capuchin which lived in Zurich Zoo for over thirty years, who had a number of friends among the regular visitors; he could pick these people out from the crowd at a great distance and he used to greet them with a loud shriek. This capuchin evidently checked every face in the thousands of humans who came and went, not only immediately in front of his cage but also in the distance. In comparison with this particular capuchin even the anthropoid apes show few signs of being extrovert and the gibbons, for example, are markedly introvert. Among the birds the most extrovert in my experience so far is the raven.

It would be rewarding to make a survey of the animal population of the zoo to find out which animals restrict their circle of interest mainly to the immediate surroundings inside their enclosures (the introverts) and those which extend their awareness beyond the limits of their own enclosure (the extroverts). Since the feeding of the animals by the public is forbidden in most zoos, at any rate in Europe, the importance of the person bringing food as an attraction outside the cage is excluded. In the case of the Capuchin monkey which reacted to my appearance, however, food played no role as over the years I had never brought it a single titbit.

By contrast the behaviour of a female orang-utan, named Moli, who was approximately 20 years old, could be described as the antithesis of the welcoming reaction of the capuchin; this orang's behaviour could be described, in my opinion, as a form of embarrassment. In my long career in zoos I have hitherto never observed anything of this nature in any animal other than in this female orang-utan. Moli arrived from Antwerp Zoo in 1959 and was accommodated in the newly built anthropoid ape house in Zurich Zoo. In Antwerp Zoo she had been living together with a male orang; unfortunately the latter escaped when a new enclosure, built on the occasion of the Brussels World Fair, was opened and unfortunately had to be shot as it was climbing around the rooftops of neighbouring houses.

The female orang, virtually widowed, was then sent to Zurich and after about a year she was given the company of a young male orang, named Adam from Hagenbeck. Adam was still not yet sexually mature but the two got on quite well together, even during puberty and after, until mating became a possibility. Sometimes the two orangs could be observed playing in wild abandon, which surprised us, because Moli usually sat looking very solemn in a car tyre, which she had chosen as her favourite spot and in which she also slept.

If the two were taken by surprise while playing by the keepers or the Director whom they knew, then Moli immediately retired to her tyre and looked solemn again. They did not seem to be disturbed when strangers watched them; it was as though they felt embarrassed in front of their acquaintances. It was not until about a year later that they ceased to pay any attention to us but by that time, we had already learned to be discreet and took care to avoid every kind of disturbance. Every effort must be made to keep orang utans in zoos and to get them to breed because this species of anthropoid ape is seriously threatened in the wild, and is only found in very restricted areas of Borneo and Sumatra (B. Harrisson 1962).

I have already mentioned the desirability, indeed the urgency, of investigating the degree to which zoo animals are introvert or extrovert; the importance of this task cannot be over-emphasized. It is essential for us to know the strength of the reactions—whether weak or strong—of the zoo animals to stimuli that are outside the boundaries of their artificial territories. The need for clarification is particularly pressing in view of the appearance of yet another catch-word, known as *stress*, which requires critical appraisal. A hundred years ago homesickness was blamed for failures in animal husbandry; more recently, so-called "traditional" methods of feeding, arterio-sclerosis and fatty degeneration through overfeeding etc. were used as an excuse and now "stress" looks as though it will become a convenient excuse. Anyone who has had much to do with the methods of investigating causes of death in zoo animals can scarcely resist the impression that fashions come and go and the use of certain catchwords is not without some influence in this subject. Is it not true that the theory and practice of human medicine also change every few years?

Let us first consider the stress theory. It is said that the poor animals in the zoo are subjected to frightful stress amounting to perpetual mental pressure, through being watched constantly by the visitors. A direct comparison is made between the situation of the zoo animals and that of the human executives who are subjected to constant worry and pressure. No wonder that animals also succumb to the popular disease of executives! In some places it has even been suggested that zoo animals should also have a five-day week, so that they can relax and rest after the fatigue of visiting days. I might add that zoo directors have never demanded a five-day week. It is doubtless said that they do not need it as they are able to take a walk in their zoo every day of the week!

Underlying this theory there is a deep-rooted misunderstanding and possibly also a projection, in the psychological sense. For many years now man has projected the fulfilment of his unattainable desires into the animal kingdom: he believes that animals exist to enjoy not only a boundless freedom in the sense of space, time and personal (including sexual) relations, but that they can also live for years and years; it is imagined for instance that birds sing and fly for pleasure, and so on. For example, even in the textbook of zoology by Claus, Grobben & Kühn (1932, p. 41) which is highly regarded there is the statement that elephants can live to an age of 200 years.

Nowadays we know for certain that elephants cannot attain even half this age, that birds do not fly and sing for pleasure, and that in spatial, temporal or personal relations wild animals are not as free as man likes to think. Man's wish-fulfilments therefore have shown

240

themselves to be nothing more than illusory day-dreams when applied to the animal kingdom.

A development now appears to be taking place that is of interest to human psychology, in which a different kind of solace is being sought in the animal.

In spite of the natural way of life of animals, they are seen as no better off than we humans. The animal also suffers from obesity, from arteriosclerosis, from frustration and naturally also from stress. We comfort ourselves with the thought that because animals are subject to social pressure and the illnesses of high-powered executives, no amount of restrictions in diet, tiresome self-denials or health formulae will be of any avail to humans. Evidently we are dealing with natural laws, from which neither man nor animal can escape, so why should we chastise ourselves.

We are not concerned here with human psychological aspects but with those relative to zoo biology. If by stress we mean pressure due to psychical and social factors, then stress in the wild is undoubtedly greater than under well-ordered conditions in the zoo. The chief preoccupation of the wild animal is with constant vigilance against enemies, the perpetual readiness for flight and the permanent need to be on the alert (Hediger 1942, 1950). This requirement is essential for the survival of the individual and for the maintenance of its species; it takes precedence over all other activity in the wild but in the zoo it disappears completely with the protection provided by the fencing. This radically reduces stress. Added to this food and water are provided regularly, thus dispensing with the need to search which is such an important factor in the wild.

As far as social stress is concerned, it is one of the elementary duties of the zoo staff to eliminate excessive or unnatural social tensions; care must be taken to achieve groups that are harmonious. It is therefore abundantly clear that stress in the zoo is minimal in comparison with stress in the wild. I see this as a reassuring factor in modern zoo management today. It is possible that stress may be decreased to an excessive extent in the zoo; when this happens the zoo biologist must step in to take control, in order to avoid obesity and insufficient activity. Here I agree with H. L. Ratcliffe (1950, p. 10) when he states that under natural conditions the animal is continually subjected to severe stress, and that, in order to survive, it must be conditioned to prolonged and strenuous activity, but that in the zoo it is completely freed from this exertion. If there is any kind of stress for the animal then it occurs only in the wild or through mistakes in zoo management.

The subject of transfers cannot be dealt with comprehensively here but even in this incomplete account, two more points must be mentioned: the doors and the threshold. In Zurich Zoo we tend to regard the doors and the threshold, like the actual house or home of the animal, as of archetypal importance. The opening of the doors (usually in the form of trap-doors, so-called slides or sliding doors) plays a prominent role in every transfer; anyone who has taken part in even a few transfer operations could not fail to be aware of the exceptional importance of the threshold.

One must remember that doors in the sense of human technology, that is doors with hinges, practically do not exist in nature; they do not even occur in this form among native peoples. Thresholds also do not exist in this sense. To the animal a door is a contrivance which suddenly opens and reveals a new space which can be entered; the space has not been visible previously and is not regarded as safe, thus the doorway in itself makes the animal uneasy. The threshold emphasizes the transition from the familiar to the unfamiliar world. It is not surprising that there are some animals that are never able to cross a threshold without hesitating or even making a drama out of it, as e.g. zebras, giraffes and many antelopes, however long they live.

In nature there is scarcely a single door in the human sense, if we disregard the trap-door spiders (family Ctenicidae). In some cases (ants, snakes, toads, pink fairy armadillo etc.) an entrance is closed by what is virtually a specially constructed part of the body such as the head or a tail plate. It is clear that in these cases however the spaces on either side of the animal—or of its living door—are familiar to it. In addition the animal can use or not use the passage way according to its own reactions; it is not a case of suddenly being confronted by a space that is either completely unknown or at least not familiar, and of being forced to enter it.

Many animals which live in subterranean burrows—from fiddler-crabs (*Uca*) to the aardvark (*Orycteropus*)—close the burrows that they live in with lumps of earth. The latter however are not removed all at once; the procedure is a gradual one, thus enabling light and scent, and everything new, to percolate through slowly. Leaving the burrow is the equivalent of stepping out of the front door; no animal that lives in a burrow, whether mouse or fox or marmot, will emerge without due care. It is typical of them all that they remain at the exit, sensing the surroundings for a while before leaving their home. Every animal should be given an opportunity to do this in every doorway. This is precisely where the keeper should not be in a hurry.

Where the door happens to have a particularly noticeable threshold, extra care should be taken. The fear of a threshold is a primitive phenomenon which should be respected in animals. In man as is well known there are all kinds of thresholds both in place and time, many of them remarkable. A threshold in time for instance is marked by a twenty-first birthday, and so on throughout one's life. An animal must come to terms with a threshold in its own way, and it is only bad keepers who drive an animal over it by force.

12

Catching Mice Without Bait

The mice which we are forced to control in zoos are of the ordinary variety, the grey house mouse (*Mus musculus*). It has a worldwide distribution and as an animal it is fascinating in its own right. As subjects of observation mice continually provide interest. The best way of watching them is to keep a pair in a vivarium, in which they have plenty of opportunity to climb, with glass walls and a fine mesh wire roof. They often hang from the mesh and climb about like small sloths. The glass sides provide considerable protection from any disturbance caused by the observer, such as noise, smell, draughts, radiant heat etc., and enable the mice to move about undisturbed. Optical stimuli have remarkably little effect on them as they hardly use their eyes at all; black and the size of a pinhead the eyes are more ornamental than functional. As a schoolboy I kept some mice as pets in the cellar and even at that age I was struck by the fact that they did not seem to react to the switching on and off of the electric lights, provided the switch did not make a click. Their sense of hearing is remarkably acute and it seems likely that ultrasonics are involved. The whiskers must also be reckoned as sense organs.

There are people with a special capacity for observation and a feeling for mice who can go a long way towards understanding them. I have come to know several of these mouse-men personally and such people are able to establish a relationship with mice that is much the same as the understanding which develops between handlers and their dogs. One such mouse-man—a woman—has published a very interesting book, under the pseudonym Besoka (1945), with the

244

whimsical title of *Don Juan, der Unbekannte* (*Don Juan, the unknown*); this deals with the life of the house mouse, in a way that largely gives the impression of fantasy but which corresponds throughout with biological fact.

In the context of zoo biology however our sympathy for mice cannot be allowed to blind us to the fact that these attractive little rodents are unfortunately one of the creatures—like rats—that must be rigorously controlled in the zoo. Man must declare war on mice, not only in zoos, but everywhere; we have no choice, it is either mice or men. This also applies to rats. As enemies of mankind we are forced to defend ourselves against them.

Rats and mice are not only unpleasant in that they damage food and stores but they also carry dangerous diseases. Each year they destroy quantities of valuable foodstuffs which starving mankind badly needs. Finally, with their tiny but very effective incisor teeth, they damage and render useless all kinds of objects and equipment. In Zurich Zoo the mice in the restaurant gnawed off the labels of the better vintages of wine, they invalidated tickets in the cash office by nibbling them, they made nests in the felt boots of the keepers in the mess-rooms and ate the inside of loaves of bread in the stores; these things are only trivial compared with the truly catastrophic damage and epidemics which can be caused by them.

There are experts who hold that in some ways the mouse can be said to be even more dangerous than the rat itself. Owing to their smaller size mice are able to get into places which are inaccessible to rats. They can also hide there and this is important bearing in mind that they carry disease.

The mouse is capable of carrying many diseases which are equally disastrous to man and animals. As well as plague (the dreaded black death) they can also carry typhus, severe enteritis, leptospirosis and tularaemia; they frequently carry salmonellosis and virus infections, also bad fungal diseases such as favus to which man is as prone as animals. The above list is by no means comprehensive; like the rat, the mouse is suspected of carrying foot-and-mouth disease, and its responsibility for swine erysipelas has been established in zoos. Corpses of mice which have somehow got into food, e.g. in grain silos, mangers or bales of hay, may also be responsible for dangerous diseases such as the dreaded botulism, which is often first recognized in humans or animals from paralysis of the eye muscles; this can lead to the death of the victim due to paralysis of the respiratory centre.

In the case of an infected mouse, even the urine of a living or dead specimen can be extremely dangerous when a trace of it gets into the smallest skin wound or scratch. The result may be leptospiral jaundice (Weil's disease) or mouse leptospirosis (harvest fever). Naturally the bite of an infected animal is also very dangerous.

When I tell the keepers that by far and away the most dangerous animals in the zoo are not the lions or venomous snakes but the rats and mice they usually smile indulgently; they may think that is an exaggeration but it is not so. Unless energetic measures are taken to keep these vermin under control they spread everywhere. The worst thing about them is that people regard them as harmless on account of their small size and they handle them carelessly; people will not accept the fact that a drop of urine, possibly invisible, from an infected rat or mouse can be lethal to man. Despite this, I have known of tragic cases in which friends and acquaintances have met their deaths in this unlikely manner or become dangerously ill.

One should be as careful in dealing with rats and mice as with venomous snakes; dead ones should not be picked up with the bare hand. To issue serious warnings about this is not enough and every zoo biologist should make it a rule that has to be obeyed in his zoo. Furthermore it should not be assumed that white rats and mice are always cleaner than those living wild. Infected animals sometimes get into laboratory cultures; one reads of this happening but I have also been unfortunate enough to have actual experience of it. White rats and mice are often kept for laboratory purposes in such a way that they attract the wild members of their species and thus get infected by them. Unless strict supervision is enforced, which unfortunately is not always the case, whole populations can become infected without any visible sign. Anyone who wants to obtain basic information on the proper care of laboratory animals, including white rats and mice, should consult the excellent *UFAW Handbook on the care and management of laboratory animals* (3rd edition, 1967). And anyone who needs convincing about the size of the problem involved in controlling these animals will find exhaustive information about the fight against rats and mice during and after the Second World War in the three volumes by D. Chitty and H. N. Southern (1954).

Rats and mice are historically important and there is an extensive literature on them. Special attention should be paid to the *Rattenbuch* (Book of rats) by R. Koller (1932) and the more recent *Rattenbiologie* (Biology of rats) by F. Steiniger (1952) which takes into account modern behaviour research.

Our concern here is simply to throw some light on the importance of rats and mice to zoo biology. Some of the available information is mentioned, in order to make it quite clear that the presence of rats and mice in the zoo is extremely dangerous to man and animals; it is for this reason that they must be dealt with by every method that is acceptable. They are killed not for sport but from a sense of duty. I emphasize this because I was once rash enough to report in one of our periodical press releases the total killed by the Zurich Zoo in a given year. The precise number is known to us because the keepers receive a reward for each dead mouse, in practice for each tail handed in. I immediately received protests from over-zealous ladies who were animal lovers; they bitterly reproached me with the fact that in Zurich Zoo we were not prepared to leave even "a pair of wee mice" alive and grudged them the little bit of food which was nothing in comparison with the food of the elephants and lions. By this time however it should be sufficiently clear why mice *must* be dealt with in the zoo.

There are still some strange notions about the methods of controlling mice in the zoo. I have been faced with the difficult task of de-mousing several zoos—at least parts of them. The usual household methods do not bring results in the zoo. In any case these methods have completely fallen into disuse; the modern skyscrapers of concrete are not suitable habitats for mice. It is also scarcely the custom nowadays to lay in stores and to save scraps of food. As a child I remember that when mice made themselves noticeable in the cellar or in the store-room, the cook and the maids then advanced on them armed with various types of traps; long discussions ensued on the best place to site the traps and particularly on the kind of bait to be used.

Great was the excitement from time to time when a mouse was actually caught in the trap, particularly if it was not a so-called tower-trap with a water dish in which the wretched mouse kicked and drowned. (I would never tolerate cruelty of this kind in the zoo).

But if it was a trap like a cage with a spring door and the mouse survived the shock of the noise as the door sprung, the problem remained of how to kill it and this led to further discussion. The methods adopted were usually abominable: the mouse might be thrown into the lavatory and then flushed, or the whole trap might be put in a bucket of water until the mouse drowned, or it might be handed over to a cat. The basket type of trap spared the mouse the shock of the clanging noise but posed the same problem of how to finish it off.

Domestic staff are relieved of such problems today because—as already mentioned—conditions in the modern skyscrapers do not suit the mice. In the zoo, on the other hand, they are still able to get a living and the discussions on baits and methods of destruction continue. Far too little consideration is given to the special conditions that prevail in the zoo; under these conditions the proverbial recipe of grandmother's time "good bait catches fine fish" does not work, nor do the most sophisticated poison baits of the chemical industry; bacteria or viruses are also ineffectual. It is a source of continual surprise to me that the methods used to combat rats and mice in some zoos, even today, can only be described as illogical and unbiological. In general the modern approach to zoology and animal psychology is a rational one but in this branch superstition still flourishes.

In European zoos for example the idea persists that the hedgehog (*Erinaceus*) can be used for the biological control of mice and that it is only necessary to let a pair of these animals loose in a building overrun with mice to keep them down. It was over a quarter of a century ago that K. Herter (1938), a great expert on hedgehogs and mice, established (p. 100) the following: "generally speaking the hedgehog cannot catch healthy adult mice in the wild or in large enclosed spaces." He showed further (p. 102), that mice which have been put into a cage with hedgehogs are not afraid of stationary hedgehogs, and they will sniff and even climb up on to them or hide beneath them. Hedgehog smell does not frighten mice.

In some zoos cats are even more popular as allegedly cheap and effective mouse-traps. It has been unequivocally established however that cats are incapable of clearing a mouse-infested area of land or a building; the best they can do is to protect a mouse-free area from incursions by mice. In the zoo, however, cats are a menace in their own right. In the first place they naturally succumb to the temptation to catch birds and eat them, particularly the young birds; this applies to valuable specimens as well as to pheasants, ducks etc. Some become astonishingly skilled at seizing small birds through the wire netting of the aviary and drawing them through the mesh, either whole or dismembered. H. L. Ratcliffe (1954, p. 14) reports from Philadelphia Zoo that stray cats have killed adult ducks and even young black swans.

The second reason why cats are out of place in the zoo is that they carry the dangerous cat distemper. The domestic cat virus also affects tigers, lions and leopards and catastrophic epidemics have been known in which the entire stock in the big cats' house has been wiped out. In the zoo therefore cats are not only worthless as destroyers of mice but they also involve additional risks.

Finally we come to the poisons, viruses and bacteria etc. recommended by industry for combating mice; these may be really effective under other conditions, e.g. in warehouses, depots, factories etc., where thousands of animals representing hundreds of species are not also present. Under the special conditions that apply in a zoo these industrial preparations are altogether contra-indicated, even though in the relevant prospectuses somewhat naïve and loose statements are often made that the recommended preparations are effective *only* against injurious animals. None of these firms could have tested their preparations on the large number of animal species which occur in even a small zoo. Each species may react differently, in totally unforeseeable ways; there are plenty of examples of this. Representatives of many animal species, from the Hawaiian goose to the panda and the kangaroo, have been killed by mouse eradication preparations that are "guaranteed non-injurious". Therefore it must be made clear here that there can be no such thing as a non-injurious preparation; in principle it cannot exist, because it is quite impossible to try it out on all zoo animals. There is only one conclusion that can be drawn from this by zoo biology: this is that poisons and biological control methods against mice (bacteria, viruses and others) ought not to be used in the zoo. In fact there is no need to use them as we shall see.

In the zoo the control of rats and mice starts with the buildings for the animals. Rules of construction for animal houses in the zoo are different from those applicable to dwelling houses and offices. In the zoo one must build houses that are rat- and mouse-proof right from the start and it is the duty of the zoo biologist to make the architects aware of this in good time; they cannot be expected to know that this is necessary and they must be briefed on the subject.

Fundamentally it is remarkably simple as it only involves following three simple rules:

1. The foundations of zoo buildings must be at least 3 feet deep. Rats in fact do not dig deeper than 3 feet, mice less deep.
2. All doors, ventilation covers and similar outlets, including the framework, must be strengthened from the start with solid metal plate or a correspondingly strong material up to a height of 18 inches from the ground.
3. All openings that are not completely sealed off, such as passages, windows, ventilation shafts etc. must be 18 inches above the ground and must also be fitted with strong wire-netting with a mesh size not greater than 8 mm. Thin wire-netting that is level with the ground will be gnawed through by rats, and if the mesh is more than 8 mm. mice can slip through.

Although these constructional faults are certainly not difficult to avoid, for some incomprehensible reason they frequently occur— as I know from wide experience—and later on, people have to grapple with the much more difficult problem of dealing with rats and mice that have already got established in the zoo. This is a procedure which involves much greater expense than the cost of constructing buildings properly from the start. In each of the zoos directed by me since 1938 and in almost every one that I have visited since then, there have been doors, windows, shafts and ventilation equipment damaged by rats and mice, all of which have had to be altered and strengthened at considerable cost. It should be borne in mind that it is very much easier to prevent the entry of rats and mice by the simple measures mentioned above than to get rid of a population that is already established.

If however the damage is already done, as is usually the case, then the following tactics should be adopted: these are based, not on the urge of these dangerous rodents to feed, but on their behaviour patterns in space and time; use is also made of the age-old principle

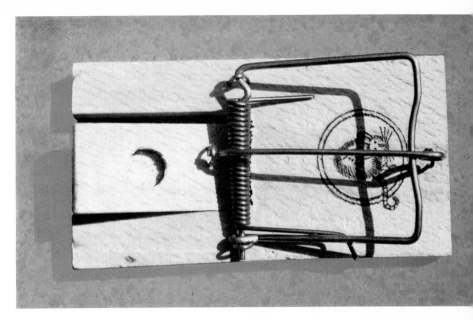

Fig. 163   One of the cheap and efficient mousetraps set for use.

Fig. 164   A House Mouse in one of the humane traps, killed immediately by the bar which is activated by a finely-set spring.

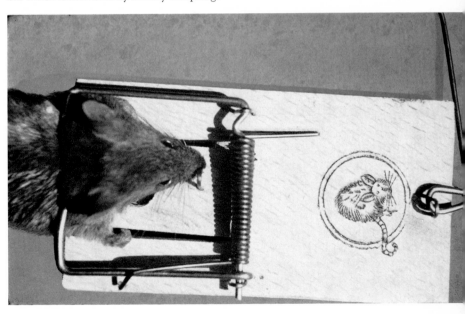

Fig. 165 These simple traps should never be set singly but always in series

Fig. 166 An example of the correct way to set out mousetraps in series on stairs.

Fig. 167 A bait is quite unnecessary. The importan thing is to set out the traps correctly in groups on the mouse runs.

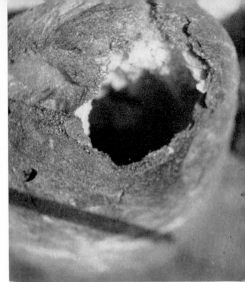

Fig. 168   Even a keeper's boots lined with felt provide the adaptable House Mouse with a place for a nest.

Fig. 169   Here House Mice have made their nest in a loaf of bread.

Fig. 170   House Mice are notorious pests in stores. In the Zurich Zoo they gnawed the tickets which led to complications with the ticket control people.

Fig. 171   Heating pipes are much used by mice as runs. The unprotected lagging is gnawed off and used as nest material.

Fig. 172   A heating pipe with lagging that is too weak and unprotected: it has already been half nibbled away by mice.

Fig. 173   Pipes denuded of their lagging by mice, showing the typical little peaks which arise from the continual passage of the mice.

of "divide and rule". This means in other words that the spatial pattern of these animals must be broken up. One area after another must be won back from them and made secure, particular attention being paid to destroying the runs between their homes and their feeding places, as well as to blocking up every possibility of going to other areas. Once this simple principle is grasped, the control of rats and mice is only child's play leading to a hundred per cent success; it could be regarded as a game, if it were not for the fact that it involves the killing of animals, even though they are of a dangerous and injurious kind.

Rats and mice are like the sparrows and other wild birds that breed in the zoo; they have their own home ranges in among the artificial territories of the most varied creatures. They move about between their own fixed points using runs which form a communication system; it is this system which must be destroyed—not, however, by stuffing a ball of steel-wool into a mouse-hole. In the first place we now know that steel-wool is one of the forbidden materials in a zoo, and secondly this line of attack does not help because the mouse circumvents the obstruction and if it is unable to gnaw or tear a new passage alongside the ball it makes a detour, like a motorist who uses a by-pass.

The runs of rats and mice are like a network of roads; there are main roads and side roads, crossings and bridges, paths and poles for climbing and there are even aerial routes, surprising though this may sound. In an area with which a mouse is familiar, it can leap up on to a smooth wall to a height of 18 inches providing it can take a run at it. But it will only do this when following a known aerial route and not in strange surroundings.

Most people have very little idea of how the mouse finds its way about in its home range. The following simile may help to explain it: the mouse's home range may be in the bird house in the zoo and within this area the mouse is as well orientated as a man would be who could find his way about, blindfolded and at a running pace, into any room he liked in a medium-sized skyscraper; if one corridor on the tenth floor were to be shut off—comparable to stopping up a mouse-hole—he would still have several other routes open to him; in other words he could still find a way round.

Part of the mouse's ability to orientate comes from a very useful sense, which in man is extremely poorly developed; this is the kinaesthetic sense, a kind of movement and muscle memory. The mouse is also helped by several other sense organs, some of which have not yet been thoroughly investigated. Based on these abilities the mouse knows its runs inside out. Amongst other things this is why a cat is rarely able to catch a mouse in its own territory. Once outside their own territory, however, they are lost because they do not know all the ins and outs and run about hither and thither, and go up blind alleys.

Returning for a moment to our man in the skyscraper, if we wanted to arrest him it would not be sufficient to lock a door here and there in the vast complex of floors, passages and rooms. We would have to proceed in a much more systematic manner, as the police do when arresting a thief in a large building. First the entrances and exits are manned, then the hall, the passage and the individual rooms. The tactical moves are the same when hunting mice, the main runs and access routes must be blocked first.

This may sound obvious but it needs emphasizing because even in the zoo people complain about the numerous mice in a store-room and still maintain that none of the traps catches anything. When one investigates these puzzling situations, one finds, for example, that a ventilator sited at ground level is inadequately wired and this is where the continual stream of mice gains access. No amount of traps laid in the room will help because the trouble has not been tackled at the root; it is essential to cover the ventilator with 8 mm. wire-mesh and make sure that there are no other similar openings.

In other cases pipes are involved or wooden partitions and disused doors which have been gnawed through; it is worth looking at places like these and making sure that they are mouse-proof.

People who despair of what they regard as the hopelessness of ever keeping the mice down in the zoo should be reminded of two irrefutable facts: in the first place, mice are not produced out of thin air, they can only come from mice and secondly, fortunately for mankind, mice are incapable of flight. Therefore if there are mice in the building they must have gained access by coming in along the ground from outside.

There is no doubt that the obvious procedure is to search for these vital points of entry and block them up; this, however, is not always done. Mice do not usually come in through the front door of a house —this also needs saying. In dealing with mice one should also bear in mind that the human brain is at least two thousand times heavier than that of the mouse. The outlook therefore is not as hopeless as it might seem but if the mice are to be dealt with successfully, then one must take the trouble to mobilize one's resources. The first question to ask oneself is: where would one enter a house if one were a mouse? Anyone with a little knowledge of the terrain and the habits of mice can work out the answer as easily as doing a simple multiplication sum. Having found the entry points and blocked these up, as well as any other likely routes which the mice might use to invade other areas, the battle is already half won; it only remains to tackle the mice that are shut in, whether they are a mere dozen or so or in their thousands.

Mention should be made of the special case of finding mice in a mouse-proof building. It can happen that mice will suddenly put in an appearance in a house built as totally proof against mice by a really competent architect. Although there is no sign of how the mice got in, nevertheless they are present inside the building. We know that mice come from mice and that they cannot fly; logically, therefore, they must have been carried into the house. And by whom? By man himself.

One should not assume that cases of this kind occur often, nevertheless the fact that they occur at all means that even an animal house which is built as guaranteed mouse-proof cannot be regarded as completely safe against mice. From this it follows that we must be prepared to do battle with mice, even in buildings that are nominally mouse-proof. It is obviously foolish to assume that the mice which are inadvertently transported into the building are always males; the introduction of only one female can result in the production of an enormous number of mice in a short period of time in the event of the particular female being pregnant. The gestation period is about 23 days and 4–8 young may be born in one litter.

In the zoo there are several possible ways in which mice can be transported by man: the mice may be present in bales of hay or straw, or inside sacks of food; they may be in paper, amongst clothing or shoes, in timber, crates, packing material, fuel, tubs of plants, inside vehicles and containers of all kinds including transport cages that are presumed to be empty, and so on. It is essential that even mouse-proof rooms are constantly checked for the possible presence of mice. This is yet another example of where it is better to be safe than sorry.

Let us now look at the problem of how to deal with a building that is infested with mice, irrespective of whether it was originally mouse-proof or subsequently protected by preventing them from coming in from outside. A population of mice that is shut up inside a building is capable not only of remaining alive but also of breeding very rapidly, providing that one condition is fulfilled: food must be present and also nest material if breeding is to take place. In point of fact the proverbial church mouse that was so poor would have been in a sorry plight if it had not gained access to the parsonage.

It is true that mice cannot exist without food but one does not often give sufficient thought to the great variety of things which can serve as food for mice, nor to how little they actually require. A church is notoriously inhospitable as far as mice are concerned but a wine-cellar or a museum is not much better and yet I have found mice in both these habitats.

In the wine-cellar the mice were gnawing the labels off the bottles, using the bits of paper for nest-building and the thin layer of gum as food. Mice are very adaptable and they will eat vegetable as well as animal matter; a cellar often has a population of various kinds of spiders, stray insects, dead flies, moths etc., which help the mice to survive.

Some years ago I was surprised to find mice in a museum that had been newly built. The surroundings appeared to be completely sterile but it transpired that initially the mice did well off the scraps of food (such as crumbs of bread, cheese rinds, sausage skins etc.) left behind by the builders after their meal breaks. Also there was plenty of paper for nest-building. After the place had been thoroughly cleaned and taken into commission only the dustproof glass-cases remained, rising out of the mirror-like expanse of polished floor which must have seemed like a barren desert to the mice. At the time I was curator of the museum and to my surprise one morning I found distinct but unusual traces of mice: there were large numbers of whitish droppings instead of the more familiar elongated black shapes. In their straitened circumstances the mice had tackled the putty fixing the panes of glass into the metal frames of the showcases, and they had been digesting the oil contained in the putty. It is not safe therefore to assume that there is nothing for mice to eat in an apparently sterile area.

Finally the problem has to be faced of getting rid of a population of mice that is virtually under siege in the zoo, with an abundant supply of food and therefore actively reproducing: this has to be done only by fair means. Methods involving cruelty are therefore not admissible, such as the spreading of a glutinous substance on the floor in which the mice get stuck; by this method the mice die a lingering death like the flies on the fly-papers which at one time were in common use.

Based on years of experience in the business in my opinion the best method which is humane, cheap and simple is with the so-called breakback traps. K. Herton (1944) who has done some interesting behaviour studies on mice described these traps as follows: a wire hoop on a small piece of wood is fixed so that when drawn back to one end of the board a strong spring is stretched. A stiff piece of wire holds the hoop in this position. When the trap is set the free end of the piece of wire lies loosely in a wire loop on a small trip-board, which moves in a rocking fashion. The bait is placed on this board. As the mouse steps on to the board this is depressed under its weight, causing the wire to slide out of the loop; the hoop is thus freed by the action of the spring and it lands with great force on the mouse.

Death is instantaneous in the great majority of cases as usually the mouse is struck on the skull, neck or vertebral column by the hoop. A quicker and more humane form of death I cannot imagine. In exceptional cases a mouse may be caught by only one foot but this may result in an equally quick death from shock. We know that mice often die as a result of a sharp retort or a loud bang. However if the mouse survives the shock it will then try to free itself from the trap. But in doing so, almost immediately it enters the area of the neighbouring traps with fatal results.

These spring traps should never be used singly but always in groups of half a dozen. One never goes out shooting with only one cartridge. Groups of traps not only avoid unnecessary suffering but also increase the probability of a catch. For this reason one can confidently dispense with any bait. In the home the bait is often fixed to the trip-board of the trap by pins or small nails but in the zoo this is not permitted on account of the danger of foreign bodies. The use of fat, dough or similar bait however is completely superfluous because there is plenty of food available for the mice all over the zoo; there is food in every den and more than enough in every store-room.

In comparison with a church a zoo must be like utopia; one has only to think of the size of just one bone left over after a big cat has been fed. A lion must leave an enormous amount of meals over for the mice. In the zoo therefore one does not catch mice with fat but with baitless spring traps, which must of course be positioned in the correct places. The main runs are the most important places and also the connecting routes in the home ranges occupied by the mice.

The mice leave tracks that enable us to find their habitual routes; these tracks are literally fingerprints. Since mice can only move along the floor, which in the zoo is usually dirty, they not only have dirty "fingers" but also dirty hands and feet; so much so that for the keen observer a conspicuous trail is left from their frequent comings and goings and the extermination plan can be based on the tracks they leave behind.

If the mouse runs are left undisturbed for some time the greasy black marks become increasingly obvious; this is because the mice not only urinate but they also defaecate somewhat at random. Droppings are likely to be found where they have had to make some extra effort, such as when jumping, climbing and balancing. Horses and elephants tend to defaecate under similarly strenuous exertions but mice are particularly prone to do so.

In contrast to the large mammals these tiny ones lose a fair number of hairs en route; these adhere to the sticky urine paths which are also strewn with faecal droppings and they build up on places that project to form what are described technically by research workers as marking pads. Through constant use, perhaps over many generations, these flat pads may grow into real marking towers; they are spaced at intervals along the route according to the gait of the mouse.

These strange looking structures occur only in conditions that are ideal for mice; I was unfortunate to find them for instance in the bird house of one of the zoos which I took over. An American colleague who was studying the habits of mice under optimal conditions in a room set aside for the purpose, eventually found them in the research room where the mice were allowed to do just as they liked. In 1955 I summarized my findings to date on this subject in the journal *Der zoologische Garten*, under the title *Mice in the Zoo*. Since then my knowledge of mice has increased somewhat.

It has become clear to me for instance that mice have no means of communicating to each other where their runs lead to; for an animal that makes such excellent runs this seems paradoxical. This was a surprise and a disappointment to me in view of the fact that the mouse is an animal which shares the same zoological class as man. Other animals which are at a much lower level in the zoological system, are able to communicate information; insects, for instance, such as bees have developed their methods of communication to an astonishingly high degree and they are able to pass on an amazing amount of information with incredible precision.

As the classical researches of Karl von Frisch (1964) have shown, bees are capable of communicating to each other the direction, distance and abundance of a given source of food by means of a special dance and other signals. Martin Lindauer (1955), a former pupil and colleague of von Frisch, has shown that the bees are also able to come to an understanding with each other about the search for a new home in an equally extraordinary manner. After bees have swarmed from the parent hive and settled in a cluster, some of them are sent out to act as scouts; they go off in search of possible places which may serve as a new home and on their return they report to the others, conveying information about the direction and distance in which they have found a nesting place of a certain size and quality. A kind of vote is then taken, the choice always falling on the best of the sites reported. The information conveyed by the returning scout workers is so clearly indicated that on several occasions Lindauer, who was watching the dance virtually as an eavesdropper, was able to get to the place before the bees actually swarmed there.

In some ways we humans ought to be thankful that mice do not have any system of communication, otherwise thousands of them would be able to invade a foodstore. On the other hand it is somewhat embarrassing to the biologist to have to admit that a mammal —albeit a small one—should be so lacking in talent in this respect.

There have been two occasions in particular on which I have been astounded by the inability of mice to communicate.

In one of the zoos of which I was director, there was a tall building that housed the birds; it had a long asphalt stairway that was used as a service passage, leading to the store-rooms and the reserve space on the upper floor; on my arrival I found that it was literally swarming with mice.

On both sides of the staircase, running all the way up, there was a conspicuous greasy blackish mouse run. The wooden door at the top of the stairs was gnawed through, as might be expected, and it gave access to the upper storey to the very active traffic from below. In accordance with the principle of "divide and rule", this important access point was made mouse-proof with a sheet of metal. By this means the main traffic artery between the two floors was ligatured. In spite of this it did not stop the flow of traffic on the staircase. Every night mice were caught in the traps placed on the steps. The mice repeatedly undertook the wearisome trip upwards to the doorway that had become impassable—and having achieved nothing came down again. I could not help feeling sorry for them; they reminded me of people plodding up the endless stairs of the Empire State Building only to arrive breathless at the top to see a notice saying the gallery was closed. In the case of the mice however one must point out that none of those disappointed was capable of warning the others that it met on the way down.

Another case of the inability of mice to communicate which struck me as even more grotesque occurred in a house in the country which we used to visit for a few weeks over a period of several years. In one room a pipe ran close to and parallel to the wall; it then bent round at a right angle through the wall and into the neighbouring room. Year after year I found little heaps of mouse droppings immediately below this place. If these were swept away there would be more droppings there on the following morning. This state of affairs was comparatively unimportant, although not particularly attractive but to a student of animal behaviour it gradually developed into an exciting puzzle. The bent pipe disappeared into a wall that was smooth and undamaged so the mice obviously could not come out from this point. This fact was beyond dispute. On the other hand there was access for mice at the other end of the pipe where it entered

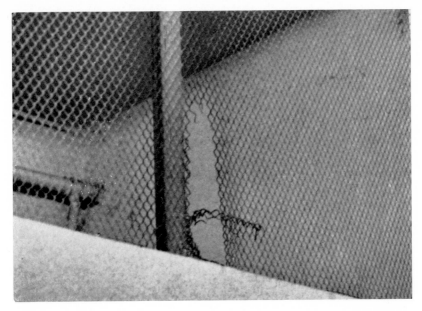

Fig. 174 A vertical piece of wire-netting, on which there is a mouse run, showing a section which has been corroded by mouse urine.

Fig. 175 Typical corrosion hole in a wire fence with marking cushion at the bottom.

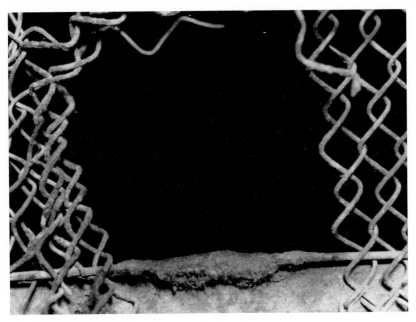

Fig. 176   A female visitor to the Zurich Zoo, who was apparently mentally deranged, managed to climb into the elephant den at night, by using an upturned dustbin; she was killed by the bull. At that time the window had no grating.

Fig. 177   On the morning after the night of the accident in November 1944 the Zurich City Police found the dismembered body of the woman; this is part of the photographic evidence which they took.

Fig. 178 Some zoos still serve as playgrounds for children and resting places for the aged. (Spring 1964).

Fig. 179 Many zoo visitors continue to believe that barriers are placed for them to climb over or slip under.

Fig. 180   The largest Elephant Seal (*Macrorhinus leoninus*) ever kept in captivity: Goliath, in Hagenbeck's Zoo at Stellingen. This animal weighed over 2·4 tons and consumed 180 lb of fish daily. It died in 1930 because a visitor had thrown the neck of a broken beer bottle into its mouth, resulting in an agonizing perforation of the gut.

the room. For years these non-communicating animals must have climbed the pipe at the accessible end and balanced themselves along its entire length until it disappeared into the smooth wall. Generations of mice must have been disillusioned by the climb and been forced to turn round, and go back the way they had come, having achieved nothing. This kind of behaviour would be inconceivable in bees; they tell each other exactly which routes lead to food and are therefore significant. Mice are resigned to senseless meanderings because of this lack of insight.

This does not apply, however, to their larger relatives the rats; in this case they do not repeatedly go astray and end up in blind alleys. Even attractive food may be regarded as suspect by rats and virtually branded as unfit for consumption; in this event the run will lead straight past it. F. Steiniger (1952, p. 36) comments on this point as follows: "When some unfamiliar object, such as a newly placed bit of poisoned bait, is rejected by the first rat that finds it, the object is not infrequently marked with scent by the rat; droppings or urine are deposited on it, with the result that none of the others will eat it." It is feasible therefore that rats receive a certain amount of information with the aid of scent substances and possibly also from other signals.

Another difference between rats and mice concerns the size of the area habitually occupied: the rat occupies an area that is relatively larger than that of the mouse. The area occupied by a mouse is also rather less flexible in that the rat will go over 100 yards from its home to collect food and it carries large scraps over considerable distances along its runs. Broadly speaking one can say that the rat brings the food to the nest, whereas the mouse has a definite tendency to build its nest within the source of food, as has already been shown in the example of the felt shoes and the loaf of bread. Having a nest which is barely the size of a man's fist the mouse can afford to build in such bizarre places. The mouse is smaller than the rat and has a greater number of enemies, and for this reason long runs in the open would be much too dangerous for it. The rat, on the other hand, is more heavily built and well able to defend itself; it is not every cat or owl for instance that will risk an encounter with a rat.

Rats sometimes set up a regular shuttle service between the source of food and their home; the runs then look like well-defined foot-paths. They have regular behaviour patterns according to a time-space system and follow an extraordinarily precise time-table, particularly on the first shuttle trips which begin just before dusk; for this reason it is easy for an experienced marksman to shoot a number of rats with a small calibre gun. It would scarcely be possible however to exterminate a whole population in this way because the intelligent survivors change their time-space system as a result of the unpleasant experience; shooting them thus becomes an increasingly wearisome and time-consuming task. Rats often make burrows in the grounds of the zoo and when this happens, according to the particular circumstances, it is recommended that the animals not killed by shooting should be exterminated by using gas cartridges. The poison gases are heavier than air and they sink into the lower parts of the rat burrows; they act so quickly that this method may be regarded as humane. Naturally one must make sure that the gas cannot injure zoo animals by drifting away into low-lying places.

It is very much simpler to destroy rats that are inside buildings; destruction can be carried out with the same type of trap recommended for mice but proportionately bigger. Similarly, groups of traps as distinct from single ones must be set along the runs.

In deciding where to place the traps one must stick to the rule that they should never be put out in the open stretches; they must always be at the point where the animal is forced to go through a narrow place, e.g. in front of gnawed holes and cracks. Traps for mice should always be laid close to the walls as these rodents are extremely wary of open spaces. One often sees traps set by people in front of a mouse-hole but at a distance—perhaps in the corner of a room—on the naïve assumption that the mouse will go straight out of the hole into the trap, like water from a tap. Nothing could be more wrong. No mouse will shoot out of its hole rashly, but like all animals leaving their home it does so only after plenty of sniffing and making sure that all is well, and it never goes diagonally across the room but always along the walls. One must therefore set a sufficient number of the prescribed traps in the correct manner against the wall, so that as the mouse comes along the wall it sets the trip-board in motion which leads to the fatal blow. Once an enclosed area, such as a store-room, has been freed of mice in this way the holes must be blocked up, if necessary with a mixture of cement and glass-wool; also, every adjoining room, at the sides as well as above and below, must be sealed off at the beginning of the campaign, in other words every connecting link must be made mouse-proof.

All mouse droppings must be carefully swept up and a periodical check should be made to see if fresh ones appear. As already mentioned, these checks are necessary even in mouse-proof buildings; they can be carried out very easily if all material (e.g. bales of hay and straw, packages of food, boxes, and all kinds of stored goods) are properly stacked. In the first place they should not be pushed right up against the wall and secondly, they should not be placed right on the ground. There is no doubt that some space is lost by observing a rule of 8 inches away from the wall and 14 inches above the ground, nevertheless one is certain of losing less material; stacking stores in this way is less inviting to the mice and their presence is also revealed immediately. Naturally the posts supporting the raised floor should not be climbable; the most suitable material for this is smooth metal tubing cemented in position.

In the fight against mice in the zoo, it is not only unnecessary to use fat or any other kind of bait, but one can also spare oneself the trouble of boiling the traps. The prospects of the catch are not affected by traces of blood from mice, or other smells as a result of their having been used. This has been found from practical experience, and it also corresponds with the experimental findings of K. Herter (1944). The importance however of setting the traps in groups against the walls on the main runs cannot be too strongly emphasized.

13

The Public in the Zoo

Zoos are visited by hundreds of thousands of people every year and even the smaller zoos have huge numbers of visitors. Not all of them however can be regarded as an asset for among the many thousands there are always a few negative or undesirable elements. Fortunately the overwhelming majority of visitors cause far less trouble in the zoo than the small minority. The former go to the zoo out of a healthy interest and for sheer relaxation and recreation; the latter however have a perverted outlook or criminal tendencies. There are various gradations between these two extremes among the undesirable elements but the rank and file can be regarded as lacking in discipline. These are the people who leave litter lying about, tread on the flower-beds and pick the flowers, disturb the animals, climb over barriers, ignore notices forbidding feeding and so on.

The negative and undisciplined visitors are by no means peculiar to zoological gardens; generally speaking they are found regularly wherever crowds collect, whether at an exhibition, a sporting event, in a public park or to enjoy some other amenity. Such people have to be reckoned with but there is no doubt that things could be run much better, more pleasantly and more cheaply without them.

All visitors who deviate from normal behaviour are virtually problem children and they are a source of considerable worry to the zoo; people who get drunk, the mentally and physically sick (such as epileptics) endanger the whole running of the zoo; they are also a nuisance to other visitors, to the staff and primarily to themselves. For this reason they should not be allowed inside the zoo but if they happen to get in and are discovered later on they should be escorted from the premises. From my own experience I would say that visitors on New Year's Day can be a particular worry because they tend to stagger into the zoo after a night of celebration. The Swiss zoos are open very early, by about 8 a.m. or earlier, and relatively often the zoo is the destination for such early morning walks. Incidents of this kind may even occur in midsummer. Thus in Zurich Zoo on 10 July 1951 a very drunken youth fell into the polar bear pool, when for some reason best known to himself he decided to give a gymnastic display on the barrier. The female polar bear leapt at the intruder but the youth managed to fend her off for a moment with his feet. He was in an extremely dangerous situation but visitors rushed to his assistance and managed to get a ladder to him which was kept nearby for cases of emergency. He was able to escape from the polar bear with the aid of the ladder but not from the police.

The feeble-minded and mentally sick need to be particularly carefully escorted and supervised in the zoo. As already mentioned, a mongol boy visiting Zurich Zoo in 1957 managed to evade his escort; he got into a staff room and from there he went into an outside cage occupied by adult chimpanzees. Another subnormal child climbed over the barrier of the same cage (which was removed in 1959) in order to stroke the chimpanzees and he had a finger joint bitten off. Even normal adults however often have ideas about zoo animals and their behaviour that are completely erroneous. For instance, when the same adult chimpanzees were transferred to the new anthropoid ape house in 1959, many friends of the zoo thought that the keepers would lead these large apes by the hand to their new quarters, and they wanted to send in their names as spectators! In fact very strong boxes are needed for transporting adult anthropoid apes. As was shown in detail in Chapter 11, every change of accommodation gives rise to exceptional excitement, a condition in which even tame animals are not to be relied upon.

Some parents pay little attention to their children while they are going round the zoo. Even small children are allowed to jump and climb around in the most dangerous manner and it is enough to make one's hair stand on end. Also adults often set a bad example to the children in that they try to stroke the animals or make them excited, disregarding all the notices, and often in spite of direct warnings by the zoo staff. There are always those who know better; many of these foolish people however, feel compelled to show how brave they are or they pose as privileged experts.

People who play jokes are also very stupid and on April Fool's Day—which fortunately only comes once a year—men and women who happen to have the name of an animal—e.g. Miss Bird, Mr Bear, Fish, Lion etc. are asked to ring a certain telephone number, which is the number of the zoo. In the smaller zoos this may mean that the whole day's work is wasted in the office. Over 100 calls of this nature were received by Zurich Zoo on 1 April 1964. In a previous year I tried to warn everyone with likely names by an announcement in the press; the net result was that the number of these senseless calls was if anything even larger than ever.

It was somewhat reassuring to us to find a report on the same subject in the excellent popular magazine *Zoonooz* of the San Diego Zoo (May 1958), under the appropriate title of "Zoo Unintelligence"; this large zoo had to deal with some 800 telephone calls of a similar nature for Messrs Fox, Wolf, Ella Fant, Bird etc. Naturally this meant that many important telephone calls were lost through the lines being engaged. It would seem therefore that this is a "joke" that is internationally popular.

At the pay-desks in zoos where children are admitted at reduced prices, it repeatedly happens that an adult will crouch in front of the pay-desk and ask for a child's ticket. Each adult seems to think that this game is entirely original but in fact this trick is played all over the world.

An international phenomenon of quite a different kind which has only been observed in Switzerland since the Second World War, has origins that are still wrapped in mystery; this is the habit of throwing coins into all the open pools, preferably into the crocodile pools. An analysis of one year's takings from the crocodile pools in Zurich Zoo showed coins from 19 different nations. The Swiss coins soon provided a special attraction to the local youngsters. They provided themselves with long sticks with chewing gum stuck on the end and they fished the more valuable coins out with this equipment—provided the keeper did not see them.

Comparative psychology is indeed forced upon one in the zoo. Both sides of the bars have to be kept under control and it is the side where the humans are that usually causes the most trouble. This state of affairs was particularly brought home to me in the anthropoid ape house at Zurich Zoo when glass panes were fitted in front of the bars. To make the glass visible and thus prevent visitors from knocking their heads against it, we had circles of coloured paint put on the inside of the glass. The chimpanzees, however, scratched the paint off so we then painted them on the side of the public. It was now the turn of *Homo sapiens* to scratch them off with his finger nails. The division between the two was only a third of an inch thick in this case.

At an earlier date (1950, p. 174) I attempted to classify the negative elements amongst zoo visitors into typical groups. Today I would submit the following categories:

1. Petty criminals

a. Swindlers who avoid paying entrance money. These people enter the zoo illegally without a ticket, by pressing themselves in with the crowd, by climbing the railings or slipping in through service doors etc.

b. Damagers and destroyers. These break the protective glass on labels, destroy horticultural exhibits and technical equipment, scratch the aquarium and vivarium glass, scatter foreign bodies and feed animals although forbidden to do so.

c. Thieves. From the viewpoint of zoo biology no particular significance need be attributed to pickpockets and cloakroom thieves, or to people who break into cash offices etc., because they occur everywhere. On the other hand, thieves who steal animals deserve special mention here; these are often pet-keepers with an obsession who are interested in rare species and as a result such people are confined to a small circle. Rabbits, birds and animals known to be edible are stolen for quite different reasons, namely for the pot. Strictly speaking intruders who open cages or smash them up out of a desire to "free" certain animals—birds are often involved—can properly be described as psychopaths.

Where thefts of a major kind are concerned or rare and costly animals are killed by giving them bad food or dangerous foreign bodies, such offenders should not of course be classed as petty criminals.

2. Psychopaths

a. Sexual perverts. The most harmless of these are the animal voyeurs, who are drawn as though by a magnet to every case of mating behaviour; such people are part of the permanent fixtures of every zoo. Then there is the type who concentrates not on the animals but on women, young people and children, eyeing them in dark and secluded corners of the zoo. There are also people who are apparently sexually stimulated by the sight of some animal or other, e.g. a long-necked terrapin, and consequently visit it with inordinate frequency. People who practise sodomy make extremely unpleasant visitors in the zoo. As is well known the most improbable things happen in this field. When something occurs that cannot be explained otherwise one should always make enquiries about visitors and also among members of staff who are not well known and not regarded as absolutely reliable.

b. Sadists and publicity-seekers. This is an exceptionally important group as far as zoo biology is concerned, not only because these people turn up relatively frequently but also because they are extremely dangerous to the animal stock. The sadist tries to torment an animal, sometimes torturing it to death by injuring it with some implement, inflicting cuts or wounds with razor blades, splinters of glass, pins of various kinds or by stabbing at it with a walking-stick, a sharp piece of wire or similar object. The seeker after immortality commits some gruesome act or indulges in some dangerous piece of mischief that may well be completely unpredictable, in order to read about his deeds or misdeeds in the papers the following day and thus achieve "fame" through notoriety.

3. Murderers and suicides

These people make use of the special conditions of the zoo, which provide opportunities that are not available elsewhere, in order to carry out their crime under cover of the zoo's routine, thus making it less easy in some circumstances to detect the crime. Suicides usually want to let themselves be killed by large carnivores that are alleged to be dangerous or by animals such as elephants that are presumed to be carnivores, either at night in the absence of witnesses or even in broad daylight in the presence of horrified spectators.

There is no doubt that every zoo, except for those that have only

Fig. 181   It is well known that people will scribble on walls and carve their initials on trees, but in a zoo they will even scrawl on the skin of the rhino while it is asleep.

Fig. 182   There are no animals in zoos that bite and snap but only careless humans, who want to 'see' with their hands instead of with their eyes. Even in museums people are not permitted to touch the exhibits.

Fig. 183 A selection of stones which were thrown in a single day at the Beavers by undisciplined visitors in the Zurich Zoo.

Fig. 184 A small selection of knives, which were offered to the apes with a slice of apple or similar titbit and thus got into their cages. The apes were far more interested in the knives than in the intended titbits.

Fig. 185 A bird cage, whose inmate was 'freed' by an eccentric visitor to the zoo.

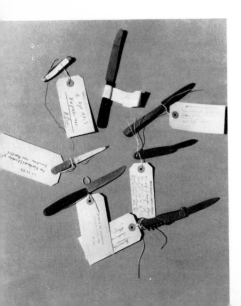

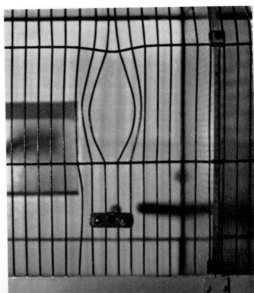

recently opened, would be able to provide data to illustrate these tragedies with the possible exception of murder. Even the latter crime however is not confined to trashy zoo novels but also takes place in reality. Only one case of murder will be referred to here. This was reported by Sir Peter Chalmers Mitchell who was Secretary of The Zoological Society of London for many years and was well known for a series of valuable publications. His account of what took place is taken from The Centenary History of The Zoological Society (1929, p. 238 *et seq.*) and reads as follows: "In 1928 a sad and inexplicable event took place, unprecedented in the history of the Society. Sayaid Ali, a Mohammedan mahout, was killed in the Gardens, and San Dwe, a younger Burmese Karen Christian, also an elephant keeper, was found guilty of murder, sentenced to death, but afterwards reprieved and the sentence commuted to imprisonment for life. During the end of 1921 and the following winter, Indiarana, a fine female elephant presented by the Maharajah of Patiala, which had been accustomed to carry children in the Gardens, became extremely nervous, and the Council decided that it was unsafe to use her in the Gardens. At the suggestion of Mr Alred Ezra, a Member of the Council, it was agreed to procure the services of a highly skilled Indian mahout, to see if Indiarana could be brought to reason. Sayaid Ali was selected and reached the Gardens in July 1922. He was extremely successful and very soon the elephant was more docile than she had ever been, became much attached to him and learned many engaging tricks. Disliking the winter, Sayaid Ali returned to India in October, but came back in 1923, as he was a great attraction in the Gardens. In addition to his pay he earned handsome sums from visitors, chiefly because he had taught the elephant to pick up and give to him any coins thrown on the ground. He stayed until October 1925 but returned again for five weeks in 1927 in charge of an elephant that had been presented to us. On June 6, 1928 he came again, bringing two elephants which Mr Ezra had commissioned him to select as a gift to the Society. The dates are of some importance, as strange myths grew up round the fatality.

In the summer of 1926, a white elephant, the property of Saw Po Min, the leader of the Karen Christians, was lent to the Society for the summer, and was kept in a house which we had set up for it, with a normally coloured companion, and the owner and a staff of Karens. In late autumn of the same year the white elephant went on a tour in America with the Karens. During the American tour, San Dwe went to America direct from Burma, to join the other Karens, and came here with them and the elephant in November 1927. They were allowed to remain in the Gardens until January 31, 1928 whilst shipment to India was being arranged. They actually remained at Barking until April, and then when the party was shipped, San Dwe, at his own request, was taken on by us and put in charge of two rather refractory elephants. White elephants have many legends attached to them, and the owners always maintained that they were in danger of their lives from Burmese who resented the sacred creature having been removed from its native land. But it is of importance to note that San Dwe had never met Sayaid Ali until the latter came to the Gardens in June 1928, and that Sayaid Ali had never been in England with the white elephant. When the two keepers were together at the Gardens they shared quarters in the special house that had been built originally for the white elephant. Sayaid Ali, as the senior and more experienced man, was given charge of the two refractory elephants and San Dwe was given sole care of a very young elephant of which he became fond and had already begun to teach to do tricks. Both men were well liked by the other keepers, and, as far as we knew, they were on good terms. The Mohammedan was a tall and powerful man, but quite good-natured; the Karen was slightly built, much younger, bright and lively, and a good musician. Then one night Sayaid Ali was brutally murdered in his sleep and all the evidence pointed to San Dwe as the criminal. We thought it right to give the man, who, in a sense, was in our charge, the help of first-rate solicitors and counsel, but the facts were irresistible. The motive was never known; there was no sufficient reason to suppose that it was an attempt at robbery, but the Oriental mind works in a way which is not easy for us to understand. There was an absurd rumour that the murder had taken place on the same evening as the white elephant died in India. That was not so, and there was no connection of any kind between the crime and the elephant." Mitchell concludes his account with this statement but the case nevertheless serves as an example of the special conditions under which a murder may take place in the zoo.

Suicides are more common in the zoo than murders. The Zurich Zoo has unfortunately not been spared in this respect. K. Huber (1954, p. 88) who wrote the history of the first 25 years of this zoo mentions the subject very briefly: "finally I would like to refer to the mysterious incident which took place on the night of 1 November 1944 and had a fatal outcome. It must be assumed from the circumstances that on the night in question a mentally deranged woman climbed through a small window into the elephant den and was crushed to death by the alarmed elephants." Having killed the woman, however, the elephants were apparently not satisfied and although it seems highly remarkable from the ethological point of view, the human corpse was found broken up into small pieces; parts of the musculature were parted from the bones and squashed out of the skin. None of the corpse had been eaten. Although many people think that elephants are carnivorous they are in fact strictly vegetarian.

In a work on punishable offences in zoological gardens by the former zoo director I. Krumbiegel (1960) numerous examples are given—from thefts of geese to sadists and suicides—which could be fitted into the classification given above. The author also mentions a trick of the pickpockets which is peculiar to zoos; by raising the alarm that the lions have got out, an artificial panic is created which enables the pickpockets to get to work more easily in the crowd.

I could also cite numerous examples from the Zurich Zoo of nearly all the types of crime mentioned in my classification. I will restrict myself however to two cases, which incidentally could have been very harmful to the miscreant.

The first case concerned the theft of a very poisonous dragonfish or lionfish (*Pterois volitans*) from one of the covered marine tanks in our aquarium. The theft was thought to be the work of an amateur aquarist who kept marine tanks at his home and knew how to look after fish of this kind. However, there are a number of amateur aquarists in every Swiss city and the person responsible was never discovered. While the thief was catching up this poisonous fish he was in far greater danger than he himself probably realized. A single prick from one of the many spines, each of which has a venom gland, would be sufficient to produce the most frightful pain and might even have fatal results. There is of course yet another possibility which is that the thief was not concerned to acquire this valuable fish for himself but merely to harm the zoo by destroying it.

The second case which I have selected from the wealth of unpleasant incidents involved the theft of exotic lizards from the tropical vivarium. The reptiles stolen were Australian blue-tongued skinks, stump-tailed skinks and bearded lizards. Once again we naturally suspected an amateur obsessed by his passion for pet-keeping, but in this case we were wrong. In a very short time the Zurich police succeeded in tracing the missing reptiles to pet-shops in the city, to whom they had been sold very cheaply under the pretext of giving up vivaria because of moving house. An arrest was soon made and the offender in fact was not one of a circle of enthusiastic keepers of reptiles. He was the type of person who steals anything: motor-cycles, radios, books or animals.

Apart from the fact that he was caught so quickly he had considerable luck because there were several specimens of the very poisonous genus *Heloderma* in the same vivarium. It was evidently pure chance—and lucky for him—that he did not happen to pick these up. Had he done so he would not have got very far.

In a chapter headed "The public in the zoo" this is a somewhat macabre subject and I will say no more about it but in the context of this book it would have been wrong to have made no reference to it at all.

* * *

As I have already emphasized in Chapter 3 the zoos of the present day, taken as a whole, are the expression of a world-embracing phenomenon and they make an impact on everybody or at least on everyone who lives in a big city. The concentration of enormous numbers of humans in very restricted spaces is particularly characteristic of our time; this trend has some alarming aspects because it gives rise to a disease of civilization that as yet has scarcely been taken into account. This is the hunger for nature, a kind of psychological deficiency phenomenon which can only be met by making secondary areas of nature available to man as emergency outlets. Parks and zoos fulfil this role.

The importance to public health of open spaces and parks as the "lungs of the big city" has been recognized for some time. I mentioned the present position on this subject briefly in Chapter 3 and there is no need to go into further detail here. In general, however, these green oases are somewhat static in appearance as no animals are visible. For this reason zoological gardens form an essential ingredient today in the life of every big city—in other words they are part of the habitat of modern man. Man needs to have access to nature but as a result of the expansion of large towns and the mechanization of the land, the countryside has been partly destroyed and the primary places of nature have been driven right back. Zoological gardens form secondary places and these provide man with the necessary contact with nature. They are scarcely less urgent than, say, an airport. Just as the latter satisfies a technical requirement, the zoo satisfies a biological requirement of our time, which is equally strong, namely the satisfaction of the deep-seated hunger for nature which cannot be shed from one generation to the next.

Nature and technical progress are two concepts that are symbolically opposed to each other and it is worth mentioning perhaps that the relationship between them is a close one. Admittedly they are strange partners but they need not be enemies. In fact the zoo, with all its technical equipment provides a good example of the virtues of partnership. Without lighting, filtration and the regulation of temperature only a few animal species could be kept in the zoo.

It is also true that as technology becomes more widespread, it intrudes increasingly upon the professional and private spheres of man's activities; as this takes place man's need to occupy himself (at least in his spare time) with non-technical matters, that is with animals and plants, becomes more powerful and pressing. The remarkable growth of zoos throughout the world has already been mentioned in Chapter 3. It is quite clear that this is a definite reaction against the alarming penetration of technology; further evidence of this reaction is to be seen in the rapid growth of the number of nature-lovers who keep aquaria and vivaria in their homes, as colourful cameos of the plant and animal kingdoms. It is indeed a pleasure today to see how interior decorators and architects have incorporated motifs from nature into their designs for shop windows, hotel entrance halls and well laid out rooms; branches of trees with the bark still on them or designs with gnarled roots have become a cult. By contrast, people going for a walk in the woods merely stumble over such things without even noticing them and country people simply use them as firewood. It takes the eye of an artist or the hunger for nature of the city-dweller, isolated in artificial surroundings, to perceive the beauty of a simple piece of wood and the charm with which nature endows it. There are many other ways in which man is turning away from technology that are symptomatic of this reaction. Thus in the field of employment a significant number of the younger generation are recruited as animal keepers from technical occupations. Due to increasing mechanization, rationalization and automation the first job that these young people learn can no longer be described as a craft and it does not appeal to them. In spite of the financial attractions, they take a dislike to looking after one anonymous machine after another to the accompaniment of the stereotyped sounds of metal parts that are dead; instead they yearn to be an individual dealing with living things under the open sky and experiencing the natural changes of the weather and the seasons. Another example of this trend is to be found in the increasing proportion of students at various agricultural colleges who come from the city. There is also an increasing interest in good nature books, wildlife films and magazines on animals. The hunger for nature of the man who is so to speak imprisoned in the big city is shown above all by the sharply rising curve of zoo visitors. Account should be taken of this growing interest both in quantitative and qualitative terms. The fact that there is an overall increase in the number of zoos and that they are being enlarged everywhere is not enough in itself. The motivation underlying this change and the newly developing interests must also be borne in mind.

In earlier times, when menageries were in vogue, the public expected in the main to gaze in astonishment at living curiosities from distant lands in old-fashioned, prison-like pits or dens; today the requirements are totally different, and at the same time the demands have become much greater.

The modern zoo visitor—fortunately—wants to see families of healthy animals in surroundings that are biologically suitable and aesthetically satisfying; the conditions under which the animals live must correspond as far as possible with the natural habitat so that the animals can express themselves fully in appropriate behaviour. The scene offered to the observer must be a pleasant one which he can enjoy in the same way as a beautiful landscape or a pretty bit of countryside. For this reason the attractiveness of the lay-out of the whole exhibit is of great importance; at one time plant decorations were completely ignored but they are now considered to be as important as the animal itself. The living animal behaving naturally can only be described as an inimitable work of art provided by nature; the zoo must do all it can to supply a suitable framework and present the animal in a way that it deserves.

In any case this is the general tendency nowadays. Where the results do not appear to be up to standard this is because there are either financial difficulties or a lack of understanding from the view-point of zoo biology.

It is important that the public as well as the animals should feel at home in the zoo. People come to see the animals as a form of recreation and there is a peculiar relationship between the animals and their visitors. It may be that even the modern man of our urban civilization retains some element of awareness concerning his surroundings that tells him when all is well and that this sense, carried on from one generation to another, makes him conscious of the harmony that obtains when an animal is completely in accord with its surroundings. In other words the spectator may well be receptive to some of this harmony in the relationship of animal to animal and of animal to environment.

The aim therefore is to make everything as natural or as similar to nature as possible in the interest of both the animals and the visitor. Plants play an important part in this, as already mentioned. They should be arranged so that they help to make the atmosphere as authentic as possible for animal and man, whether the desired background is a tropical rain-forest or a desert. The visitor looking at tropical animals must receive something of the illusion of the tropical habitat with its luxuriance of vegetation.

A demand for this, particularly in some American zoos, has recently led however to a departure from sound practice, that is as curious as it is questionable from the viewpoint of zoo biology. Generally speaking it is not easy to obtain tropical vegetation in sufficient quantity and variety in the temperate and cold regions of our globe. It is expensive and difficult to maintain, in particular because some animals destroy all the plants immediately, by nibbling and eating them, breaking the stems or digging them up etc. Some people therefore have taken to using artificial plants made of plastic, a practice that should be avoided at all costs on the principles of zoo biology. Nowadays a highly developed industry offers a surprisingly rich assortment of astonishingly natural-looking artificial plants and flowers and the temptation therefore is that much greater.

Zoological museums should certainly make use of this modern material but zoological gardens ought never to do so. Logically the next step would be to put plastic animals in among the plastic plants and deceive people by making the animals move about with the aid of suitably camouflaged machinery.

Is this an exaggerated fear for the future? Certainly not. It may sound like pure fantasy at present as far as Europe is concerned but in America it has already been done. In fact Disneyland in California is a town of fantasy built by Walt Disney as a gigantic tourist attraction; it is more than a town, it is like fairyland itself depicted in American superlatives. It is also a huge commercial enterprise.

One part of this dreamland for instance contains a jungle. Ready for a romantic and adventurous journey, the visitors board a small longboat which travels along a typical winding tropical river; as the boat sets off the captain loads his heavy revolver, ready to meet all eventualities. There are numerous adventures awaiting the occupants of the boat but I will only mention the herd of elephants which are surprised while bathing at a bend in the meandering river. Among the herd are some young elephants which splash about in the water, flapping their ears and squirting water from their trunks. The models are so remarkably true to life that even zoo experts have to look twice to make sure that a few live young elephants have not invaded Disneyland and joined the extraordinarily lifelike models.

One can only point out that the fake zoo already exists in Disneyland with its automatic plastic animals in the plastic jungle and with all the appropriate jungle noises recorded on tape. In other habitats of Disneyland one can see plastic deer fighting one another; there are behaviour patterns to be seen in a group of black bears, such as the marking of a tree, which only a trained worker on behaviour could simulate with such accuracy.

The functions of the zoo have been confused with those of the museums and waxworks for a very long time and this confusion still exists today. The attempt to introduce artificial plastic plants into the zoo touches on basic principles and calls for a fresh appraisal of the situation, with a clear definition of what the zoo means at the present time.

It is worth mentioning in passing that as well as animal species which destroy plants in the zoo there are also some which help to preserve certain plants. Thus for example in Zurich Zoo in the enclosure with Himalayan black bears, Malay bears and sloth bears, small fig trees thrive which have evidently developed from seeds of the figs fed to the bears; after being passed out in the faeces the seeds grow in the crevices of the stone slabs. In San Francisco Zoo an adult chimpanzee tolerates a small shrub in its cage; baboons in Brookfield Zoo in Chicago do no harm to certain plants and so on.

Another reason for retaining live plants as distinct from artificial ones is that amongst other things living plants have an important function in that they serve as biological or ecological indicators: they show whether temperature, humidity, ventilation, lighting etc. are working properly and whether the optimal micro-climate appropriate to the animals is present. Plants are also important indicators of conditions in the ground. It is essential therefore that the plants shown in a zoo should be just as real as the animals.

To recapitulate briefly: man's hunger for nature has been deeply rooted in him for generation after generation. A zoo has the important function of replacing the primary sources of nature, which are rapidly dwindling, and thus offering the big-city dweller nature at secondhand. At the same time a zoo must also serve the purposes of popular education and scientific research, which should benefit not only the animals but also man, through the comparative approach. Zoo biology can be enriched by many different disciplines and for its part it is in a position to promote many branches of science. Finally the zoo should be a refuge for animal species that are in danger and thus provide a centre for the vital task of animal and nature conservation. It is not a case of preserving preparations and specimens but of conserving live species, the animals living together in family groups and retaining their characteristic behaviour in the purest possible form.

All this needs to be constantly stressed because from the time of the cabinets of curiosities there has been—and still is in some quarters—a lack of clarity concerning the widely divergent tasks of museums and zoos. The principle that the museum is concerned with dead material and the zoo exclusively with the living is quite clear but this is not the only difference. There are zoos for instance which collect species out of a desire to exhibit representatives of as many species as possible. This particular objective, however, should be left entirely to the museum; in the zoo such an aim can only lead to the presentation of unbiological units, e.g. to endless rows of small bird cages, often stacked one above the other and each containing a single individual, or sometimes even two or three representatives of the species in the same cage.

This kind of exhibit shows a total misunderstanding of the functions of the zoo, which I have come across in more than one of the zoos that I have taken over. A zoo's ambition should be directed not towards exhibiting the largest possible number of species, but towards the most natural presentation of a selection of breeding groups, chosen to represent certain aspects. The final aim should be the achievement of breeding successes because these are the fruits of keeping animals according to correct biological principles.

The reproductive behaviour is the *crucial part* of the total behaviour. When breeding does not take place something is wrong with the methods of keeping the animals; reproductive behaviour is therefore the decisive factor, the touchstone of zoo biology.

In this important aspect the zoos have made considerable progress in the last two decades; in general the results have been gratifying. It has been shown that better accommodation and improved diet have helped many animal species to a more natural, indeed to an optimal development of their behaviour. Some of the species which were previously thought to be impossible to breed are now doing so. These include rhinoceros, okapi, gorilla, cheetah, giant panda, Malay bear and sloth bear, flamingo, Congo peacock, gerenuk, kea, giant tortoise, *Heloderma* and many others, some of which are even breeding regularly.

Based on the principle of steadily improved living conditions the animals in the zoo must be shown in typical family or herd groups, behaving in an undisturbed manner, free from stress. As already mentioned this function of the zoo is of the greatest importance because it enables the big-city dweller to have an excellent opportunity of observing and enjoying animals that are almost completely natural. There is hardly any truly wild life left nowadays; animals can no longer live wild in the sense that they used to, not even in national parks and reserves. Even though it is necessary for man to play some part in these reserves, his role can scarcely be described as a natural one.

This state of affairs leads us to an important conclusion which is fraught with consequence of a serious nature, namely that in the last few decades a far-reaching change has occurred in the places where animals live. As a result of the growing needs of man and the increasing application of modern techniques, the wild animals living free in their natural habitats are constantly being forced to retreat; this applies particularly to the larger animals. At the same time there has been an increase in the number of animals that have moved into cities all over the world and these now occupy territories that are under the protection of man. At present there are roughly five hundred zoos in the world and if one reckons up the large numbers of zebras, giraffes, chimpanzees, elephants, lions, tigers, hippopotamuses, antelopes etc. which are kept in these zoos, the sum total represents herds of gigantic proportions. A large and imposing fauna is now living far from its original areas of distribution in the centres of large towns, in neo-habitats and reserves, and in newly fashioned habitats in the zoos situated in the big-city biotope.

A complete change has taken place in which the habitats of man and animals have been re-organized. We are all witnesses of this massive change; we are taking part in the transformation and we are also subjected to its influences. This vast and important event in the biological world has scarcely received any attention from the scientific side. Every zoo has its own problems but these are comparatively small and for large-scale research projects, which extend beyond the bounds of the zoo, unfortunately there seems to be a general lack of awareness and an absence of the means to deal with them.

The biological process that is involved in this transformation can only be compared in extent and importance with that of domestication, that is with the keeping of domestic animals by man. Nowadays we take the existence of domestic animals and their daily use for

277

granted but without them we would still be living at the stage of Stone Age man. The ability to live together in urban communities, the very existence of our civilization would be quite impossible without domestic animals.

There are various parallels to be drawn between domestication and civilization (H. Zeiss and K. Pintschovius 1944). The production of domestic animals out of wild ones has changed not only animals but man as well. The reciprocal effects between zoo animals and urban man, particularly in the psychological field, are more intimate than one might at first imagine. Some readers will doubtless laugh at this and regard it as a classic example of attaching undue weight to the importance of one's own profession. As far as I am concerned they can still laugh but I hope they will bear with me a little further in order to understand what I mean. We have to accept the fact that today we are already condemned to living among skyscrapers, surrounded by heavy traffic, power stations, and factories; we are also forced to accept fully automated farms for the production of protein. What a dismal world it would be if the only animals we had were pigs for fattening, cows for milk production, poultry for eggs, white mice and rats and perhaps a few others. Unfortunately we are already well on the way towards this state of affairs.

Anyone who doubts this is politely invited to inspect a large-scale American farm, fully automated, in which the "farmer" sits at a control panel. The small farms in the style of our grandfathers are rapidly becoming uneconomic. The more complete the automation the greater the profit; it is not only in America that profitability dictates future development. Even in a country the size of Switzerland one can already get a definite foretaste by studying modern methods of poultry farming and these should serve as an object lesson. Under the battery system the eggs are laid on a moving belt, passed along to the incubator, thence after hatching into the cages containing different age groups for rearing and fattening; still on the conveyor belt they pass through the killing machine and come out the other end bleeding and minus their heads. Before they are ready for the pot they are processed by other machines that pluck and eviscerate them. The entrails are passed automatically to the factories for the production of fat, that is, to live pigs. Like the hens, in many cases the pigs are nothing but abstract production units and they never see a patch of sky or a bit of green grass throughout their lives. In fact their lives could be better described as a wretched test-tube existence in an environment that is cluttered with machinery. Domestication has made these animals into mere caricatures of their original forms; their wild ancestors however were living only a few thousand years ago as wild fowl in the jungles of India and as wild pigs in the forests of Europe and Asia. Automation in the production of domestic animals can neither be challenged nor halted.

The second incontrovertible fact is that in historic times one species of wild animal after another has been exterminated by man and this process goes on continually and at an ever increasing rate. It is doubtful for example whether it will be possible to preserve the last of the Arabian oryx, which were given sanctuary in Arizona in 1964. In the case of the Tasmanian wolf, it must be accepted that by 1964 there were no living survivors. I will not cite here the long and macabre list of animals, both interesting and beautiful, which have been exterminated by man during recent years.

The extermination of wild life, like the increasing automation in the production of domestic animals, is not something that is happening only in far away places; it is also taking place in central Europe and indeed on our very doorstep. For instance I regard it as very doubtful, in fact extremely unlikely, that there are still otters living wild in Switzerland. Yet in 1914 E. A. Goldi stated in his book on the animal life of Switzerland (p. 251): "the number of otters killed every year is still in the neighbourhood of 200." During the last few decades wolf, wild cat, lynx, bear and beaver have been exterminated in Switzerland. After considerable trouble it has been possible to re-establish the alpine ibex which had been exterminated, and welcome efforts have been made at various times on behalf of the beaver.

Taking wildlife as a whole there can be no doubt as to the rapidity of its decline. In stemming the tide of this steadily increasing impoverishment, nature reserves and zoos are of the greatest importance. But nature reserves may be subjected to exceptional vicissitudes, as has been shown by the conditions in Africa following the movements for independence since 1960. In the Second World War we also experienced the destruction of zoos. These disasters indicate the need to get them recognized as part of our cultural heritage and therefore sacrosanct.

279

As already emphasized in Chapter 1, zoos are not merely zoological institutions but are cultural in the widest sense. Animals play a much greater role in our culture, in history, art and literature than most people suspect. This undoubtedly also applies to wild animals that are so seriously threatened in modern times. If we were to eliminate everything relating to wild animals from our art collections, from the literature and history of the world we should be left with a wretchedly truncated torso. If mankind were to be finally deprived of the opportunity to see lions and elephants, bears and crocodiles, antelopes and parrots, what a bleak outlook the future would hold. Under such circumstances the theory mentioned earlier regarding the psychological effect on man of the total removal of wild life would be seriously put to the test. As it is, my brief comments should have been sufficient to demonstrate that the disappearance of the wild animal would be a real loss to mankind, a fate which we must avoid.

The keeping of animals for domestic production has a purpose which is diametrically opposed to that of the zoological garden. Farm production moves away from nature in the interests of maximal increase in production; the zoos, on the other hand, aim at preserving natural features as far as this is possible. They have to fight against the phenomena of domestication, of which there are already signs, with all the means at their disposal. Both of these major undertakings are extremely important to mankind, but confusion still exists between them here and there. The differences are not clearly understood, misunderstandings arise and serious mistakes are made. To put up a fight against this is one of the first duties of zoo biology but it is by no means easy, as I attempted to show with regard to feeding methods.

It is far from every zoo that fully recognizes the basic requirement of avoiding all domestication effects in keeping wild animals. In view of this attention should be drawn to a remarkable book on diseases of civilization written by P. Bugard, M. Henry and L. Joubert (1962).

Although zoo animals were far from the minds of the authors when they wrote their book, nevertheless the text is of interest in this connection. The authors, a medical man, a veterinarian and a biochemist, were concerned only with indicating the danger of excessive domestication to the domesticated animal and to the humans feeding on domesticated animals. In issuing a warning on this subject they gave a clear and concise account of the effects of domestication:

"Man is largely dependent for his food on protein which is available to him in the form of domesticated animals (cattle, pigs, sheep, poultry etc.) but even today the supply of these is inadequate. The farmer therefore has to make every effort to produce the maximum amount of protein with the minimum of feeding-stuffs in the least possible time. The domesticated animal therefore becomes more and more a protein-producing machine; in order to satisfy man's hunger for protein the pressure for production is such that the animal's metabolism is forced in a way that is highly unnatural; the targets are early maturity and maximal growth with optimal utilization of the minimum amount of feeding-stuffs. This is a trend which leads away from the normal and natural and takes us to the frontiers of the abnormal and even beyond. This gives rise to serious disturbances of the metabolism, the hormone economy, the nervous system and of behaviour, and also makes the animal extremely susceptible to infection. Man not only feeds himself on these animals, but he is also subject to the harmful influences of civilization which correspond to the effects of domestication. The result is an increasing tendency towards degeneration; this manifests itself in such conditions as early maturity, excessive growth, metabolic diseases (diabetes, obesity), circulatory diseases, neuroses, susceptibility and pathological fatigue.

The ceaseless efforts of those who rear domestic animals to "improve" the performances of their stock to an excessive degree leads in fact to the reverse, namely to an increasing degeneration which reflects on man himself in much the same way. This so-called neopathology of domestic animals and mankind can only be recognized, studied and perhaps halted by making comparisons with organisms closer to nature, that is with wild animals and native races of man."

In our context it only remains to establish the immense importance of the points mentioned in relation to the keeping of wild animals in the zoo so that they can retain their natural character as much as possible. The production of protein must govern the conditions under which domestic animals are kept. The zoo's efforts on the other hand must in principle be directed towards a totally different goal; its wild animals must be kept in purely natural conditions and as free as possible from all effects of domestication. In the zoo therefore any rationalization of the techniques of husbandry, such as automatic or stereotyped feeding, is misplaced. The keeper ought not to be given the role of a robot or an automation engineer; on the contrary his role should be the old-fashioned one in which he is naturally accepted as a familiar fellow-being, or in some cases as a socially superior member of the species, the super-alpha animal.

All over the world zoos have already become important cultural institutions. Tomorrow and in the near future they will assume an even greater significance as reservoirs of original, natural behaviour. There are already generations of domestic cows in existence which have never had even a distant view of a bull. Artificial insemination is undertaken by the veterinarian and even artificial fertilization has been achieved with a view to producing a particularly valuable strain of animals, known for its good performance in relation to large yields of milk and meat.

The germ cell fertilized *in vitro* is implanted in an ordinary cow which merely represents a cheap test-tube, enabling further development to take place. For the purpose of increasing production artificial twin births can also be arranged.

This raises the question however of whether in the long run fertility will not be affected by the use of artificial insemination over generations and to what extent behaviour has already become simplified—or even degenerate—among domesticated animals which are mated by the male covering the female, a method which is already outdated. But what should our yardstick be? The aurochs is no longer with us—it became extinct in the 17th century and we are now only left with the related park cattle as the ancestors of domestic cattle. Thus we should take a look at the bison and study it in reserves or in zoos, preferably in the latter as they provide opportunities for detailed observation.

Things are not much better in the world of man—he too is exhibiting signs of tension as a result of domestication. Artificial insemination in man is also gaining ground, particularly in America at present—and this is raising exceptionally difficult problems which are not merely of a sociological and legal nature. In Italy, as might

Fig. 186   Simultaneous training of two Pilot Whales (*Globicephala*) in Marineland of the Pacific, California.

Fig. 187   A tame White Whale (*Beluga*) in the New York Aquarium on Coney Island.

Fig. 188   Simultaneous leap by two dolphins in Marineland of the Pacific (1 August 1962). Since then groups of several dolphins have been trained to give this beautifully synchronized performance, which requires exceptional concentration right from the start. As soon as the under-water command has been given through a hydrophone they dash off, perfectly in line.

be expected, artificial fertilization and test-tube culture have caused uproar.

Quite apart from these major problems gynaecologists often look to the zoo for information from the animal kingdom on superfecundation and superfoetation; they are interested in such matters as how the animals most similar to man behave in relation to the birth, how they deal with the placenta and start suckling, the duration of lactation and so on. There are large scientific primate centres which cannot provide the answers to even the simplest questions of this kind; this is because experimental work which necessitates separating the young immediately from the mother takes precedence over the study of natural behaviour. One must therefore turn to the zoos for this kind of information as in this respect they try to maintain conditions that are as close to nature as possible.

It was from a paper read at an international conference of zoo directors in 1964 that I learnt with horror of the confusion which still exists in some quarters regarding the basic functions of zoological gardens. It reached a climax with a recommendation to speed up the breeding of chimpanzees by removing the newly born young and rearing them artificially. Normally the mother does not become pregnant again until after weaning has taken place, that is for about three years, but after losing her young she can become pregnant again much earlier.

This is another case of a total confusion between the maintenance of wild animals in the zoo and the production methods of farming. Since chimpanzees are not eaten as a rule, the acceleration of their reproduction can only be for financial reasons. The zoo however ought never to develop into some kind of commercial factory for producing chimpanzees at a profit. On the contrary it should provide visitors and also research workers with the opportunity to observe the natural growth of these anthropoid apes in family groups, in which juvenile behaviour and the reciprocal relations between the mother, father and siblings can develop and the whole group can be seen in relationship to its surroundings, and so on. The first birth in captivity of a chimpanzee, indeed of any anthropoid ape, took place as long ago as the year 1915—and this was in far away Cuba. But there are still a humiliating number of questions left unanswered which are of the greatest interest to comparative biology and physiology.

U

These questions which are of direct interest to man could be answered today much better and with far greater accuracy if only the meagre funds available to zoos could be used for research work rather than for the improvement of the drains or the repair of rusty wire-netting. The fact that research work unfortunately comes last on the list in zoos has already been mentioned in Chapter 1. Whilst economy is still the order of the day in most zoos, man is making use of animals as pioneer cosmonauts and projecting them far into outer space for his own ends. Man appears to want to hold fast to the disastrous principle of studying the most distant and remote problems first whilst overlooking those that are near at hand.

It is a fact that today we know far less about the larger animals of the earth than about the very smallest things. In one sense inanimate matter is more real to us today than the largest living representatives of the animal kingdom—many of which are quite closely related to us. The efficiency of optical instruments and nuclear machines brings the remotest organisms closer to us than the largest forms of animal life and the smallest is made more manifest than the largest. This is all the more strange when you consider that the larger mammals are our contemporaries on earth and are living creatures of flesh and blood with emotions like us—even if to a lesser degree.

It is not exaggeration to say that in regard to what we know about these impressive fellow-inhabitants of our planet our knowledge, or lack of it, is more appropriate to the Dark Ages or to ancient times. In the field of elementary zoology we are like a Pliny, an Aristotle or a Herodotus as far as our knowledge goes in relation to many of the simplest facts about the life of the animals of the modern era. At the same time we are admitted in a Faustian atmosphere of necromancy to the secret world of the atoms and of the stars. There still exists an alarming gap in human knowledge which must eventually be filled in. The zoos are in a strong position to redress the balance with the wealth of animal life, in all its variety, that is collected and looked after by them.

Zoos are faced with all sorts of difficulties, many of them inconceivable, but they carry on and make every effort to contribute to the advancement of scientific knowledge. The development of the menagerie into the zoo, of the bear-pit into the equivalent of a home for the animal, as well as the steady and impressive increase in the variety of species which can now be bred successfully, are both striking and satisfying evidence of this progress.

Zoo biology has not stood still even though little is known about it. In spite of all the difficulties and the lack of full recognition progress is being made, and we can make some prognosis for the future.

First of all there is a shift of emphasis away from the technical aspects of pure animal husbandry to the biological, and in addition from the morphological to the psychological.

The discovery of the territory and of the social hierarchy formed an important milestone. This came with the realization that the so-called free-living animal does not live free but is restricted by considerations of space, time and individual relationships—in short, it is inescapably tied to a space-time system and to a social hierarchy. Linked with this is the fact that the zoo animal—provided it has suitable care and attention—does not feel like a prisoner but rather as the occupier of a territory.

Another milestone was the collapse of the concept of the animal as a dumb creature which was based on the theory that animals have no speech because they have nothing to say to each other. In actual fact the human ear is not delicate enough to perceive the finer distinctions of sound produced by animals and thus interpret them. Moreover it is now clear that many animals are far superior to us in respect of their sensory organization (ultra-sonic, ultra-violet radiation, radar, vibrations) and their reaction time etc; this also applies in certain other ways, even with regard to their brain structure.

Let us dwell for a moment on the subject of speech in animals. F. Kainz (1961) has written an excellent summary on this but he could well have done without adorning the word speech with inverted commas every time he uses it in connection with the speech of animals. The use of inverted commas in this way is completely superfluous because everyone knows that animals do not have any kind of human speech. Neither does any animal have a human skull or a human liver. Where would we be in comparative anatomy if we were to print the vertebral column of monkeys, the legs of the dog or the jaws of the rabbit in inverted commas, simply to indicate that these were not human vertebral columns, legs or jaws?

The speech of animals is different from that of man, but it is certainly something more than just a series of screams that happen to slip out. It is impossible to go into greater detail here on the sounds produced by many insects, birds, apes and whales; these have already been analysed and interpreted. In conclusion it should be pointed out that the finer points of animal speech can become apparent to us only in so far as technology is able to compensate for the inadequacy of the human sense of hearing. As a result we are forced to interpret the richness and variety of animal sounds visually by means of electronic apparatus, before we can even perceive them and subsequently interpret them. This means we should approach the subject with due circumspection.

A proper respect is something that we should constantly bear in mind in the zoo. For example every chimpanzee is far superior to us in strength and speed of reaction; a small bat is capable of an acoustic perception which extends far into the ultra-sonic range. When a venomous snake strikes it develops a speed that is too fast for our eyes; an electric fish can do something which we are unable to do and which we still do not fully understand. This applies also to the symbiosis between certain giant sea-anenomes and the anenome-fish (*Amphiprion*) and to thousands of other phenomena of animal life represented in a zoo.

The sheer size of an elephant compared with man is always disconcerting but it is also somewhat disturbing when one realizes that the brain of an elephant is about four times that of a human. Here man can take comfort from the fact that it is not only the size but also the number of cells, the nerve connections etc. which are of importance. By means of careful experiments, however, B. Rensch and R. Altevogt (1955) have shown that an elephant has a remarkably efficient brain which completely confirms the old saying "an elephant never forgets".

Watching the public gazing at the elephants in the zoo, it always seems a pity to me that they go home convinced that they have seen the largest of all animals. Elephants, rhinoceroses and hippopotamuses are certainly the largest land animals, but they are insignificant dwarfs in comparison with the blue whale (*Balaenoptera musculus*), which can reach a length of 90–100 feet and a weight of 120 tons.

This would be equivalent to about 40 average-sized elephants.

A newly born blue whale weighs about two tons, which is the same weight as a medium-sized elephant, and it is about 20 feet long; bearing this in mind it is remarkable that the gestation period of the blue whale is only about half as long (11 months) as that of the elephant (21–22 months).

A young blue whale grows about $1\frac{1}{2}$ inches in a day, and its daily intake of food is about 200 lbs which is the equivalent of the weight of a new-born elephant. In 7 months the young blue whale grows about 20 feet to 40 feet and increases its weight by 21 tons, so that the 7-month old youngster weighs some 23 tons. Two railway wagons would scarcely be sufficient to transport it. (E. J. Slijper 1962).

It seems doubtful to me whether a zoo will ever be able to exhibit specimens of this species, the largest which the world has ever seen. This is not on account of the dimensions of the tank or any other technical difficulty; no technical problem is really insoluble nowadays. But there are many problems in zoo biology that are unsolved or perhaps insoluble. The blue whale, the largest of the baleen whales, feeds only on very small animals the size of a matchstick, namely the small crustaceans of the genus *Euphausia* which it requires by the ton. It might be possible to accustom these giants of the animal kingdom to a substitute food. This would have to be tipped by the truck-load into the tank—possibly a circular one—in which the huge animals could move around the whole time, rather like the sharks in the Seaquarium in Miami. Craig Phillips, the founder and curator of the Seaquarium, who has had considerable experience of modern oceanaria, has written about this subject in his book *The captive sea* (1964).

So far we have not advanced very far. Nevertheless out of the 110 or so different species of whale, which include the dolphins and their relatives, several have already been kept and even bred in huge tanks (Hediger 1963). The keeping of whales—but only the small toothed whales—started about a century ago. About 1860 the naturalist Frank Buckland, already mentioned as a pioneer, was nearly driven to despair in his efforts to keep some dolphins alive at the London Zoo. Other zoos and aquaria also made attempts at keeping toothed whales with varying degrees of success; one of these was the aquarium at Battery Park, New York which was famous in its time.

A turning point in the keeping of whales came in 1938 with the opening of Marine Studios in Marineland on the east coast of Florida. Various toothed whales (especially *Tursiops*) have been kept for years in the tanks of this establishment; they have also bred and responded to training in an astonishing manner. Similar undertakings and to some extent on an even larger scale, followed after the Second World War, as for example at Marineland of the Pacific south of Los Angeles, in Miami etc.

A further milestone in the history of whale-keeping was the opening in 1961 of the Seven Seas Panorama in the Brookfield Zoo, Chicago, which was the first installation of its kind to be emancipated from the immediate vicinity of the coast—virtually in the heart of a continent. With this development the keeping of whales far from the sea was inaugurated. The tank is heated and is in effect a covered swimming-pool, provided with fresh water to which salts are added by the ton, to give a salinity of 2 or 1 per cent which is essential for marine toothed whales. Another possibility for inland aquaria would to be exhibit freshwater dolphins, thus doing away with the necessity for salt and its attendant technical complications. This has been done at Fort Worth Zoo in Texas (L. Z. Curtis 1962) and also at Silver Springs in Florida (J. N. Loyned, D. K. Caldwell 1964).

It is not difficult to predict that in the near future the smaller toothed whales will become as common in European zoos as sealions were some decades ago. In the long run one cannot afford to ignore whales, even in Switzerland or in any other part of the interior far from the sea. Some years ago it was the anthropoid apes which were regarded as essential exhibits in zoos; although keeping them in captivity was thought to be impossible at the start they are now not only kept with great success but they even breed. It only requires a few men with sufficient initiative and adequate funds at their disposal to make the keeping of whales a practical proposition in Europe. One day these animals will make their debut and research on them will eventually get under way in Europe.

It is a particularly promising subject since it has been found for example that dolphins have a brain which is in many respects even superior to that of the anthropoid apes, coming uncomfortably close to that of man himself. Directly connected with this is the capacity of these animals to learn (Hediger 1963), which is quite unique.

Some remarkable facts have already come to light, in particular that many of the toothed whales possess speech that is differentiated to a remarkable degree; they are capable of imitating human speech to an extent which is perhaps significantly greater than in the parrots, if J. C. Lilly (1961) is correct.

It is possible that on the subject of the relationship of man and animal we are now facing the beginning of a breakthrough such as has never been known in the history of science. In any event G. Pilleri, a research worker on the brain in Bern, stated in 1962 that the degree of centralization in the brain forms of certain toothed whales goes far beyond that of man; this throws doubt on the previously held view that the brain of *Homo sapiens* occupies the highest position in the scale of mammals.

* * *

We now come to the inevitable question of whether those who bear the responsibility for the financing of the zoos of Europe give greater weight to the virtues of economy—which are often exaggerated—than to the necessity for far-sighted, large-scale projects of a pioneering nature. This is not a question of the ambition of zoo directors nor is zoo biology as outlined in this book anything to do with individual ambition. We are dealing here with a question of values. Do we attach more importance to the remarkable animal life that shares this planet with us than we do to what is usually called technical progress?

It seems to me that it is not only possible for man to continue to learn all kinds of things from the animals but it is also right that he should do so. When my father was at school he was taught that man would never be able to fly with the aid of a machine. The theory underlying this statement was that because of the exceptionally powerful motor that would be necessary, the machine would be so heavy that it would never be able to lift itself off the ground. What has become of this theory today?

There are also people who argue with similar logic today that there always have been wars and therefore there always will be wars, both now and in the future. This argument is just as untenable as that of the impossibility of flight. One fine day man was able to fly, and the day will come—an even finer one—when there will be no more wars.

This will happen when man takes the final step of raising himself above the rest of the animal kingdom and wars will be at an end.

To be able to do this man must know about the world of living organisms; zoos all over the world can give him a helping hand in this. To zoo experts and animal psychologists it is common knowledge that an animal species with several weapons at its disposal only uses its most deadly weapon against enemies of other species; the more harmless weapons are used, often according to specific rules, against members of its own species.

It is known for example that bull giraffes can smash the skull of a lion with one blow of their fore-feet but when fighting with each other they use only the short horns which are padded by a covering of thick skin. Rattlesnakes and other very venomous snakes, with their highly effective chemical weapon, can even kill animals that are a hundred times larger and heavier than themselves; nevertheless when fights take place between rivals they do not bite each other but settle their contest virtually on points, according to a ritual. When the superfluous males or drones have to be expelled from a colony of bees they are not killed by the poisonous stings of the workers, but simply nipped with the mandibles and then thrown out. Skunks never squirt their stinking secretion at each other. And so on.

Man appears to be the only living animal which uses his most deadly weapons against members of his own species and who is perpetually seeking more lethal weapons. One day perhaps he will bring himself up to the level of the animal and will renounce this unbiological use of weapons. If he restricted himself to intellectual weapons in the exercise of his authority, he could finally reach a stage which would place him above the so-called lower creatures.

REFERENCES

Alving, Th.	1932	Flußpferdgeburt und andere Ereignisse im Zoo Kopenhagen. *Zoolog. Garten* (N.F.), Vol. 5, 34–37.
Anonymus	1961	Dimensions of Animal Enclosures. Ditches at Detroit Zoo, USA. *Internat. Zoo Yearbook*, Vol. 2, 63–67.
Barrows, W. B.	1889	The English Sparrow (*Passer domesticus*) in North America. Washington, D.C.
Bassermann, W.	1911	Der Strauß und seine Zucht. Berlin.
van Bemmel, A. C. V., Zwart, P. und Peters, J. C.	1962	Report on Births and Deaths occurring in the Gardens of the Royal Rotterdam Zoo during the Years 1959 and 1960. *Tijdschr. Dierengeneesk.*, Vol. 87, 826–836.
Besoka	1945	Don Juan, der Unbekannte (Ein Mäusebuch). Francke, Bern.
Bettelheim, B.	1959	Feral Children and Autistic Children. *Amer. J. Sociol.*, Vol. 64, 455–467.
Bigalke, R.	1954	The National Zoological Gardens of South Africa. Pretoria.
Bigalke, R.	1961	The Use of Moats in Zoological Gardens. *Internat. Zoo Yearbook*, Vol. 2, 62.
Böker, H.	1937	Einführung in die vergleichende biologische Anatomie der Wirbeltiere Bd. II, Biologische Anatomie der Ernährung. Fischer, Jena.
Boulenger, E. G.	1937	The London Zoo, London.
Brightwell, L. R.	1949	House to House at the Zoo. Sea Lions. *Zoo Life*, Vol. 4, 21–23.
Brightwell, L. R.	1952	The Zoo Story. London.
Brock, F.	1934	Jahrmarktsdressur wilder Mäuse als Grundlage einer wissenschaftlichen Verhaltensanalyse. *Verh. dtsch. Zool. Ges.*, 235–246.
Burton, R. G.	1931	A Book of Man-eaters. Hutchinson, London.
Chitty, D. and Southern, H. N.	1954	Control of Rats and Mice. 3 Vols. Oxford.

Chombart de Lauwe, Y. M.-J.	1959	Psychopathologic sociale de l'enfant inadapté. Travaux du Groupe d'Ethnologie sociale. C.N.R.S., Paris.
Claus, C., Grobben, K. und Kühn, A.	1932	Lehrbuch der Zoologie. 10. Edn. Berlin und Wien.
Corbett, J.	1949	The Man-eating Leopard of Rudraprayag. Oxford University Press.
Corbett, J.	1957	The Temple Tiger. Oxford University Press.
Cott, H. B.	1961	Scientific Results of an Inquiry into the Ecology and Economic Status of the Nile Crocodile (*Crocodilus niloticus*) in Uganda and Northern Rhodesia. *Trans. Zool. Soc. London*, Vol. 29, 211–356.
Crandall, L. S.	1964	The Management of Wild Mammals in Captivity. The University of Chicago Press, Chicago and London.
Curtis, L.	1962	The Amazon Dolphin, *Inia geoffrensis*, at the Fort Worth Zoological Park. *Internat. Zoo Yearbook*, Vol. 4, 7–10.
Darling, F. F.	1937	A Herd of Red Deer. Oxford University Press.
Delacour, J.	1961	Cage and Aviary Design. *Avicult. Mag.* 67, 3, 107.
Ditmars, R. L. and Crandall, L. S.	1945	Guide to the New York Zoological Park.
Dobberstein, J.	1936	Über die häufigsten Todesursachen der in zoologischen Gärten gehaltenen Tiere. *Med. Klin.*, 32. Jhrg., Nr. 10, 311–315.
Dobberstein, J.	1951	Wesen und Aufgabe einer vergleichenden Pathologie. *Sitzber. Dt. Akad. Wiss. Berlin* (Med.), Jhrg. 1950, Nr. 4.
Fiedler, W.	1964	Die Haut der Säugetiere als Ausdrucksorgan. *Studium Generale*, Jhrg. 17, 6, 362–390.
Fiennes, R. N. T.-W.	1963	Report of the Society's Pathologist for the Year 1961. *Proc. Zool. Soc. London*, Vol. 140, 25–46.
Fischel, W.	1938	Psyche und Leistung der Tiere. Berlin.
Fisher, L. E.	1954	Lead Poisoning in a Gorilla. *J. Amer. Vet. Med. Ass.* 125, No. 933, 478–479.
Fox, H.	1923	Disease in Wild Mammals and Birds. Philadelphia.

Friedmann, H.	1955	The Honey-Guides. V. 5. *Nat. Mus. Bull.* 208. Smithsonian Inst., Washington, D.C.
v. Frisch, K.	1959	Bestrafte Gefräßigkeit. *Z. Tierpsychol.*, Vol. 16, 647–650.
v. Frisch, K.	1964	Aus dem Leben der Bienen. Springer, Berlin.
Garnett, R. A.	1924	A Man in the Zoo. London.
Gillespie, T. H.	1932	A Book of King Penguins. London.
Gillespie, T. H.	1964	Story of the Edinburgh Zoo. Old Castle, Slains.
G.K.B.	1958	Der Lainzer Tiergarten. *Der Fremdenverkehr* (Offiz. Mittbl. österr. Fremdenverk.), Jhrg. 31, Wien.
Groth, H. W.	1951	Coping with Vandalism through Area and Facility Planning. *Parks and Recreation*, Vol. 34, 8–10.
Hagenbeck, C.	1909	Von Tieren und Menschen. Berlin.
Hall, E. T.	1963a	Proxemics. The Study of Man's Spatial Relations. In. Men's Image in Medicine and Anthropology.
Hall, E. T.	1963b	Quality in Architecture: An Anthropological View. *J. Amer. Inst. Architects.*
Harrisson, B.	1962	Orang Utan. Collins, London.
Hayes, C.	1952	The Ape in our House. New York.
Heck, L.	1929	Merkwürdige Todesursache eines Straußes. *Zoolog. Garten* (N.F.), Vol. 1, 335.
Hediger, H.	1938	Wildtiere in Gefangenschaft. *Ciba Zs.*, No. 54, Basel.
Hediger, H.	1942	Wildtiere in Gefangenschaft. Ein Grundriß der Tiergartenbiologie. Basel.
Hediger, H.	1944	Biologische und psychologische Tiergartenprobleme. *Vierteljahresschr. Natf. Ges. Zürich*, Vol. 89, 92–108.
Hediger, H.	1950	Wild Animals in Captivity. An Outline of the Biology of Zoological Gardens. Butterworths, London. New edition 1964, Dover Publications, Inc., New York.
Hediger, H.	1951	Observations sur la Psychologie Animale dans les Parcs Nationaux du Congo. Institut des Parcs Nationaux du Congo. Bruxelles.
Hediger, H.	1953a	Vorbemerkungen zum Besuch des neuen Elefantenhauses im Basler Zoologischen Garten. *Revue Suisse Zool.*, Vol. 60, 439–440.

Hediger, H.   1953b Neue exotische Freunde im Zoo, Basel.

Hediger, H.   1953c Bedeutung und Aufgabe der Zoologischen Gärten. *Jahresbericht des Zürcher Zoologischen Gartens.*

Hediger, H.   1953d Operative Fremdkörper-Entfernung aus dem Magen eines Gorillas. *Zoolog. Garten* (N.F.), Vol. 20, 89–95.

Hediger, H.   1956 Tiergartenbiologie und vergleichende Verhaltensforschung. *Zs. Säugetierkunde*, Vol. 21, 1–28.

Hediger, H.   1958 Kleine Tropenzoologie. *Acta tropica*, Suppl. I, Basel.

Hediger, H.   1961 Beobachtungen zur Tierpsychologie im Zoo und im Zirkus. Basel.

Hediger, H.   1963 Weitere Dressurversuche mit Delphinen und anderen Walen. *Zs. Tierpsychol.*, Vol. 20, 487–497.

Hediger, H.   1964 Die Kea-Familie auf dem Zürichberg. *Vogel-Kosmos*, Stuttgart, H. 8, 169–173.

Hediger, H.   1965 Environmental Factors in the Reproduction of Zoo Animals.

Hediger, H. und   1962 Primaten-ethologische Schnappschüsse aus
Zweifel, F.   dem Zürcher Zoo. *Bibl. primat.*, Vol. 1, 252–276.

Hediger, H. und   1964 Eine Tschaja-Brut im Zürcher Zoo. *Zoolog.*
Bucher, F.   *Garten* (N.F.), Vol. 29, 75–81.

Hediger-Zurbuchen, 1964 Einige ungewöhnliche Lokomotionsweisen
H. u. K.   bei Säugetieren. *Revue Suisse Zool.*, Vol. 71, 299–310.

Heinroth, O. und M. 1924–33 Die Vögel Mitteleuropas. Berlin.

Heinroth, O.   1941 Aufopferung und Eigennutz im Tierreich. Kosmos, Stuttgart.

Heinroth, O.   1955 Aus dem Leben der Vögel. Springer, Berlin.

Henderson, J. Y.   1951 Circus Doctor, Boston.

Herre, W.   1959 Über Domestikationserscheinungen bei Tier und Mensch. *Dtsch. med. Wschr.* 84, 2334–2338.

Herter, K.   1938 Die Biologie der europäischen Igel. Leipzig.

Herter, K.   1944 Mäuse und Mäusefallen. *Zs. Tierpsychol.*, Vol. 6, 87–110.

Hill, W. C. Osman	1955	Report of the Society's Prosector for the Year 1954. *Proc. Zool. Soc. London*, Bd. 125, 533–539.
Hinde, R. A.	1962	Some Aspects of the Imprinting Problem. *Symp. Zool. Soc. London*, No. 8, 129–138.
Huber, K.	1954	25 Jahre Zoologischer Garten Zürich. Zürich.
Hubert, E.	1947	La faune des grands mammifères de la plaine Rwindi-Rutshuru (Lac Edouard). Bruxelles.
Hume, C. W.	1962	Man and Beast, London, U.F.A.W.
Huxley, Elspeth	1963	Foreword. *East African Wildlife Journal*, Vol. 1.
Iles, G.	1960	At Home in the Zoo. Allen, London.
Inhelder, E.	1955a	Zur Psychologie einiger Verhaltensweisen, besonders des Spiels, von Zootieren. *Zs. Tierpsychol.*, Vol. 12, 88–144.
Inhelder, E.	1955b	Über das Spielen mit Gegenständen bei Huftieren, *Revue Suisse Zool.*, Vol. 62, 240–250.
Inhelder, E.	1962	Skizzen zu einer Verhaltenspathologie reaktiver Störungen bei Tieren. *Schweiz. Arch. Neurol. Neurochir. Psychiatrie*, Vol. 89, 276–326.
IUCN Publications, New Series:		Supplementary Paper No. 3. Symposium «Zoos and Conservation». Report. Publ. by IUCN in conjunction with ICBP and IUDZG, London.
Jackson, P. B. M.	1962	Why do Nile Crocodiles attack boats? *Copeia*, No. 1, 204–206.
Jaspers, K.	1963	Gesammelte Schriften zur Psychopathologie. Springer, Berlin.
Juon, P.	1963	Über neuere Erkenntnisse zur Frage der Rehwildernährung. Dissertation ETH Zürich.
Kainz, F.	1961	Die «Sprache» der Tiere. Stuttgart.
Katz, D.	1948	Mensch und Tier. Studien zur vergleichenden Psychologie. Zürich.
Kaufmann, J. H.	1962	Ecology and Social Behaviour of the Coati, *Nasua narica* on Barro Colorado Island, Panama. University of California Press.
Koehler, O.	1950	Besprechung des Buches von Singh, J.A.L. und Zingg, R.M. (1942): Wolf-Children and Feral Man. *Zs. Tierpsychol.*, Vol. 7, 148–160.

References

Koehler, O.   1952   «Wolfskinder», Affen im Haus und verglei-
                       chende Verhaltensforschung. *Fol. Phoniatrica*,
                       Vol. 5, 29–53.
Koford, C. B. 1957   The Vicunia and the Puma. *Ecol. Monogr.* 27,
                       153–219.
Koller, R.   1932   Das Rattenbuch. Hanover.
Krause, C.   1939   Pathologie und pathologische Anatomie des
                       Nutz-und Raubwildes sowie sonstiger wildle-
                       bender Säugetiere und Vögel. *Erg. Allg.
                       Pathol. Path. Anat. Menschen und Tiere*, Vol. 34,
                       München.
Krieg, H.   1929   Biologische Reisestudien in Südamerika.
                       XV. Zur Ökologie großen Nager des Gran
                       Chaco und seiner Grenzgebiete. *Zs. Morphol.
                       Ökol. Tiere*, Vol. 15, 755–785.
Krieg, H.   1948   Zwischen Anden und Atlantik, München.
Krumbiegel, I. 1949   Wie füttere ich gefangene Tiere? 2. Aufl.,
                       Verlag Naturkunde, Hanover und Berlin.
Krumbiegel, I. 1954   Die Biologie der Säugetiere. Krefeld.
Krumbiegel, I. 1960   Straftaten in Zoologischen Gärten. *Arch.
                       Kriminol.*, Vol. 126, 61–69.
Kurt, F.   1963   Zur Carnivorie bei *Cephalophus dorsalis*. *Zs.
                       Säugetierkunde*, Vol. 28, 5, 309–313.
Lang, E. M.   1956   Geburt eines Panzernashorns. 84. Jahres-
                       bericht des Zoologischen Gartens Basel.
Lang, E. M.   1958   Zur Haltung des Strandwolfes (*Hyaena
                       brunnea*). *Zoolog. Garten* (N.F.), Vol. 24, 81–
                       90.
Lang, E. M.   1961   Beobachtungen am indischen Panzernashorn
                       (*Rhinoceros unicornis*). *Zool. Garten* (N.F.), Vol.
                       25, 369–409.
Layne, J. N. and 1964 Behavior of the Amazon Dolphin (*Inia
Caldwell, D. K.   geoffrensis*) (Blainville) in Captivity. *Zoo-
                       logica*, Vol. 49, 81–108.
Lehrman, D. S. 1961   Hormonal Regulation of Parental Behavior
                       in Birds and Infrahuman Mammals. In:
                       Sex and Internal Secretion, edited by W. C.
                       Young, Baltimore.
Lilly, J. C.   1961   Man and Dolphin. Doubleday, New York.
Lindauer, M.   1955   Schwarmbienen auf Wohnungssuche. *Zs.
                       vgl. Physiol.*, Vol. 37, 263–324.

Lint, K. C.   1965   Hummingbirds in Zoological Gardens . . .
                                    Living Jewels. *Zoonooz*, Vol. 38, Nr. 2, 3–7.

Lorenz, K.   1940   Durch Domestikation verursachte Störungen
                                    arteigenen Verhaltens. *Zs. angew. Psychol.*
                                    Charakterkde., Vol. 59, 2–81.

Lorenz, K.   1966   On Aggression. London, Methuen.

Lutz, J. und   1964   Kontroverse über «Wolfskinder?». *Heilpäda-*
Kobi, E. E.   *gog. Werkbl.* 33, 5, 228–232.

Meyer-Holzapfel, M. 1964   Tierpsychologie, Verhaltensforschung und
                                    Psychiatrie. *Akt. Fragen Psychiat. Neurol.*,
                                    Vol. 1, 253–294.

Meyerhardt, O.   1954   Untersuchungen über den Mechanismus der
                                    Enuresis nocturna. *Zs. Kinderpsychiatrie*, 21.
                                    Jhrg., 4, 129–135.

Mitchell, P. Ch.   1929   Centenary History of the Zoological Society
                                    of London.

Murer, B.   1939   Pathologisch-anatomische Untersuchungen
                                    an gefangen gehaltenen wilden Tieren des
                                    Basler zoologischen Gartens. Basel.

Nachtsheim, H.   1944   Gefangenschaftsveränderungen beim Tier –
                                    Parallelerscheinungen zu den Zivilisations-
                                    schäden am Menschen. In: Zeiß, H. und
                                    Pintschovius, K., Zivilisationsschäden am
                                    Menschen. 2. Aufl., Lehmann, München.

Neutra, R.   1962   Auftrag für Morgen. Claassen, Hamburg.

Nouvel, J.   1957   Rapport sur la mortalité et la natalité
Bullier, P. et   enregistrées au Parc Zoologique pendant
Rinjard, J.   l'année 1956. *Bull. Mus. Nat. Hist. Nat.*, No.
                                    4, 297–309.

Nouvel, J.,   1958   Rapport sur la mortalité et la natalité
Bullier, P. et   enregistrées au Parc Zoologique pendant
Rinjard, J.   l'année 1957. *Bull. Mus. Nat. Hist. Nat.*, No.
                                    3, 241–254.

O'Connor   1955   A Bibliography of References to Diseases in
Halloran, P.   Wild Mammals and Birds. Amer. Vet. Med.
                                    Ass., New York.

Patterson, J. H.   1958   The Man-eaters of Tsavo. Macmillan,
                                    London.

Phillips, C.   1964   The captive Sea. Life behind the Scenes of
                                    the great modern Oceanarium. Chilton
                                    Company, Philadelphia and New York.

References

Pichot, P.-A.	1873	Le Jardin d'Acclimatation illustré. Hachette, Paris.
Pilleri, G.	1962	Die zentralnervöse Rangordnung der Cetacea (*Mammalia*). *Acta anat.* 51, 241–258.
Pournelle, H.	1963	Telltale Stripes. *Zoonooz*, San Diego, Vol. 36, Nr. 6.
Pratt, A.	1937	The Call of the Koala. Melbourne.
Raethel, H. S.	1958	Tierverluste in Zoologischen Gärten, ihre Ursachen und Maßnahmen zu ihrer Verhütung. *Monatsheft Vet. Med.*, Vol. 13, H. 9/10, Leipzig.
Ratcliffe, H. L.	1940	Diets for a Zoological Garden: Some Results during a Test Period for Five Years. *Zoologica*, Vol. 25, 463–472.
Ratcliffe, H. L.	1950	Report of the Penrose Research Laboratory of the Zoological Society of Philadelphia.
Ratcliffe, H. L.	1956	Adequate Diets for Captive Wild Animals and Notes on Tuberculin Tests for Apes and Monkeys. A Bulletin from the Penrose and Research Lab. Zool. Soc., Philadelphia.
Ratcliffe, H. L., and Cronin, M. T. I.	1958	Changing Frequency of Arteriosclerosis in Mammals and Birds at the Philadelphia Zoological Garden. *Circulation*, Vol. 18, 41–52.
Reed, T. H.	1963	The 1963 Snake-Bite Serum Survey. Amer. Ass. Zool. Parks, Aquariums. Oglebay Park, Wheeling, West Virginia.
Reichenow, A.	1913	Die Vögel. Handbuch der systematischen Ornithologie. Stuttgart.
Rensch, B. und Altevogt, R.	1955	Das Ausmaß visueller Lernfähigkeit eines indischen Elefanten. *Zs. Tierpsychol.*, Vol. 12, 68–76.
Rewell, R. E.	1948	Report of the Pathologist for the Year 1947. *Proc. Zool. Soc. London*, Vol. 118, 501–514.
Richter, C. P.	1945	Incidence of Rat Bites and Rat Bite Fever in Baltimore. *J. Amer. Med. Ass.*, Vol. 128, 324–326.
Saporiti, E. J.	1949	Contribución al Conocimiento de la Biologia del Oso de Lentes. *An. Soc. Cientif. Argentina*, Vol. 147, 3–12.
Sarasin, F.	1924	Geschichte des Zoologischen Gartens in Basel, 1874–1924. Basel.

References

Schaller, G. B.	1963	The Mountain Gorilla. Ecology and Be haviour. University of Chicago Press.
Schäperclaus, W.	1954	Fischkrankheiten, 3. Aufl., Berlin.
Schenkel, R.	1959	Lebensformung in sozialen Feld und menschliche Sprache. *Home*, Vol. 10.
Schmidt-Hoensdorf, F.	1930	Tod eines Straußenhahnes durch eine verschluckte Modelliernadel. *Zoolog. Garten* (N.F.), Vol. 2, 137.
Schmidt, H. D.	1958	Tod durch Futtermid. *Zoolog. Garten* (N.F.), Vol. 24, 104–105.
Schneider, K.M.	1928	Einige Bilder zur Fortpflanzung des Emus. *Zoolog. Garten* (N.F.), Vol 1, 28–32.
Schneider, K. M.	1937	Leipzig, Bericht über das Kalenderjahr 1935. *D. Zoolog. Garten* (N.F.), Vol. 9, 65–71.
Scott, J. P.	1958	Animal Behavior. University of Chicago Press.
Seton, E. T.	1953	Lives of Game Animals. 4 Vols. Boston.
Singh, J. A. L. and Zingg, R. M.	1942	Wolf-Children and Feral Men. New York and London.
Slijper, E. J.	1962	Riesen des Meeres; Eine Biologie der Wale und Delphine, Springer, Berlin.
Sommer, R.	1925	Tierpsychologie. Leipzig.
Sommer, R.	1959	Studies in Personal Distance.
Spindler, M. und Bluhm, E.	1934	Kleine Beiträge zur Psychologie der Seelöwen (*Eumetopias californianus*). *Zs. vgl. Physiol.*, Vol. 21, 616–631.
Srbich, A. L.	1963	Application of Modern Production Management Techniques to Large Metropolitan Zoo Operations. Bur. Bus. Ec. Res. San Diego, State College, Monogr. 5, 1.
Stähli, A.	1944	Beiträge zur Feststellung der Todesursachen von Haustieren und Wild. Jena.
Steinbacher, G.	1937	Zur Haltung und Pflege des Schuhschnabels (*Balaeniceps rex* J. Gd.). *Zool. Garten* (N.F.), Vol. 9, 101–106.
Steiniger, F.	1952	Rattenbiologie und Rattenbekämpfung einschließlich der Toxikologie der gebräuchlichen Rattengifte. Stuttgart.
Stevenson-Hamilton, H.	1947	Wild Life in South Africa. Cassell, London.

References

Talbot, L. M. and Talbot, M. H.	1963	The Wildebeest in Western Masailand, East Africa. *Wildlife Monographs*, No. 12, University of Louisville, Kentucky.
Thomas, W. D.	1958	Observations on the Breeding in Captivity of a Pair of Lowland Gorillas. *Zoologica*, Vol. 43, 95–104.
Thorpe, W. H.	1956	Learning and Instinct in Animals. London.
Tillman, H.	1944	Durch Fremdkörper verursachte Hauben- und Herzbeutelentzündung beim Trampeltier (*Camelus bactrianus* L.). *Zoolog. Garten* (N.F.), Vol. 16, 31–33.
Uexhüll, von, J. J.	1928	Theoretische Biologie. Springer, Berlin.
Urbain, A., Nouvel, J., Bullier, P. et Rinjard, J.	1949	Rapport sur la mortalité et la natalité enregistrées au Parc Zoologique du Bois de Vincennes pendant l'année 1948. *Bull. Mus. Nat. Hist. Nat.*, Vol. 21, 178–193.
Urbain, A., Nouvel, J., Bullier, P. et Rinjard, J.	1955	Rapport sur la mortalité et la natalité enregistrées au Parc Zoologique du Bois de Vincennes pendant l'année 1954. *Bull. Mus. Nat. Hist. Nat.*, Vol. 27, 117–134.
Wackernagel, H.	1960	Moderne Methoden der Fütterung von Wildtieren im Zoologischen Garten. F. Hoffmann-La Roche & Co., Basel.
Wegeforth, H. M. and Morgan, N.	1953	It began with a Roar. The Story of San Diego's World-Famed Zoo. San Diego.
Windecker, W. und Zeller, F.	1960	Wegweiser durch den Zoologischen Garten Köln.
Lane-Petter, W. et. al.	1967	The UFAW Handbook on the Care and Management of Laboratory Animals. 3rd Edition, London, W.C.1.
Zuckerman, S.	1959	The Zoological Society of London. *Nature* 183, 1082–1084.
Zukowsky, L.	1929	Carl Hagenbecks Reich. Bücherfreunde, Berlin.
Zwingmann, Ch.	1962	Das nostalgische Phänomen. In: Zur Psychologie der Lebenskrisen (Akademische Reihe), Frankfurt a. M.

INDEX

301

Index